ANCIENT
CELTIC
ROMANCES

ANCIENT
CELTIC
ROMANCES

Translated from the Gaelic

by

P. W. Joyce, L.L.D., T.C.D., M.R.I.A.

Author of
"The origin and history of irish names of places,"
"A short history of ireland"
etc., etc.

"I shall tell you a pretty tale."

—Coriolanus.

Third Edition, Revised and Enlarged.

PARKGATE
BOOKS

First published by David Nutt, 1894
This edition published in 1997 by

Parkgate Books Ltd
London House
Great Eastern Wharf
Parkgate Road
London SW11 4NQ
Great Britain

9 8 7 6 5 4 3 2 1

ISBN 1 85585 390 6

Cover design by
Book Creation Services, London

Printed and bound in Finland by WSOY

PREFACE.

———•◇•———

Among the Celtic people of Ireland and the north-west of Scotland, story-telling has always been a favourite amusement. In the olden time, they had professional story-tellers, variously designated according to rank—ollaves, shanachies, filès, bards, etc.—whose duty it was to know by heart a number of old tales, poems, and historical pieces, and to recite them at festive gatherings, for the entertainment of the chiefs and their guests. These story-tellers were always well received at the houses of princes and chiefs, and treated with much consideration; and on occasions when they acquitted themselves well, so as to draw down the applause of the audience, they were often rewarded with costly presents.

To meet the demand for this sort of entertainment, ingenious " men of learning," taking legends or historical events as themes, composed stories from time to time; of which those that struck the popular fancy were caught up and remembered, and handed down from one generation of story-tellers to another. In course of time, a body of romantic literature grew up, consisting chiefly of prose tales, which were classified, according to subject, into Battles, Voyages, Tragedies, Military Expeditions, Cattle-Raids, Courtships, Pursuits, Adventures, Visions, etc.*

Some of these tales were historical, *i.e.* founded on historical events, and corresponded closely with what is now called the historical romance ; while others were altogether fictitious—pure creations of the imagination. But it is to be observed that even in the fictitious tales, the main characters are always historical, or such as were considered so. The old ollaves wove their fictions round Conor Mac Nessa and his Red Branch Knights, or Finn and his Fena, or Luga of the Long Arms and his Dedannans, or Conn the Hundred-fighter, or Cormac Mac Art; like the Welsh legends of Arthur and his Round Table, or the Arabian romances of Haroun-al-Raschid and his Court.

The greater number of the tales were, as I have said, in prose. But some were in poetry; and in many of the prose tales the leading characters are often made to express themselves in verse, or some striking incident of the story is repeated in a poetical

---

* In the Book of Leinster, a manuscript now in Trinity College, Dublin, which was transcribed about the year 1130, there is a very interesting list of ancient historic tales—187 in all—classified in the manner indicated above, which an ollave was obliged to master, so as to be able to repeat any one of them from memory, whenever his patron required him to do so. (See O'Curry, " Lectures on the MS. Materials of Irish History," pages 243 and 584.)

form. Not unfrequently the fragments of verse
introduced into a prose tale are quotations from an
older poetical version of the same tale ; and hence it
often happens that while the prose may be plain
enough, the poetry is often archaic and obscure.

At some very early period in Ireland—how early
we have now no means of determining with certainty
—Celtic thought began to be committed to writing ;
and as everything seems to have been written down
that was considered worth preserving, manuscripts
accumulated in course of time, which were kept either
in monasteries, or in the houses of the hereditary
professors of learning. But in the dark time of the
Danish ravages, and during the troubled centuries
that followed the Anglo-Norman invasion, the manuscript collections were gradually dispersed, and a
large proportion lost or destroyed. Yet we have
remaining—rescued by good fortune from the general
wreck—a great body of manuscript literature. Our
two most important collections are those in Trinity
College and in the Royal Irish Academy, Dublin ;
where we have manuscripts of various ages, from the
year 1100 down to the present century, on every
conceivable subject—Annals, History, Biography,
Theology, Romance, Legend, Science, etc. These
manuscripts, which, it should be remarked, are nearly
all copies from older books, contain a vast collection
of romantic literature : it may, indeed, be said that
there is scarcely one important event in our early
history, or one important native personage or native

legend, that has not been made the subject of some fanciful story.

The volume I now offer to the notice of the public contains eleven tales, selected and translated from the manuscripts of Trinity College and of the Royal Irish Academy. Some have been already published, with original text and *literal* translation, and are to be found in the Transactions of various literary societies, where, however, they are inaccessible to the general run of readers; and even if they were accessible, they are almost unreadable, the translations having been executed, not for literary, but for linguistic purposes. Others 'have never been translated or given to the public in any shape or form till now.

Of the whole collection of eleven tales, therefore, it may be said that they are quite new to the general mass of the reading public. And furthermore, this is the first collection of the old Gaelic prose romances that has ever been published in fair English translation.

Scraps and fragments of some of these tales have been given to the world in popular publications, by writers who, not being able to read the originals, took their information from printed books in the English language. But I am forced to say that many of these specimens have been presented in a very unfavourable and unjust light—distorted to make them look *funny*, and their characters debased to the mere modern conventional stage Irishman. There is none of this silly and odious vulgarity in the originals of these fine old tales, which are high and dignified in tone and feeling—quite as much so as the old romantic tales of Greece and Rome.*

A translation may either follow the very words, or reproduce the life and spirit, of the original; but no translation can do both. If you render word for word, you lose the spirit; if you wish to give the spirit and manner, you must depart from the exact words, and frame your own phrases. I have chosen this latter course. My translation follows the original closely enough in narrative and incident; but so far as mere phraseology is concerned, I have used the English language freely, not allowing myself to be trammelled by too close an adherence to the very words of the text. The originals are in general simple in style; and I have done my best to render them into simple, plain, homely English. In short, I have tried to tell the stories as I conceive the old shanachies themselves would have told them, if they had used English instead of Gaelic.

* Macpherson never sinned in this way. He caught the true keynote; and his "Poems of Ossian," however perverted in other respects, are always dignified in thought and expression. Among other examples of the true interpretation of the spirit of these old romances, prose and poetry, I may mention Miss Brooke's "Reliques of Irish Poetry," published in the end of the last century; the Rev. Dr. Drummond's "Ancient Irish Minstrelsy," published in 1852; Lady Ferguson's graceful and interesting book, "The Story of the Irish before the Conquest" (1868); and Mr. Standish O'Grady's ably written volume, the "History of Ireland" (Vol. I., The Heroic Period 1878).

In the originals, the stories run on without break or subdivision;* but I have thought it better to divide the longer ones into chapters, with appropriate headings.

In almost all cases I had at my command several copies of the same story, some of them differing in phraseology and in minor points of detail, though agreeing, in the main, in narrative and incident. I found this a considerable advantage, as it gave me more freedom in the choice of expression.

I have made full use of the literal translations of those tales that have been already published in the Transactions of the Ossianic Society, in the *Atlantis*, in the Proceedings of the Royal Irish Academy, and in the Journal of the Royal Historical and Archæological Association of Ireland. But, in order to secure the advantage of various readings, I compared, in every case, the published text with at least one copy of the story, in the Royal Irish Academy, in Trinity College, or in my own private manuscript collection.

The ancient institution of professional story-telling held its ground both in Ireland and in Scotland down to a very recent period; and it is questionable if it be even yet quite extinct. Within my own memory,

* With one partial exception. In " The Book of the Dun Cow," "The Voyage of Maildun " is divided into parts or chapters, which are numbered on the margin in Roman numerals, each chapter relating to one particular island; but no spaces are left, and the chapters have no headings. In this tale I have followed the old sub-division.

this sort of entertainment was quite usual among the
farming classes of the south of Ireland. The family
and workmen, and any neighbours that chose to drop
in, would sit round the kitchen fire after the day's
work—or perhaps gather in a barn on a summer or
autumn evening—to listen to some local shanachie reciting one of his innumerable Gaelic tales. The story-
teller never chose his own words—he always had the
story by heart, and recited the words from memory,
often gliding into a sort of recitative in poetical
passages, or when he came to some favourite grandiose
description abounding in high-sounding alliterative
adjectives. And very interesting it was to mark the
rapt attention of the audience, and to hear their
excited exclamations when the speaker came to relate
some mighty combat, some great exploit of the hero,
or some other striking incident. Three years ago, I
met a man in Kilkee, who had a great number of these
stories by heart, and who actually repeated for me,
without the slightest hitch or hesitation, more than
half—and if I had not stopped him would have given
me the whole—of "Cúirt an Mheadhon-Oidhche"
("The Midnight Court"), a poem about six times as
long as Gray's "Elegy."

I will now proceed to give a few particulars concerning these tales, including a short account of the
manuscript or manuscripts from which each has been
translated.

THE THREE TRAGIC STORIES OF ERIN.

Among the ancient Gaelic tales, three were known as " the three most sorrowful (tales) of story-telling," or " The Three Tragic Stories of Erin ; " viz., " The Fate of the Children of Usna," " The Fate of the Children of Lir," and " The Fate of the Children of Turenn." I have not included the first in this volume, but a poetical version of it has been written and published by my brother.*

THE FATE OF THE CHILDREN OF LIR.

Two translations of this tale have been published : one literal, with the Gaelic text, by Professor O'Curry, in the *Atlantis* (Nos. vii. and viii.) ; and another, less literal, by Gerald Griffin, in his "Tales of a Jury-Room."

The oldest known copies of the tale are, one in the Catholic University, Dublin, made by Andrew Mac Curtin, a well-known Gaelic scholar and scribe of the county Clare, who lived between 1680 and 1740; one in Trinity College, Dublin, made by Hugh O'Daly, in 1758 ; and one in the British Museum, made by Richard Tipper of Dublin, in 1718.† There is also a very good copy in the Royal Irish Academy (23. C. 26), of which I made considerable use, written in or about 1782, by Peter O'Connell, a good Gaelic scholar of the county Clare. From a comparison of several of these versions, O'Curry made his copy of the text as published in the *Atlantis*.

There may be, and there probably are, older copies, in Trinity College, in the British Museum, or elsewhere, if we knew only where to find them. And this observation applies to several of the tales that follow, of which we have at hand only modern copies.

THE FATE OF THE CHILDREN OF TURENN.

In the Book of Lecan (folio 28), which was compiled by the Mac Firbises, about A.D. 1416, is a short account, partly in prose and partly in verse, of the celebrated eric-fine imposed on the three

---

* "Deirdrè," by Robert D. Joyce, M.D., M.R.I.A. Boston: Roberts Brothers. Dublin: M. H. Gill and Son.

† O'Curry, *Atlantis*, Nos. vii. and viii., page 390.

sons of Turenn, by Luga of the Long Arms, for killing his father Kian; but this old book does not give the story of the quest for the fine. The full tale, text and literal translation, has been published by O'Curry in the *Atlantis*. There are several good copies in the Royal Irish Academy: one in 23. G. 10, transcribed by Patrick Brown of the county Clare, in 1805; another in 23. E. 16, written out by Michael Oge O'Longan, in 1797; and a third (imperfect) in 23. M. 47, copied by Andrew Mac Curtin, in 1734.

There are references to these three sons of Turenn, and to the manner of their death, in two very old authorities, viz., Cormac's "Glossary" (about A.D. 900); and a poem by Flann of Monasterboice (who died A.D. 1056), a copy of which is in the Book of Leinster, written about A.D. 1130.

In the older references to the sons of Turenn, they are called Brian, Iuchar, Iucharba; but in some comparatively modern copies of the tale the names are a little different—for instance, Peter O'Connell calls them Uar, Iuchar, and Iucharba; and they vary still further in other copies. I have taken advantage of this variety to give the names in a more pronounceable form in my translation.

In the original, this tale is introduced by an anecdote of Nuada of the Silver Hand and the two great Dedannan leeches, Midac and Armedda (see page 92, *infra*), which has nothing whatever to do with the story, and which I have omitted.

THE OVERFLOWING OF LOUGH NEAGH.

"Leabhar na h-Uidhre," or "The Book of the Dun Cow," from which this and the two following tales are taken, is the oldest manuscript of miscellaneous Gaelic literature we possess. It was transcribed from older books by Maelmuire Mac Ceilechair, who died A.D. 1106; and it is now deposited in the Royal Irish Academy, Dublin—or rather, I should say, a large fragment of it, for the book has suffered much mutilation. This venerable book may now be said to be in the hands of the public, as it has been lately reproduced in lithograph fac-simile, and published by the Council of the Royal Irish Academy, at the Government expense.

The story of "The Overflowing of Lough Neagh" (called in the original "The Destruction of Eocho Mac Mairedo") has been published, with text and literal translation, by the late J. O'Beirne Crowe, in the Kilkenny Archæological Journal (volume for 1870-1).

In this story I have been obliged to make a few transpositions in the mere order of the incidents, for the narrative in the original is in some places very ill arranged.

It is now nearly eight hundred years since this story was *transcribed* from some old authority into "The Book of the Dun Cow;" and it is singular that the tradition of the formation of Lough Neagh, by the overflow of an enchanted well which was neglected by the woman in charge of it, still maintains a vivid existence among the peasantry. (See on this subject the author's "Origin and History of Irish Names of Places," Series I. 4th edition, page 176.)

CONNLA OF THE GOLDEN HAIR, AND THE FAIRY MAIDEN.

This tale (called in the original "Echtra Condla Cain," "The Adventures of Connla the Comely") is taken from "The Book of the Dun Cow." It has been published, with text and literal translation, by the late J. O'Beirne Crowe, in the Kilkenny Archæological Journal (volume 1874-5, page 128).

This is one of the many tales that illustrate the ancient and widespread superstition that fairies sometimes take away mortals to their palaces in the fairy forts and pleasant green hills; [19] of which the last story in this book—"Oisin in Tirnanoge"—is another example. This superstition prevailed in Ireland and the Scottish Highlands as far back as either history or tradition reaches; it flourished in full vigour within my own memory; and it is scarcely quite extinct—in Ireland at least—at the present day.* In connection with the antiquity of this superstition, it must be borne in mind that the present story was transcribed into "The Book of the Dun Cow" in or about the year 1100, from some older book; and that it relates to the time of Conn the Hundred-fighter, king of Ireland, who reigned in the second century of the Christian era.

* See the ballad and air of "The Fairy King's Courtship," in the author's "Ancient Irish Music," page 1.

THE VOYAGE OF MAILDUN.

Of this tale (which is now given to the public for the first time) the oldest copy is in "The Book of the Dun Cow" (about the year 1100); but it is imperfect at both beginning and end—a portion having been torn away when the book was mutilated at some former time. There is a perfect copy in the Yellow Book of Lecan, in Trinity College, Dublin, and another in the British Museum (MS. Harl. 5280).

After I had made a rough translation of the greater part of this piece, I discovered a good literal translation in manuscript in the Royal Irish Academy, made by the late J. O'Beirne Crowe, which was of great use to me, as it helped to explain some strange terms, and to clear up some obscure passages.

This voyage would appear from internal evidence to have been made in the beginning of the eighth century (O'Curry says about the year 700); for I think it likely that Maildun did actually go on a voyage, which was afterwards made the framework of the story. On my translation of this tale, Lord Tennyson founded his poem " The Voyage of Maeldune."

Of the *Imrama* or voluntary sea expeditions (to which the present story belongs) there are, according to O'Curry (Lect. MS. Mat. 289), only four remaining, all very ancient. Of these the best known is the " Voyage of St. Brendan," undertaken in the sixth century, which was at one time celebrated all over Europe, and which has been lately made the theme of a fine poem by Denis Florence M'Carthy.

Another of these *Imrama* is the " Voyage of the Sons of O'Corra," which has been described at some length by Professor O'Curry (Lect. MS. Mat. 289). Of this I have a copy which I made from the MS. 23. M. 50, Royal Irish Academy (and which I afterwards carefully compared with another copy lent me by my friend, Mr. W. M. Hennessy). I made a translation of this story, intending to print it in the present volume; but as there is a much older and better copy in the ancient " Book of Fermoy," which I had not time to consult in detail, I have thought it better to hold back for the present the strange adventures of the sons of O'Corra. A beautiful poetical translation of the whole tale has been made by Mr. T. D. Sullivan of Dublin, and published in his volume of Poems.

THE FAIRY PALACE OF THE QUICKEN TREES.

The "Bruighean Caerthainn," or "The Fairy Palace of the Quicken Trees," which is now translated for the first time, is one of the most popular of the Gaelic romances. I had three of the Royal Irish Academy MSS. before me when translating it—viz., 23. C. 30, transcribed in 1733, by the Irish writer and lexicographer, Andrew Mac Curtin of the county Clare; 24. B. 15, written in 1841; and 23. L. 24, copied in 1766, by Dermot O'Mulqueen of the county Clare.

This is one of a type of stories very common in Gaelic romantic literature :—One or more of the heroes are entrapped by some enchanter and held under a spell in a castle, or a cave, or a dungeon; till, after a series of adventures, they are released by the bravery or mother-wit of some of their companions. "The Chase of Slieve Fuad" and "The Chase of Slieve Cullinn" are two other examples of this class of Gaelic tales.

THE PURSUIT OF THE GILLA DACKER AND HIS HORSE.

This is a humorous story of a trick—a very serious practical joke—played by Avarta, a Dedannan enchanter, on sixteen of the Fena, whom he carried off to "The Land of Promise;" and of the adventures of Finn, Dermat O'Dyna, and the others, in their pursuit of Avarta (who had taken the shape of the Gilla Dacker) to recover their companions. It may be regarded as belonging to the same class as the last story.

O'Curry described the opening of this tale in his Lectures (MS. Mat. 316); and he was the first, so far as I know, to draw attention to it. I think it strange that such a story should not have been noticed before by writers on Gaelic literature; for as a work of imagination, it seems to me a marvellous and very beautiful creation.

The battles fought by the king of Sorca, aided by Finn and his Fena, against the King of the World, are described at much length in the original; but I have cut them down to a very short compass; and I have omitted altogether a long episode towards the end, which travels away from the main story.

This tale has never been translated till now. I translated it chiefly from the Royal Irish Academy MS., 24. B. 28, a well-written manuscript, which was copied out by Edmond Terry, in 1728: but I kept another good copy beside me for comparison, viz., that contained in the Royal Irish Academy MS., 23. G. 21, written in 1795, by Michael Oge O'Longan of Cork, father of Mr. Joseph O'Longan, now the Irish scribe in the Royal Irish Academy, and the transcriber in fac-simile of "Leabhar na h-Uidhre," "Leabhar Breac," and "Leabhar Laighneach."

THE PURSUIT OF DERMAT AND GRANIA.

This tale is one of those mentioned in the list contained in the Book of Leinster, which was written about A.D. 1130 (see note, page iv.); but though this proves the tale to be an ancient one, I have never come across a copy older than the last century.

"The Pursuit of Dermat and Grania" has been published, with text and a very racy idiomatic literal translation, by Mr. Standish Hayes O'Grady, in the Transactions of the Ossianic Society for 1855, from a comparison of two manuscripts, one of 1780 and the other of 1842. In addition to Mr. O'Grady's published text, I made use of another good copy (MS. Royal Irish Academy, 23. G. 21) written in 1795, by Michael Oge O'Longan, already spoken of.

I cannot help believing that this fine story originally ended with the death of Dermat; though in all the current versions (including Mr. O'Grady's printed text) there is an additional part recounting the further proceedings of Grania and her sons, after the death of the hero. But this part is in every respect inferior to the rest—in language, in feeling, and in play of imagination. It seems to me very clear that it was patched on to the original story by some unskilful hand; and I have accordingly omitted it, and ended the story with the death of Dermat. I have also omitted two short episodes—that of the *cnumh* or reptile of Corca Divna, as a mere excrescence; and Finn's expedition to Scotland for aid against Dermat. And, for the sake of clearness, I have slightly changed the place of that part of the tale which recounts the origin of the Fairy Quicken Tree of Dooros. There are one or two other trifling but very necessary modifications, which need not be mentioned here.

THE CHASE OF SLIEVE CULLINN: THE CHASE OF SLIEVE FUAD: OISIN IN TIRNANOGE.

In the original Gaelic these are three poetical tales. All three have been printed, with Gaelic text and literal translation, in the Transactions of the Ossianic Society: the two first by the late John O'Daly, and "Oisin in Tirnanoge" by Professor O'Looney. There are many good copies of these tales in the manuscripts of the Royal Irish Academy; though of not one of them have I seen a copy older than the last century.

"The Chase of Slieve Cullinn" (commonly known as "The Poem of the Chase") has been translated into English verse by Miss Brooke; and there is another metrical translation in the *Irish Penny Journal* (page 93). And of "Oisin in Tirnanoge," Mr. T. D. Sullivan has given a graceful poetical rendering in his volume of Poems, already mentioned.

In this edition there is one additional tale, "The Voyage of the Sons of O'Corra," a notice of which will be found at page xiii of the Preface to the First Edition.

LYRE-NA-GRENA, LEINSTER-ROAD,
RATHMINES, 1891.

CONTENTS.

———•◇•———

The Fairy Palace of the Quicken Trees.

The Pursuit of the Gilla Dacker and his Horse.

THE PURSUIT OF DERMAT AND GRANIA.

THE

FATE OF THE CHILDREN OF LIR;

OR,

THE FOUR WHITE SWANS.

——◆——

Silent, O Moyle, be the roar of thy water;
Break not, ye breezes, your chain of repose;
While murmuring mournfully, Lir's lonely daughter
Tells to the night-star her tale of woes.

MOORE.

CHAPTER I.

BOVE DERG CHOSEN KING OF THE DEDANNANS.

AFTER the battle of Tailltenn,* the Dedannans[1]† of the five provinces of Erin assembled in one place of meeting, to consider on their state, and to choose a king. For their chiefs said it was better for them to have one king over all, than to be divided, as they were, serving sundry lords and princes.

Now of those who expected the sovereignty for themselves, the following chiefs were the noblest, namely:—Bove Derg,‡ son of the Dagda; his brother

---

* Now Teltown, on the river Blackwater, between Kells and Navan, in Meath. (See note 1 at the end, for this battle.)

† The numbers refer to the notes at the end of the book.

‡ At the end of the book will be found an alphabetical list of all the names of persons and places mentioned through the volume, with their Gaelic forms, and, in many cases, their meanings.

Angus, of Bruga on the Boyne, who, however, had no
earnest wish to become king, preferring to remain as
he was; Ilbrec of Assaroe; Lir of Shee Finnaha; and
Midir the Haughty of Bri-Leth.[1]

Then the chief people went into council, all except
the five above named; and the decision they came to
was to elect Bove Derg, son of the Dagda, king over
the whole of the Dedannan race. When the election
was made known, none of those who were disappointed
took the matter to heart except Lir of Shee Finnaha
alone. And when Lir found that the chiefs had
chosen Bove Derg, he was greatly offended, and
straightway left the assembly in anger, without
taking leave of any one, and without showing any
mark of respect or obedience to the new king.

When the chiefs heard this, they were wroth; and
they said they would follow him to Shee Finnaha,*
and slay him with spear and sword, and burn his
house, because he did not yield obedience to the king
they had elected in lawful council.

But Bove Derg would not permit them to do so.
"This man," he said, "will defend his territory, and
many will be slain; and I am none the less your king,
although he has not submitted to me."

Matters remained so for a long time. But at last
a great misfortune happened to Lir, for his wife died
after an illness of three days. This weighed heavily

* Shee Finnaha, Lir's residence, is thought to have been situated
near the boundary of Armagh and Monaghan, not far from Newtown
Hamilton.

on him, and his heart was weary with sorrow after
her. Her death, moreover, was a great event at that
time, and was much spoken of throughout Erin.

When the tidings reached the mansion of Bove
Derg, where the chief men of the Dedannans were
then assembled, the king said—

"As Lir's wife is now dead, my friendship would
be of service to him, if he were willing to accept it.
For I have in my house three maidens, the most
beautiful and the best instructed in all Erin, namely,
Eve, Eva, and Alva, my own foster children, and
daughters of Allil of Ara."*

The Dedannans agreed to this, and said that their
king had spoken wisely and truly.

Messengers were accordingly sent to Lir, and they
were told to say to him—

" If thou art willing to submit to the king, he will
give thee for a wife one of his three foster children;
and thou shalt have his friendship for ever."

It was pleasing to Lir to make this alliance; and
accordingly he set out next day from Shee Finnaha
with a company of fifty chariots; and they never
halted or turned aside till they reached the palace of
Bove Derg, on the shore of the Great Lake.† Their
arrival gave much joy and happiness to the king and
his household; for although Lir did not submit at first
to Bove Derg, he was a good man, and was greatly

---

* Ara, the islands of Aran, in Galway Bay.
† The Great Lake, *i.e.* Lough Derg, on the Shannon, above
Killaloe.

beloved by the king himself and by all his subjects. So Lir and his followers got a kindly welcome; and they were supplied with everything necessary, and were well attended to that night.

Next day, the three daughters of Allil of Ara sat on the same couch with the queen their foster mother; and the king said to Lir—

"Take thy choice of the three maidens, and which-ever thou choosest, she shall be thy wife."

"They are all beautiful," said Lir, "and I cannot tell which of them is best; but I will take the eldest, for she must be the noblest of the three."

Then the king said, "Eve is the eldest, and she shall be given to thee if it be thy wish."

So Lir chose Eve for his wife, and they were wedded that day.

Lir remained a fortnight in the king's palace, and then departed with his wife to his own house, Shee Finnaha, where he celebrated his marriage by a great royal wedding feast.

CHAPTER II.

THE CHILDREN OF LIR.

IN course of time, Lir's wife bore him two children at a birth, a daughter and a son, whose names were Finola and Aed. A second time she brought forth twins, two sons, who were named Ficra and Conn:

and she died in giving them birth. This was a cause
of great anguish to Lir; and he would almost have
died of grief, only that his mind was turned from his
sorrow by his great love for his four little children.

When the news of Eve's death reached the
mansion of Bove Derg, the king was in deep grief,
and the people of his household raised three great
cries of lamentation for her. And when their mourning was ended, the king said—

"We grieve for our foster child, both on her own
account, and for the sake of the good man to whom
we gave her; for we are thankful for his alliance
and his friendship. But our acquaintance shall not
be ended, and our alliance shall not be broken; for
I will give him her sister to wife, my second foster
child, Eva."

Messengers were sent to Lir to Shee Finnaha, to tell
him of this; and he consented. So after some time he
came to the king's house to espouse her, and they
were united; and he brought her home with him to
his own house.

The four children grew up under Eva's care. She
nursed them with great tenderness, and her love for
them increased every day. They slept near their
father; and he would often rise from his own bed at
the dawn of morning, and go to their beds, to talk
with them and to fondle them.

The king, Bove Derg, loved them almost as well as
did their father. He went many times every year to
Shee Finnaha to see them; and he used to bring them

often to his palace, where he kept them as long as he could on each occasion, and he always felt sad when he sent them home.

At this time, too, the Dedannans used to celebrate the Feast of Age[2] at the houses of their chiefs by turns; and whenever it happened that the festival was held at Shee Finnaha, these children were the delight and joy of the Dedannans. For nowhere could four lovelier children be found; so that those who saw them were always delighted with their beauty and their gentleness, and could not help loving them with their whole heart.

CHAPTER III.

THE FOUR CHILDREN OF LIR ARE TURNED INTO FOUR WHITE SWANS BY THEIR STEPMOTHER.

Now when Eva saw that the children of Lir received such attention and affection from their father, and from all others that came to his house, she fancied she was neglected on their account; and a poisonous dart of jealousy entered her heart, which turned her love to hatred; and she began to have feelings of bitter enmity for her sister's children.

Her jealousy so preyed on her that she feigned illness, and lay in bed for nearly a year, filled with gall and brooding mischief; and at the end of that time she committed a foul and cruel deed of treachery on the children of Lir.

One day she ordered her horses to be yoked to her chariot, and she set out for the palace of Bove Derg, bringing the four children with her.

Finola did not wish to go, for it was revealed to her darkly in a dream that Eva was bent on some dreadful deed of fratricide ;* and she knew well that her stepmother intended to kill her and her brothers that day, or in some other way to bring ruin on them. But she was not able to avoid the fate that awaited her.

When they had gone some distance from Shee Finnaha on their way to the palace, Eva tried to persuade her attendants to kill the children. " Kill them, and you shall be rewarded with all the worldly wealth you may desire; for their father loves me no longer, and has neglected and forsaken me on account of his great love for these children."

But they heard her with horror, and refused, saying, " We will not kill them. Fearful is the deed thou hast contemplated, O Eva ; and evil will surely befall thee for having even thought of killing them."

Then she took the sword to slay them herself ; but her woman's weakness prevented her, and she was not able to strike them.

So they set out once more, and fared on till they came to the shore of Lake Darvra,† where they alighted, and the horses were unyoked.

* The word " fratricide " is the nearest English equivalent to the original word, *fionghal*, which means the murder of a relative.

† Lake Darvra, now Lough Derravaragh, in Westmeath.

She led the children to the edge of the lake, and
told them to go to bathe; and as soon as they had
got into the clear water, she struck them one by one
with a druidical[3] fairy wand, and turned them into
four beautiful snow-white swans. And she addressed
them in these words—

> Out to your home, ye swans, on Darvra's wave;
> With clamorous birds begin your life of gloom:
> Your friends shall weep your fate, but none can save;
> For I've pronounced the dreadful words of doom.

After this, the four children of Lir turned their
faces to their stepmother; and Finola spoke—

"Evil is the deed thou hast done, O Eva; thy
friendship to us has been a friendship of treachery;
and thou hast ruined us without cause. But the deed
will be avenged; for the power of thy witchcraft is
not greater than the druidical power of our friends to
punish thee; and the doom that awaits thee shall be
worse than ours."

> Our stepmother loved us long ago;
> Our stepmother now has wrought us woe:
> With magical wand and fearful words,
> She changed us to beautiful snow-white birds;
> And we live on the waters for evermore,
> By tempests driven from shore to shore.

Finola again spoke and said, "Tell us now how
long we shall be in the shape of swans, so that we
may know when our miseries shall come to an end."

"It would be better for you if you had not put
that question," said Eva; "but I shall declare the
truth to you, as you have asked me. Three hundred

years on smooth Lake Darvra; three hundred years on the Sea of Moyle, between Erin and Alban;* three hundred years at Irros Domnann and at Inis Glora† on the Western Sea. Until the union of Largnen, the prince from the north, with Decca, the princess from the south; until the Taillkenn ‡ shall come to Erin, bringing the light of a pure faith; and until ye hear the voice of the Christian bell. And neither by your own power, nor by mine, nor by the power of your friends, can ye be freed till the time comes."

Then Eva repented what she had done; and she said, "Since I cannot afford you any other relief, I will allow you to keep your own Gaelic speech; and ye shall be able to sing sweet, plaintive, fairy music, which shall excel all the music of the world, and which shall lull to sleep all that listen to it. Moreover, ye shall retain your human reason; and ye shall not be in grief on account of being in the shape of swans."

And she chanted this lay—

> Depart from me, ye graceful swans;
>   The waters are now your home:
> Your palace shall be the pearly cave,
> Your couch the crest of the crystal wave,
>   And your mantle the milk-white foam!

---

* The sea between Erin and Alban (Ireland and Scotland) was anciently called the Sea of Moyle, from the Moyle, or Mull, of Cantire.

† Irros Domnann; Erris, in the county Mayo. Inis Glora; a small island about five miles west from Belmullet, in the same county, still known by the same name.

‡ Taillkenn, a name given by the druids to St. Patrick.

Depart from me, ye snow-white swans
  With your music and Gaelic speech :
The crystal Darvra, the wintry Moyle,
The billowy margin of Glora's isle ;—
  Three hundred years on each !

Victorious Lir, your hapless sire,
  His lov'd ones in vain shall call ;
His weary heart is a husk of gore,
His home is joyless for evermore,
  And his anger on me shall fall !

Through circling ages of gloom and fear
  Your anguish no tongue can tell ;
Till Faith shall shed her heavenly rays,
Till ye hear the Taillkenn's anthem of praise,
  And the voice of the Christian bell !

Then ordering her steeds to be yoked to her chariot she departed westwards, leaving the four white swans swimming on the lake.

Our father shall watch and weep in vain ;
He never shall see us return again.
Four pretty children, happy at home ;
Four white swans on the feathery foam ;
And we live on the waters for evermore,
By tempests driven from shore to shore.

CHAPTER IV.

THE FOUR WHITE SWANS ON LAKE DARVRA.

WHEN Eva arrived at the house of Bove Derg, the chiefs bade her welcome ; and the king asked her why she had not brought the Children of Lir to him.

"Because," she replied, "Lir no longer loves thee; and he does not wish to intrust his children to thee, lest thou shouldst harm them."

The king was greatly astonished and troubled at this, and he said, "How can that be? For I love those children better than I love my own."

But he thought in his own mind that Eva had played some treachery on them. And he sent messengers with all speed northwards to Shee Finnaha, to inquire for the children, and to ask that they might be sent to him.

When the messengers had told their errand, Lir was startled; and he asked, "Have the children not reached the palace with Eva?"

They answered, "Eva arrived alone, and she told the king that you refused to let the children come."

A sad and sorrowful heart had Lir when he heard this; and he now felt sure that Eva had destroyed his four lovely children. So, early next morning, his chariot was yoked for him, and he set out with his attendants for the king's palace; and they travelled with all speed till they arrived at the shore of Lake Darvra.

The children of Lir saw the cavalcade approaching; and Finola spoke these words—

> I see a mystic warrior band
> From yonder brow approach the strand;
> I see them winding down the vale,
>   Their bending chariots slow advancing;
> I see their shields and gilded mail,
>   Their spears and helmets brightly glancing.

Ah! well I know that proud array;
I know too well their thoughts to-day:
The Dannan host and royal Lir;
   Four rosy children they are seeking:
Too soon, alas! they find us here,
   Four snowy swans like children speaking!

Come, brothers dear, approach the coast,
To welcome Lir's mysterious host.
Oh, woful welcome! woful day,
   That never brings a bright to-morrow!
Unhappy father, doomed for aye
   To mourn our fate in hopeless sorrow!

When Lir came to the shore, he heard the birds speaking, and, wondering greatly, he asked them how it came to pass that they had human voices.

"Know, O Lir," said Finola, "that we are thy four children, who have been changed into swans and ruined by the witchcraft of our stepmother, our own mother's sister, Eva, through her baleful jealousy."

When Lir and his people heard this, they uttered three long mournful cries of grief and lamentation.

After a time, their father asked them, "Is it possible to restore you to your own shapes?"

"It is not possible," replied Finola; "no man has the power to release us until Largnen from the north and Decca from the south are united. Three hundred years we shall be on Lake Darvra; three hundred years on the sea-stream of Moyle; three hundred years on the Sea of Glora in the west. And we shall not regain our human shape till the Taillkenn come with his pure faith into Erin, and until we hear the voice of the Christian bell."

And again the people raised three great cries of sorrow.

" As you have your speech and your reason," said Lir, " come now to land, and ye shall live at home, conversing with me and my people."

" We are not permitted to leave the waters of the lake, and we cannot live with our people any more. But the wicked Eva has allowed us to retain our human reason, and our own Gaelic speech; and we have also the power to chant plaintive, fairy music, so sweet that those who listen to us would never desire any other happiness. Remain with us to-night, and we will chant our music for you."

Lir and his people remained on the shore of the lake; and the swans sang their slow, fairy music, which was so sweet and sad, that the people, as they listened, fell into a calm, gentle sleep.

At the glimmer of dawn next morning, Lir arose, and he bade farewell to his children for a while, to seek out Eva.

> The time has come for me to part :—
> 　　No more, alas! my children dear,
> Your rosy smiles shall glad my heart,
> 　　Or light the gloomy home of Lir.
>
> Dark was the day when first I brought
> 　　This Eva in my home to dwell!
> Hard was the woman's heart that wrought
> 　　This cruel and malignant spell !
>
> I lay me down to rest in vain;
> 　　For, through the livelong, sleepless night,
> My little lov'd ones, pictured plain,
> 　　Stand ever there before my sight.

Finola, once my pride and joy ;
  Dark Aed, adventurous and bold ;
Bright Ficra, gentle, playful boy ;
  And little Conn, with curls of gold ;—

Struck down on Darvra's reedy shore,
  By wicked Eva's magic power :
Oh, children, children, never more
  My heart shall know one peaceful hour !

Lir then departed, and travelled south-west till he arrived at the king's palace, where he was welcomed ; and Bove Derg began to reproach him, in presence of Eva, for not bringing the children.

"Alas!" said Lir; "it was not by me that the children were prevented from coming. But Eva, your own foster child, the sister of their mother, has played treachery on them; and has changed them by her sorcery into four white swans on Lake Darvra."

The king was confounded and grieved at this news ; and when he looked at Eva, he knew by her countenance that what Lir had told him was true; and he began to upbraid her in a fierce and angry voice.

"The wicked deed thou hast committed," said he, " will be worse for thee than for the children of Lir; for their suffering shall come to an end, and they shall be happy at last."

Again he spoke to her more fiercely than before ; and he asked her what shape of all others, on the earth, or above the earth, or beneath the earth, she most abhorred, and into which she most dreaded to be transformed.

And she, being forced to answer truly, said, "A demon of the air."*

"That is the form you shall take," said Bove Derg; and as he spoke he struck her with a druidical magic wand, and turned her into a demon of the air. She opened her wings, and flew with a scream upwards and away through the clouds; and she is still a demon of the air, and she shall be a demon of the air till the end of time.

Then Bove Derg and the Dedannans assembled on the shore of the lake, and encamped there; for they wished to remain with the birds, and to listen to their music. The Milesian people† came and formed an encampment there in like manner; for historians say that no music that was ever heard in Erin could be compared with the singing of these swans.

And so the swans passed their time. During the day they conversed with the men of Erin, both Dedannans and Milesians, and discoursed lovingly with their friends and fellow nurselings; and at night they chanted their slow, sweet, fairy music, the most delightful that was ever heard by men; so that all who listened to it, even those who were in grief, or sickness, or pain, forgot their sorrows and their sufferings, and fell into a gentle, sweet sleep, from which they awoke bright and happy.

So they continued, the Dedannans and the Mile-

---

* A demon of the air was held in great abhorrence by the ancient Irish.

† The Milesian people; the colony who conquered and succeeded the Dedannans. (See note 1 at end.)

sians, in their encampments, and the swans on the lake, for three hundred years.* And at the end of that time, Finola said to her brothers—

"Do you know, my dear brothers, that we have come to the end of our time here; and that we have only this one night to spend on Lake Darvra?"

When the three sons of Lir heard this, they were in great distress and sorrow; for they were almost as happy on Lake Darvra, surrounded by their friends, and conversing with them day by day, as if they had been in their father's house in their own natural shapes; whereas they should now live on the gloomy and tempestuous Sea of Moyle, far away from all human society.

Early next morning, they came to the margin of the lake, to speak to their Father and their friends for the last time, and to bid them farewell; and Finola chanted this lay—

I.

Farewell, farewell, our father dear!
  The last sad hour has come:
Farewell, Bove Derg! farewell to all,
  Till the dreadful day of doom!†
We go from friends and scenes beloved,
  To a home of grief and pain;
    And that day of woe
    Shall come and go,
  Before we meet again!

---

* The Dedannans were regarded as gods, and were immortal or semi-immortal. (See note 1 at the end.)

† It must be remembered that the children of Lir had some obscure foreknowledge of the coming of Christianity.

II.

We live for ages on stormy Moyle,
  In loneliness and fear;
The kindly words of loving friends
  We never more shall hear.
Four joyous children long ago;
  Four snow-white swans to-day;
    And on Moyle's wild sea
    Our robe shall be
The cold and briny spray.

III.

Far down on the misty stream of time,
  When three hundred years are o'er,
Three hundred more in storm and cold,
  By Glora's desolate shore;
Till Decca fair is Largnen's spouse;
  Till north and south unite;
    Till the hymns are sung,
    And the bells are rung,
At the dawn of the pure faith's light.

IV.

Arise, my brothers, from Darvra's wave,
  On the wings of the southern wind;
We leave our father and friends to-day
  In measureless grief behind.
Ah! sad the parting, and sad our flight
  To Moyle's tempestuous main;
    For the day of woe
    Shall come and go,
Before we meet again!

The four swans then spread their wings, and rose
from the surface of the water in sight of all their
friends, till they reached a great height in the air;
then resting, and looking downwards for a moment,

they flew straight to the north, till they alighted on the Sea of Moyle between Erin and Alban.

The men of Erin were grieved at their departure, and they made a law, and proclaimed it throughout the land, that no one should kill a swan in Erin from that time forth.

CHAPTER V.

THE FOUR WHITE SWANS ON THE SEA OF MOYLE.

As to the children of Lir, miserable was their abode and evil their plight on the Sea of Moyle. Their hearts were wrung with sorrow for their father and their friends; and when they looked towards the steep, rocky, far-stretching coasts, and saw the great, dark wild sea around them, they were overwhelmed with fear and despair. They began also to suffer from cold and hunger, so that all the hardships they had endured on Lake Darvra appeared as nothing compared with their suffering on the sea-current of Moyle.

And so they lived, till one night a great tempest fell upon the sea. Finola, when she saw the sky filled with black, threatening clouds, thus addressed her brothers—

"Beloved brothers, we have made a bad preparation for this night; for it is certain that the coming

storm will separate us; and now let us appoint a
place of meeting, or it may happen that we shall never
see each other again."

And they answered, " Dear sister, you speak truly
and wisely; and let us fix on Carricknarone, for that
is a rock that we are all very well acquainted with."

And they appointed Carricknarone as their place
of meeting.

Midnight came, and with it came the beginning of
the storm.   A wild, rough wind swept over the dark
sea, the lightnings flashed, and the great waves rose,
and increased their violence and their thunder.

The swans were soon scattered over the waters, so
that not one of them knew in what direction the others
had been driven.   During all that night they were
tossed about by the roaring winds and waves, and it
was with much difficulty they preserved their lives.

Towards morning the storm abated, and the sea
became again calm and smooth; and Finola swam
to Carricknarone.   But she found none of her brothers
there, neither could she see any trace of them when
she looked all round from the summit of the rock over
the wide face of the sea.

Then she became terrified, for she thought she
should never see them again; and she began to lament
them plaintively in these words—

> The heart-breaking anguish and woe of this life
>   I am able no longer to bear:
> My wings are benumbed with this pitiless frost;
> My three little brothers are scattered and lost;
>   And I am left here to despair.

> My three little brothers I never shall see
>   Till the dead shall arise from the tomb:
> How I sheltered them oft with my wings and my breast,
> And I soothed their sorrows and lulled them to rest,
>   As the night fell around us in gloom!
>
> Ah, where are my brothers, and why have I lived,
>   This last worst affliction to know?
> What now is there left but a life of despair?—
> For alas! I am able no longer to bear
>   This heart-breaking anguish and woe.*

Soon after this she looked again over the sea, and she saw Conn coming towards the rock, with his head drooping, and his feathers all drenched with the salt spray; and she welcomed him with joyful heart.

Not long after, Ficra appeared, but he was so faint with wet and cold and hardship, that he was scarce able to reach the place where Finola and Conn were standing; and when they spoke to him he could not speak one word in return. So Finola placed the two under her wings, and she said—

"If Aed were here now, all would be happy with us."

In a little time they saw Aed coming towards them, with head erect and feathers all dry and radiant and Finola gave him a joyful welcome. She then placed him under the feathers of her breast, while Conn and Ficra remained under her wings; and she said to them—

"My dear brothers, though ye may think this

---

* Many of these old poems begin and end with the same line or couplet.

night very bad, we shall have many like it from this time forth."

So they continued for a long time on the Sea of Moyle, suffering hardships of every kind, till one winter night came upon them, of great wind and of snow and frost so severe, that nothing they ever before suffered could be compared to the misery of that night. And Finola uttered these words—

Our life is a life of woe ;
  No shelter or rest we find :
How bitterly drives the snow ;
  How cold is this wintry wind !

From the icy spray of the sea,
  From the wind of the bleak north-east,
I shelter my brothers three,
  Under my wings and breast.

Our stepmother sent us here,
  And misery well we know :—
In cold and hunger and fear ;
  Our life is a life of woe !

Another year passed away on the Sea of Moyle ; and one night in January, a dreadful frost came down on the earth and sea, so that the waters were frozen into a solid floor of ice all round them. The swans remained on Carricknarone all night, and their feet and their wings were frozen to the icy surface, so that they had to strive hard to move from their places in the morning ; and they left the skin of their feet, the quills of their wings, and the feathers of their breasts clinging to the rock.

"Sad is our condition this night, my beloved

brothers," said Finola, "for we are forbidden to leave the Sea of Moyle; and yet we cannot bear the salt water, for when it enters our wounds, I fear we shall die of pain."

And she spoke this lay—

> Our fate is mournful here to-day;
>   Our bodies bare and chill,
> Drenched by the bitter, briny spray,
>   And torn on this rocky hill!
>
> Cruel our stepmother's jealous heart
>   That banished us from home;
> Transformed to swans by magic art,
>   To swim the ocean foam.
>
> This bleak and snowy winter day,
>   Our bath is the ocean wide;
> In thirsty summer's burning ray,
>   Our drink the briny tide.
>
> And here 'mid rugged rocks we dwell,
>   In this tempestuous bay;
> Four children bound by magic spell;—
>   Our fate is sad to-day!

They were, however, forced to swim out on the stream of Moyle, all wounded and torn as they were; for though the brine was sharp and bitter, they were not able to avoid it. They stayed as near the coast as they could, till after a long time the feathers of their breasts and wings grew again, and their wounds were healed.

After this they lived on for a great number of years, sometimes visiting the shores of Erin, and sometimes the headlands of Alban. But they always returned to the sea-stream of Moyle, for it was destined to be their home till the end of three hundred years.

One day they came to the mouth of the Bann, on the north coast of Erin, and looking inland, they saw a stately troop of horsemen approaching directly from the south-west. They were mounted on white steeds, and clad in bright-coloured garments, and as they wound towards the shore their arms glittered in the sun.

"Do ye know yonder cavalcade?" said Finola to her brothers.

"We know them not," they replied; "but it is likely they are a party of the Milesians, or perchance a troop of our own people, the Dedannans."

They swam towards the shore, to find out who the strangers were; and the cavalcade on their part, when they saw the swans, knew them at once, and moved towards them till they were within speaking distance.

Now these were a party of the Dedannans; and the chiefs who commanded them were the two sons of Bove Derg, the Dedannan king, namely, Aed the Keen-witted, and Fergus the Chess-player, with a third part of the Fairy Host.* They had been for a long time searching for the children of Lir along the northern shores of Erin, and now that they had found them, they were joyful; and they and the swans greeted each other with tender expressions of friendship and

* Fairy host; *i.e.* the Dedannans. (See note 1 at the end of the book.)

love. The children of Lir inquired after the Dedannans, and particularly after their father Lir, and
Bove Derg, and all the rest of their friends and
acquaintances.

"They are all well," replied the chiefs; "and they
and the Dedannans in general are now gathered
together in the house of your father, at Shee Finnaha,
celebrating the Feast of Age,[2] pleasantly and agreeably.
Their happiness would indeed be complete, only that
you are not with them, and that they know not where
you have been since you left Lake Darvra."

"Miserable has been our life since that day," said
Finola; "and no tongue can tell the suffering and
sorrow we have endured on the Sea of Moyle."

And she chanted these words—

> Ah, happy is Lir's bright home to-day,
> With mead and music and poet's lay:
> But gloomy and cold his children's home,
> For ever tossed on the briny foam.
>
> Our wreathèd feathers are thin and light
> When the wind blows keen through the wintry night:
> Yet oft we were robed, long, long ago,
> In purple mantles and furs of snow.
>
> On Moyle's bleak current our food and wine
> Are sandy sea-weed and bitter brine:
> Yet oft we feasted in days of old,
> And hazel-mead drank from cups of gold.
>
> Our beds are rocks in the dripping caves;
> Our lullaby song the roar of the waves:
> But soft rich couches once we pressed,
> And harpers lulled us each night to rest.

Lonely we swim on the billowy main,
Through frost and snow, through storm and rain:
Alas for the days when round us moved
The chiefs and princes and friends we loved!

My little twin brothers beneath my wings
Lie close when the north wind bitterly stings,
And Aed close nestles before my breast;
Thus side by side through the night we rest.

Our father's fond kisses, Bove Derg's embrace,
The light of Mannanan's [1] godlike face,
The love of Angus [1]—all, all are o'er;
And we live on the billows for evermore!

After this they bade each other farewell, for it was not permitted to the children of Lir to remain away from the stream of Moyle. As soon as they had parted, the Fairy Cavalcade returned to Shee Finnaha, where they related to the Dedannan chiefs all that had passed, and described the condition of the children of Lir. And the chiefs answered—

"It is not in our power to help them; but we are glad that they are living; and we know that in the end the enchantment will be broken, and that they will be freed from their sufferings."

As to the children of Lir, they returned to their home on the Sea of Moyle, and there they remained till they had fulfilled their term of years.

CHAPTER VI.

THE FOUR WHITE SWANS ON THE WESTERN SEA.

AND when their three hundred years were ended, Finola said to her brothers—

"It is time for us to leave this place, for our period here has come to an end."

> The hour has come; the hour has come;
>   Three hundred years have passed:
> We leave this bleak and gloomy home,
>   And we fly to the west at last!
>
> We leave for ever the stream of Moyle;
>   On the clear, cold wind we go;
> Three hundred years round Glora's isle,
>   Where wintry tempests blow!
>
> No sheltered home, no place of rest,
>   From the tempest's angry blast:
> Fly, brothers, fly, to the distant west,
>   For the hour has come at last!

So the swans left the Sea of Moyle, and flew westward, till they reached Irros Domnann and the sea round the isle of Glora. There they remained for a long time, suffering much from storm and cold, and in nothing better off than they were on the Sea of Moyle.

It chanced that a young man named Ebric, of good family, the owner of a tract of land lying along the shore, observed the birds and heard their singing.

He took great delight in listening to their plaintive music, and he walked down to the shore almost every day, to see them and to converse with them; so that he came to love them very much, and they also loved him. This young man told his neighbours about the speaking swans, so that the matter became noised abroad; and it was he who arranged the story, after hearing it from themselves, and related it as it is related here.

Again their hardships were renewed, and to describe what they suffered on the great open Western Sea would be only to tell over again the story of their life on the Moyle. But one particular night came, of frost so hard that the whole face of the sea, from Irros Domnann to Achill, was frozen into a thick floor of ice; and the snow was driven by a north-west wind. On that night it seemed to the three brothers that they could not bear their sufferings any longer, and they began to utter loud and pitiful complaints. Finola tried to console them, but she was not able to do so, for they only lamented the more; and then she herself began to lament with the others.

After a time, Finola spoke to them and said, " My dear brothers, believe in the great and splendid God of truth, who made the earth with its fruits, and the sea with its wonders ; put your trust in Him, and He will send you help and comfort."

" We believe in Him," said they.

" And I also," said Finola, " believe in God, who is perfect in everything, and who knows all things."

And at the destined hour they all believed, and
the Lord of heaven sent them help and protection;
so that neither cold nor tempest molested them from
that time forth, as long as they abode on the
Western Sea.

So they continued at the point of Irros Domnann,
till they had fulfilled their appointed time there.   And
Finola addressed the sons of Lir—

"My dear brothers, the end of our time here has
come; we shall now go to visit our father and our
people."

And her brothers were glad when they heard this.

Then they rose lightly from the face of the sea,
and flew eastward with joyful hopes, till they reached
Shee Finnaha.   But when they alighted they found
the place deserted and solitary, its halls all ruined and
overgrown with rank grass and forests of nettles;
no houses, no fire, no mark of human habitation.

Then the four swans drew close together, and they
uttered three loud mournful cries of sorrow.

And Finola chanted this lay—

> What meaneth this sad, this fearful change,
>   That withers my heart with woe?
> The house of my father all joyless and lone,
> Its halls and its gardens with weeds overgrown,—
>   A dreadful and strange overthrow!
>
> No conquering heroes, no hounds for the chase,
>   No shields in array on its walls,
> No bright silver goblets, no gay cavalcades,
> No youthful assemblies or high-born maids,
>   To brighten its desolate halls!

An omen of sadness—the home of our youth
    All ruined, deserted, and bare.
Alas for the chieftain, the gentle and brave;
His glories and sorrows are stilled in the grave,
    And we left to live in despair!

From ocean to ocean, from age unto age,
    We have lived to the fulness of time;
Through a life such as men never heard of we've passed,
In suffering and sorrow our doom has been cast,
    By our stepmother's pitiless crime!

The children of Lir remained that night in the ruins of the palace—the home of their forefathers, where they themselves had been nursed; and several times during the night they chanted their sad, sweet, fairy music.

Early next morning they left Shee Finnaha, and flew west to Inis Glora, where they alighted on a small lake. There they began to sing so sweetly that all the birds of the district gathered in flocks round them on the lake, and on its shore, to listen to them; so that the little lake came to be called the Lake of the Bird-flocks.

During the day the birds used to fly to distant points of the coast to feed, now to Iniskea of the lonely crane,* now to Achill, and sometimes southwards to Donn's Sea Rocks,† and to many other islands

---

* Iniskea; a little rocky island near the coast of Erris, in Mayo. "The lonely crane of Iniskea" was one of the "Wonders of Ireland." According to an ancient legend, which still lives among the peasantry of Mayo, a crane—one lonely bird—has lived on the island since the beginning of the world, and will live there till the day of judgment.

† Donn's Sea Rocks—called in the text *Teach-Dhuinn*, or Donn's House, which is also the present Irish name; a group of three rocks

and headlands along the shore of the Western Sea, but they returned to Inis Glora every night.

They lived in this manner till holy Patrick came to Erin with the pure faith; and until Saint Kemoc came to Inis Glora.

The first night Kemoc came to the island, the children of Lir heard his bell at early matin time, ringing faintly in the distance. And they trembled greatly, and started, and ran wildly about; for the sound of the bell was strange and dreadful to them, and its tones filled them with great fear. The three brothers were more affrighted than Finola, so that she was left quite alone; but after a time they came to her, and she asked them—

"Do you know, my brothers, what sound is this?"

And they answered, "We have heard a faint, fearful voice, but we know not what it is."

"This is the voice of the Christian bell," said Finola; "and now the end of our suffering is near; for this bell is the signal that we shall soon be freed from our spell, and released from our life of suffering; for God has willed it."

And she chanted this lay—

> Listen, ye swans, to the voice of the bell,
>   The sweet bell we've dreamed of for many a year;
> Its tones floating by on the night breezes, tell
>   That the end of our long life of sorrow is near!

---

off Kenmare Bay, where Donn, one of the Milesian brothers, was drowned. These remarkable rocks are now called in English the "Bull, Cow, and Calf."

Listen, ye swans, to the heavenly strain;
  'Tis the anchoret tolling his soft matin bell:
He has come to release us from sorrow, from pain,
  From the cold and tempestuous shores where we dwell!

Trust in the glorious Lord of the sky;
  He will free us from Eva's druidical spell:
Be thankful and glad, for our freedom is nigh,
  And listen with joy to the voice of the bell!

Then her brothers became calm; and the four swans remained listening to the music of the bell, till the cleric had finished his matins.

"Let us sing our music now," said Finola.

And they chanted a low, sweet, plaintive strain of fairy music, to praise and thank the great high King of heaven and earth.

Kemoc heard the music from where he stood; and he listened with great astonishment. But after a time it was revealed to him that it was the children of Lir who sang that music; and he was glad, for it was to seek them he had come.

When morning dawned he came to the shore of the lake, and he saw the four white swans swimming on the water. He spoke to them, and asked them were they the children of Lir.

They replied, "We are indeed the children of Lir, who were changed long ago into swans by our wicked stepmother."

"I give God thanks that I have found you," said Kemoc; "for it is on your account I have come to this little island in preference to all the other islands of Erin. Come ye now to land, and trust in me; for it is in this place that you are destined to be freed from your enchantment."

So they, filled with joy on hearing the words of the cleric, came to the shore, and placed themselves under his care. He brought them to his own house, and, sending for a skilful workman, he caused him to make two bright, slender chains of silver; and he put a chain between Finola and Aed, and the other chain he put between Ficra and Conn.

So they lived with him, listening to his instructions day by day, and joining in his devotions. They were the delight and joy of the cleric, and he loved them with his whole heart; and the swans were so happy that the memory of all the misery they had suffered during their long life on the waters caused them neither distress nor sorrow now.

CHAPTER VII.

THE CHILDREN OF LIR REGAIN THEIR HUMAN SHAPE AND DIE.

THE king who ruled over Connaught at this time was Largnen, the son of Colman; and his queen was Decca, the daughter of Finnin,* king of Munster,—the same king and queen whom Eva had spoken of in her prophecy long ages before.

---

* These are well-known historical personages, who flourished in the seventh century.

Now word was brought to queen Decca regarding these wonderful speaking swans, and their whole history was related to her; so that even before she saw them, she could not help loving them, and she was seized with a strong desire to have them herself. So she went to the king, and besought him that he would go to Kemoc and get her the swans. But Largnen said that he did not wish to ask them from Kemoc. Whereupon Decca grew indignant; and she declared that she would not sleep another night in the palace till he had obtained the swans for her. So she left the palace that very hour, and fled southwards towards her father's home.

Largnen, when he found she had gone, sent in haste after her, with word that he would try to procure the swans; but the messengers did not overtake her till she had reached Killaloe. However, she returned with them to the palace; and as soon as she had arrived, the king sent to Kemoc to request that he would send the birds to the queen; but Kemoc refused to give them.

Largnen became very angry at this; and he set out at once for the cleric's house. As soon as he had come, he asked the cleric whether it was true that he had refused to give the swans to the queen. And when Kemoc answered that it was quite true, the king, being very wroth, went up to where the swans stood, and seizing the two silver chains, one in each hand, he drew the birds from the altar, and turned towards the door of the church, intending to bring them by force to the queen; while Kemoc followed him, much alarmed lest they should be injured.

The king had proceeded only a little way, when suddenly the white feathery robes faded and disappeared; and the swans regained their human shape, Finola being transformed into an extremely old woman, and the three sons into three feeble old men, white-haired and bony and wrinkled.

When the king saw this, he started with affright, and instantly left the place without speaking one word; while Kemoc reproached and denounced him very bitterly.

As to the children of Lir, they turned towards Kemoc; and Finola spoke—

"Come, holy cleric, and baptise us without delay, for our death is near. You will grieve after us, O Kemoc; but in truth you are not more sorrowful at parting from us than we are at parting from you. Make our grave here and bury us together; and as I often sheltered my brothers when we were swans, so let us be placed in the grave—Conn standing near me at my right side, Ficra at my left, and Aed before my face."*

> Come, holy priest, with book and prayer;
> Baptise and shrive us here:
> Haste, cleric, haste, for the hour has come,
> And death at last is near!

---

* Among the ancient Celtic nations, the dead were often buried standing up in the grave. It was in this way Finola and her brothers were buried.

Dig our grave—a deep, deep grave,
　　Near the church we loved so well;
This little church, where first we heard
　　The voice of the Christian bell.

As oft in life my brothers dear
　　Were sooth'd by me to rest—
Ficra and Conn beneath my wings,
　　And Aed before my breast;

So place the two on either hand—
　　Close, like the love that bound me;
Place Aed as close before my face,
　　And twine their arms around me.

Thus shall we rest for evermore,
　　My brothers dear and I :
Haste, cleric, haste, baptise and shrive,
　　For death at last is nigh!

Then the children of Lir were baptised, and they died immediately. And when they died, Kemoc looked up; and lo, he saw a vision of four lovely children, with light, silvery wings, and faces all radiant with joy. They gazed on him for a moment; but even as they gazed, they vanished upwards, and he saw them no more. And he was filled with gladness, for he knew they had gone to heaven; but when he looked down on the four bodies lying before him, he became sad and wept.

And Kemoc caused a wide grave to be dug near the little church; and the children of Lir were buried together, as Finola had directed—Conn at her right hand, Ficra at her left, and Aed standing before her face. And he raised a grave-mound over them, placing a tombstone on it, with their names graved in Ogam;* after which he uttered a lament for them, and their funeral rites were performed.

So far we have related the sorrowful story of the Fate of the Children of Lir.

* Ogam, a sort of writing, often used on sepulchral stones to mark the names of the persons buried.

FATE OF THE CHILDREN OF TURENN;

OR,

THE QUEST FOR THE ERIC-FINE.

———◦◇◦———

For the blood that we spilled,
For the hero we killed,
Toil and woe, toil and woe, till the doom is fulfilled!

CHAPTER I.

THE LOCHLANNS INVADE ERIN.

WHEN the Dedannans [1] held sway in Erin, a prosperous free-born king ruled over them, whose name was Nuada of the Silver Hand.[4]

In the time of this king, the Fomorians,[5] from Lochlann,[6] in the north, oppressed the Dedannans, and forced them to pay heavy tributes; namely, a tax on kneading-troughs, a tax on querns, and a tax on baking flags; and besides all this, an ounce of gold for each man of the Dedannans. These tributes had to be paid every year at the Hill of Usna;* and if any one refused or neglected to pay his part, his nose was cut off by the Fomorian tyrants.

* The Hill of Usna, in the parish of Conry, in Westmeath, one of the royal residences of Ireland.

At this time a great fair-meeting was held by the king of Ireland, Nuada of the Silver Hand, on the Hill of Usna. Not long had the people been assembled, when they saw a stately band of warriors, all mounted on white steeds, coming towards them from the east; and at their head, high in command over all, rode a young champion, tall and comely, with a countenance as bright and glorious as the setting sun.

This young warrior was Luga of the Long Arms.[7] He was accompanied by his foster brothers, namely, the sons of Mannanan Mac Lir; and the troop he led was the Fairy Host from the Land of Promise.[8]

Now in this manner was he arrayed. He rode the steed of Mannanan Mac Lir,[8] namely, Enbarr of the Flowing Mane: no warrior was ever killed on the back of this steed, for she was as swift as the clear, cold wind of spring, and she travelled with equal ease on land and on sea. He wore Mannanan's coat of mail: no one could be wounded through it, or above it, or below it. He had on his breast Mannanan's breast-plate, which no weapon could pierce. His helmet had two glittering precious stones set in front, and one behind; and whenever he took it off, his face shone like the sun on a dry day in summer. Mannanan's sword, The Answerer, hung at his left side: no one ever recovered from its wound; and those who were opposed to it in the battle-field were so terrified by looking at it, that their strength left them till they became weaker than a woman in deadly sickness.

This troop came forward to where the king of

Erin sat surrounded by the Dedannans, and both parties exchanged friendly greetings.

A short time after this they saw another company approaching, quite unlike the first, for they were grim and fierce and surly looking; namely, the tax-gatherers of the Fomorians, to the number of nine nines, who were coming to demand their yearly tribute from the men of Erin.   When they reached the place where the king sat, the entire assembly—the king himself among the rest—rose up before them.   For the whole Dedannan race stood in great dread of these Fomorian tax-collectors; so much so that no man dared even to chastise his own son without first seeking their consent.

Then Luga of the Long Arms spoke to the king and said, "Why have ye stood up before this hateful-looking company, when ye did not stand up for us?"

"We durst not do otherwise," replied the king; "for if even an infant of a month old remained seated before them, they would deem it cause enough for killing us all."

When Luga heard this he brooded in silence for a little while, and then he said, "Of a truth, I feel a great desire to kill all these men!"

Then he mused again, and after a time, said, "I am strongly urged to kill these men!"

"That deed would doubtless bring great evil on us," said the king, "for then the Fomorians would be sure to send an army to destroy us all."

But Luga, after another pause, started up, exclaim-

ing, " Long have ye been oppressed in this manner ! "
and so saying, he attacked the Fomorians, dealing red
slaughter among them.   Neither did he hold his hand
till he had slain them all except nine.   These he
spared, because they ran with all speed and sat nigh
the king, that he might protect them from Luga's
wrath.

Then Luga put his sword back into its scabbard,
and said, " I would slay you also, only that I wish you
to go and tell your king, and the foreigners in general,
what you have seen."

These nine men accordingly returned to their own
country, and they told their tale to the Fomorian
people from beginning to end—how the strange, noble-
faced youth had slain all the tax-collectors except
nine, whom he spared that they might bring home the
story.

When they had ended speaking, the king, Balor[9] of
the Mighty Blows and of the Evil Eye, asked the
chiefs, "Do ye know who this youth is ? "

And when they answered, " No," Kethlenda,[9]
Balor's queen, said—

" I know well who the youth is : he is the
Ildana,* Luga of the Long Arms, the son of your
daughter and mine ; and it has been long foretold that
when he should appear in Erin, our sway over the
Dedannans should come to an end."

Then the chief people of the Fomorians held

---

* Luga of the Long Arms is often called The Ildana, *i.e.* the
Man of many sciences, to signify his various accomplishments.

council; namely, Balor of the Mighty Blows, and his twelve sons, and his queen Kethlenda of the Crooked Teeth; Ebb and Sencab, the grandsons of Neid; Sotal of the Large Heels; Luath the Long-bodied; Luath the Story-teller; Tinna the Mighty, of Triscadal; Loskenn of the Bare Knees; Lobas, the druid; besides the nine prophetic poets and philosophers of the Fomorians.

After they had debated the matter for some time, Bres, the son of Balor, arose and said, "I will go to Erin with seven great battalions of the Fomorian army, and I will give battle to the Ildana, and I will bring his head to you to our palace of Berva." [6]

The Fomorian chiefs thought well of this proposal, and it was agreed to.

So the ships were got ready for Bres; abundant food and drink and war stores were put into them, their seams were calked with pitch, and they were filled with sweet-smelling frankincense. Meantime the two Luaths, that is to say, Luath the Story-teller and Luath of the Long Body, were sent all over Lochlann to summon the army. And when all the fighting men were gathered together, they arrayed themselves in their battle-dresses, prepared their arms, and set out for Erin.

Balor went with them to the harbour where they were to embark, and when they were about to go on board, he said to them—

"Give battle to the Ildana, and cut off his head. And after ye have overcome him and his people, put your cables round this island of Erin, which gives us

so much trouble, and tie it at the sterns of your ships:
then sail home, bringing the island with you, and
place it on the north side of Lochlann, whither none
of the Dedannans will ever follow it."

Then, having hoisted their many-coloured sails and
loosed their moorings, they sailed forth from the
harbour into the great sea, and never slackened speed
or turned aside from their course till they reached the
harbour of Eas-Dara.*   And as soon as they landed,
they sent forth an army through West Connaught,
which wasted and spoiled the whole province.

CHAPTER II.

THE MURDER OF KIAN.

Now the king of Connaught at that time was Bove
Derg, the son of the Dagda,† a friend to Luga of the
Long Arms.   It chanced that Luga was then at Tara,‡
and news was brought to him that the Fomorians
had landed at Eas-Dara, and were spoiling and wasting
the province.   He immediately got ready his steed,
Enbarr of the Flowing Mane; and early in the morning,
when the point of night met the day, he went to the
king and told him that the foreigners had landed, and

* Eas-Dara, now Ballysodare, in the county Sligo.
† See page 1.
‡ Tara, in Meath, the chief seat of the kings of Ireland.

that' they had wasted and plundered the province of Bove Derg.

"I shall give them battle," said Luga; "and I wish to get from thee some help of men and arms."

"I will give no help," said the king; "for I do not wish to avenge a deed that has not been done against myself."

When Luga heard this reply he was wroth, and departing straightway from Tara, he rode westward. He had not travelled long when he saw at a distance three warriors, fully armed, riding towards him. Now these were three brothers, the sons of Canta; namely, Kian and Cu and Kethen; and Kian was Luga's father. And they saluted each other, and conversed together for a time.

"Why art thou abroad so early?" said they.

"Cause enough have I," replied Luga; "for the Fomorians have landed in Erin, and have wasted the province of Bove Derg, the son of the Dagda. It is well indeed that I have met you, for I am about to give them battle, and I wish now to know what aid I shall get from you."

"We will go into the battle with you," said they; "and each of us will ward off from you a hundred of the Fomorian warriors."

"That, indeed, is good help," said Luga; "but, for the present, I wish you to go to the several places throughout Erin where the Fairy Host * are abiding, and summon them all to me."

* Fairy Host, *i.e.* the Dedannans.   (See notes 1 and 8 at end.)

The three brothers accordingly separated, Cu and Kethen going south, while Luga's father, Kian, turned his face northwards, and rode on till he came to Moy Murthemna.* He had not been long travelling over the plain when he saw three warriors, clad in armour and fully armed, coming towards him. These were three Dedannan chiefs, the sons of Turenn, and their names were Brian, Ur, and Urcar. Now these three and the three sons of Canta were at deadly feud with each other, on account of an old quarrel, and whenever they met there was sure to be a fight for life or death.

As soon as Kian saw these three, he said, "If my two brothers were now with me, we should have a brave fight; but as they are not, and as I am only one against three, it is better to avoid the combat." So saying, he looked round, and seeing near him a herd of swine, he struck himself with a golden druidical[5] wand, and changed himself into a pig; and he quickly joined the herd.

No sooner had he done so than Brian, the eldest of the sons of Turenn, said to his brothers, "Tell me, my brothers, do you know what has become of the warrior that we saw just now approaching us on the plain?"

"We saw him," said they, "but we know not whither he has gone."

"You deserve great blame," said he, "that you are not more watchful while traversing the country during this time of war. Now I know what has happened

---

* Moy Murthemna, a plain in the county of Louth.

to this warrior; he has changed himself, by a druidical spell, into a pig; and he is now among yonder herd. And whoever he may be, of this be sure—he is no friend of ours."

"This is an unlucky matter," said they; "for as these pigs belong to one of the Dedannans, it would be wrong for us to kill them; and even if we should do so, the enchanted pig might escape after all."

"But," answered Brian, "I think I can manage to distinguish any druidical beast from a natural one; and if you had attended well to your learning, you would be able to do the same."

Saying this, he struck his brothers one after the other with his golden druidical wand, and turned them into two fleet, slender, sharp-nosed hounds. The moment he had done so they put their noses to the earth, and, yelping eagerly, set off towards the herd on the trail of their enemy. When they had come near, the druidical pig fell out from the herd, and made towards a thick grove that grew hard by; but Brian was there before him, and drove his spear through his chest.

The pig screamed and said, "You have done an ill deed to cast your spear at me, for you know well who I am."

"Your voice, methinks, is the voice of a man," said Brian; "but I know not who you are."

And the pig answered, "I am Kian, the on of Canta; and now I ask you to give me quarter."

Ur and Urcar, who had regained their shape and

come up, said, "We will give you quarter indeed, and
we are sorry for what has happened to you."

But Brian, on the other hand, said, "I swear by the
gods of the air, that if your life returned to you seven
times, I would take it from you seven times."

"Then," said Kian, "as you will not grant me
quarter, allow me first to return to my own shape."

"That we will grant you," said Brian; "for I often
feel it easier to kill a man than to kill a pig."

Kian accordingly took his own shape; and then he
said, "You indeed, ye sons of Turenn, are now about
to slay me; but even so, I have outwitted you. For
if you had slain me in the shape of a pig, you would
have to pay only the eric-fine [10] for a pig; whereas,
now that I am in my own shape, you shall pay the
full fine for a man. And there never yet was killed,
and there never shall be killed, a man for whom a
greater fine shall be paid, than you will have to pay
for me. The weapons with which I am slain shall
tell the deed to my son; and he will exact the fine
from you."

"You shall not be slain with the weapons of a
warrior," said Brian; and so saying, he and his
brothers laid aside their arms, and smote him fiercely
and rudely with the round stones of the earth, till they
had reduced his body to a disfigured mass; and in this
manner they slew him.

They then buried him a man's height in the earth;
but the earth, being angry at the fratricide,* refused

* Fratricide; Gaelic, *fionghal*, the murder of a relative. (See note,

to receive the body, and cast it up on the surface. They buried him a second time, and again the body was thrown up from beneath the clay. Six times the sons of Turenn buried the body of Kian a man's height in the earth, and six times did the earth cast it up, refusing to receive it. But when they had buried him the seventh time, the earth refused no longer, and the body remained in the grave.

Then the sons of Turenn prepared to go forward after Luga of the Long Arms to the battle. But as they were leaving the grave, they thought they heard a faint, muffled voice coming up from the ground beneath their feet—

> The blood you have spilled,
> The hero you've killed,
> Shall follow your steps till your doom be fulfilled !

CHAPTER III.

DEFEAT AND FLIGHT OF THE LOCHLANNS.

Now as to Luga. After parting from his father, he journeyed westward till he reached Ath-Luan,* thence

page 7.) The sons of Turenn and the sons of Canta appear to have been related to each other (see the third stanza of the poem, page 94).

* *Ath-Luan,* now Athlone; *Ros-Coman,* now Roscommon; *Moy-Lurg,* a plain in the county Roscommon; Curlieu Hills, a range of hills near Boyle, in Roscommon; Kesh-Corran, a well-known mountain in Sligo. The "Great Plain of the Assembly" must have been near Ballysodare, in Sligo.

to Ros-Coman, and over Moy-Lurg to the Curlieu Hills, and to the mountain of Kesh-Corran, till he reached the " Great Plain of the Assembly," where the foreigners were encamped, with the spoils of Connaught around them.

As he drew nigh to the Fomorian encampment, Bres, the son of Balor, arose and said—

" A wonderful thing has come to pass this day ; for the sun, it seems to me, has risen in the west."

" It would be better that it were so," said the druids,[3] " than that matters should be as they are."

" What else can it be, then ? " asked Bres.

" The light you see," replied the druids, " is the brightness of the face, and the flashing of the weapons of Luga of the Long Arms, our deadly enemy, he who slew our tax-gatherers, and who now approaches."

Then Luga came up peacefully and saluted them.

" How does it come to pass that you salute us," said they, " since you are, as we know well, our enemy ? "

" I have good cause for saluting you," answered Luga ; " for only one half of my blood is Dedannan ; the other half comes from you ; for I am the son of the daughter of Balor of the Mighty Blows, your king.[7] And now I come in peace, to ask you to give back to the men of Connaught all the milch cows you have taken from them."

" May ill luck follow thee," said one of the Fomorian leaders, in a voice loud and wrathful, " until thou get one of them, either a milch cow or a dry cow ! "

And the others spoke in a like strain.

Then Luga put a druidical spell upon the plundered
cattle; and he sent all the milch cows home, each to
the door of her owner's house, throughout all that
part of Connaught that had been plundered.   But the
dry cows he left, so that the Fomorians might be
cumbered, and that they might not leave their encampment till the Fairy Host should arrive to give
them battle.

Luga tarried three days and three nights near
them, and at the end of that time the Fairy Host
arrived, and placed themselves under his command.
They encamped near the Fomorians, and in a little
time Bove Derg, son of the Dagda, joined them with
twenty-nine hundred men.

Then they made ready for the fight.   The Ildana
put on Mannanan's coat of mail and his breast-plate;
he took also his helmet, which was called Cannbarr,
and it glittered in the sun with dazzling brightness;
he slung his broad, dark-blue shield from his shoulder
at one side; his long, keen-edged sword hung at his
thigh; and lastly, he took his two long, heavy-handled
spears, which had been tempered in the poisonous
blood of adders.   The other kings and chiefs of the
men of Erin arrayed their men in battle ranks;
hedges of glittering spears rose high above their
heads; and their shields, placed edge to edge, formed
a firm fence around them.

Then at the signal they attacked the Fomorians,
and the Fomorians, in no degree dismayed, answered
their onset.   At first a cloud of whizzing javelins flew

from rank to rank across the open space, and as the warriors rushed together in closer conflict, their spears were shivered in their hands. Then they drew their gold-hilted swords, and fought foot to foot and shield to shield, so that a forest of bright flashes rose high above their helmets, from the clashing of their keen-tempered weapons.

In the midst of the fight, Luga looked round, and seeing at some distance, Bres, surrounded by his Fomorian warriors, dealing havoc and death among the Dedannans, he rushed through the press of battle, and attacked first Bres's guards so fiercely that in a few moments twenty of them fell beneath his blows.

Then he struck at Bres himself, who, unable to withstand his furious onset, cried aloud—

"Why should we be enemies, since thou art of my kin? Let there be peace between us, for nothing can withstand thy blows. Let there be peace, and I will undertake to bring my Fomorians to assist thee at Moytura,[11] and I will promise never again to come to fight against thee."

And Bres swore by the sun and the moon, by the sea and land, and by all the elements,* to fulfil his engagement; and on these conditions Luga granted him his life.

Then the Fomorians, seeing their chief overcome, dropped their arms, and sued for quarter. The Fomo-

---

* A usual form of oath among the ancient Irish. (See, for an account of this oath, the author's " Origin and History of Irish Names of Places," Series II. chap. XIV.)

rian druids and men of learning next came to Luga
to ask him to spare their lives; and Luga answered
them—

"So far am I from wishing to slay you, that in
truth, if you had taken the whole Fomorian race
under your protection, I would have spared them."

And after this, Bres, the son of Balor, returned to
his own country with his druids, and with those of
his army who had escaped from the battle.

CHAPTER IV.

THE ERIC-FINE ON THE SONS OF TURENN FOR THE SLAYING OF KIAN.

TOWARDS the close of the day, when the battle was
ended, Luga espied two of his near friends; and he
asked them if they had seen his father, Kian, in the
fight. And when they answered, "No," Luga said—

"My father is not alive; for if he lived he would
surely have come to help me in the battle. And now
I swear that neither food nor drink will I take till
I have found out who has slain him, and the manner
of his death."

Then Luga set out with a small chosen band of
the Fairy Host, and he halted not till he reached the
place where he had parted from his father. And from
that he travelled on to the plain of Murthemna, where

Kian had been forced to take the shape of a pig to avoid the sons of Turenn, and where they had slain him.

When he had come near to the very spot, he walked some little way before his companions, and the stones of the earth spoke beneath his feet, and said—

"Here thy father lies, O Luga. Grievous was Kian's strait when he was forced to take the shape of a pig on seeing the three sons of Turenn; and here they slew him in his own shape!"

> The blood that they spilled,
> The hero they killed,
> Shall darken their lives till their doom be fulfilled!

Luga stood for a while silent, pondering on these words. But as his companions came up, he told them what had happened; and having pointed out the spot from which the voice came, he caused the ground to be dug up. There they found the body, and raised it to the surface; and when they had examined it, they saw that it was covered all over with gory wounds and bruises.

Then Luga spoke after a long silence, "A cruel and merciless death has my beloved father suffered at the hands of the sons of Turenn!"

He kissed his father's face three times, and again spoke, grieving, "Ill fare the day on which my father was slain! Woful is this deed to me, for my eyes see not, my ears hear not, and my heart's pulse has ceased to beat, for grief. Why, O ye gods whom I worship,

why was I not present when this deed was done?
Alas! an evil thing has happened, for the Dedannans
have slain their brother Dedannan. Ill shall they fare
of this fratricide, for its consequences shall follow
them, and long shall the crime of brother against
brother continue to be committed in Erin!"

And he spoke this speech—

> A dreadful doom my father found
>   On that ill-omened even-tide;
> And here I mourn beside the mound,
>   Where, whelmed by numbers, Kian died,—
> This lonely mound of evil fame,
> That long shall bear the hero's name!
>
> Alas! an evil deed is done,
>   And long shall Erin rue the day:
> There shall be strife 'twixt sire and son,
>   And brothers shall their brothers slay;
> Vengeance shall smite the murderers too,
> And vengeance all their race pursue!
>
> The light has faded from mine eyes;
>   My youthful strength and power have fled
> Weary my heart with ceaseless sighs;
>   Ambition, hope, and joy are dead;
> And all the world is draped in gloom—
> The shadow of my father's tomb!

Then they placed the hero again in the grave, and
they raised a tomb over him with his name graved in
Ogam;* after which his lamentation lays were sung,
and his funeral games were performed.

When these rites were ended, Luga said to his
people, "Go ye now to Tara, where the king of Erin

* A kind of writing. (See note, page 36.)

sits on his throne with the Dedannans around him; but do not make these things known till I myself have told them."

So Luga's people went straightway to Tara, as he had bade them; but of the murder of Kian they said naught. Luga himself arrived some time after, and was received with great honour, being put to sit high over the others, at the king's side; for the fame of his mighty deeds at the battle of the Assembly Plain had been noised over the whole country, and had come to the ears of the king.

After he was seated, he looked round the hall, and saw the sons of Turenn in the assembly. Now these three sons of Turenn exceeded all the champions in Tara, in comeliness of person, in swiftness of foot, and in feats of arms; and, next to Luga himself, they were the best and bravest in the battles against the Fomorians; wherefore they were honoured by the king beyond most others.

Luga asked the king that the chain of silence * should be shaken; and when it was shaken, and when all were listening in silence, he stood up and spoke—

"I perceive, ye nobles of the Dedannan race, that you have given me your attention, and now I have a question to put to each man here present: What vengeance would you take of the man who should knowingly and of design kill your father?"

---

* Chain of silence; a chain, probably hung with little bells, which the lord of a mansion shook when he wished to get silence and attention.

They were all struck with amazement on hearing this, and the king of Erin said—

"What does this mean? For that your father has not been killed, this we all know well!"

"My father has indeed been killed," answered Luga; "and I see now here in this hall those who slew him. And furthermore, I know the manner in which they put him to death, even as they know it themselves."

The sons of Turenn, hearing all this, said nothing; but the king spoke aloud and said—

"If any man should wilfully slay my father, it is not in one hour or in one day I would have him put to death; but I would lop off one of his members each day, till I saw him die in torment under my hands!"

All the nobles said the same, and the sons of Turenn in like manner.

"The persons who slew my father are here present, and are joining with the rest in this judgment," said Luga; "and as the Dedannans are all now here to witness, I claim that the three who have done this evil deed shall pay me a fitting eric-fine for my father. Should they refuse, I shall not indeed transgress the king's law nor violate his protection; but of a certainty they shall not leave this hall of Micorta * till the matter is settled."

And the king of Erin said, "If I had killed your

* Micŏ′rta; the name of the great banqueting hall of Tara, the ruins of which are to be seen to this day.

father, I should be well content if you were willing to accept an eric-fine from me."

Now the sons of Turenn spoke among themselves; and Ur and Urcar said, "It is of us Luga speaks this speech. He has doubtless found out that we slew his father; and it is better that we now acknowledge the deed, for it will avail us naught to hide it."

Brian, however, at first set his face against this, saying that he feared Luga only wanted an acknowledgment from them in presence of the other Dedannans, and that afterwards he might not accept a fine. But the other two were earnest in pressing him, so that he consented, and then he spoke to Luga—

"It is of us thou speakest all these things, Luga; for it has been said that we three have been at enmity with the three sons of Canta. Now, as to the slaying of thy father Kian, let that matter rest; but we are willing to pay an eric-fine for him, even as if we had killed him."

"I shall accept an eric-fine from you," said Luga, "though ye indeed fear I shall not. I shall now name before this assembly the fine I ask, and if you think it too much, I shall take off a part of it.

"The first part of my eric-fine is three apples; the second part is the skin of a pig; the third is a spear; the fourth, two steeds and a chariot; the fifth, seven pigs; the sixth, a hound-whelp; the seventh, a cooking-spit; and the eighth, three shouts on a hill. That is my eric," said Luga; "and if ye think it too much, say so now, that I may remit a part; but if not, then it will be well that ye set about paying it."

"So far," said Brian, "we do not deem it too great. It seems, indeed, so small that we fear there is some hidden snare in what you ask, which may work us mischief."

"I do not deem my eric too small," said Luga; "and now I engage here, before the assembled Dedannans, that I will ask no more, and that I will seek no further vengeance for my father's death. But, as I have made myself answerable to them for the faithful fulfilment of my promise, I demand the same guarantee from you, that you also be faithful to me."

"Alas that you should doubt our plighted word!" said the sons of Turenn. "Are we not ourselves sufficient guarantee for the payment of an eric-fine greater even than this?"

"I do not deem your word sufficient guarantee," answered Luga; "for often have we known great warriors like you to promise a fine before all the people, and afterwards to go back of their promise."

And the sons of Turenn consented, though unwillingly, for they grieved that their word should be doubted. So they bound themselves on either side— Luga not to increase his claims; and the sons of Turenn, on their part, to pay him the full fine. And the king of Erin and Bove Derg, son of the Dagda, and the nobles of the Dedannans in general, were witnesses and sureties of this bond.

Then Luga stood up and said, "It is now time that I give you a full knowledge of this eric-fine.

"The three apples I ask are the apples of the

Garden of Hisberna,* in the east of the world, and
none others will I have. There are no apples in the
rest of the world like them, for their beauty and for
the secret virtues they possess. Their colour is the
colour of burnished gold; they have the taste of honey;
and if a wounded warrior or a man in deadly sickness
eat of them, he is cured immediately. And they are
never lessened by being eaten, being as large and
perfect at the end as at the beginning. Moreover,
any champion that possesses one of them may perform
with it whatsoever feat he pleases, by casting it from
his hand, and the apple will return to him of itself.
And though you are three brave warriors, ye sons of
Turenn, methinks you will not find it easy to bring
away these apples; for it has been long foretold that
three young champions from the Island of the West
would come to take them by force, so that the king
has set guards to watch for your coming.

"The pig's skin I seek from you belongs to Tuis,
the king of Greece. When the pig was alive, every
stream of water through which she walked was turned
into wine for nine days, and all sick and wounded
people that touched her skin were at once cured,
if only the breath of life remained. Now the king's
druids told him that the virtue lay, not in the pig
herself, but in her skin; so the king had her killed and
skinned, and he has her skin now. This, too, ye valiant
champions, is a part of my eric-fine which you will
find it hard to get, either by force or by friendship.

* The Garden of the Hesperides.

" The spear I demand from you is the venomed spear of Pezar, king of Persia. Its name is Slaughterer. In time of peace, its blazing, fiery head is always kept in a great caldron of water, to prevent it from burning down the king's palace; and in time of war, the champion who bears it to the battle-field can perform any deed he pleases with it. And it will be no easy matter to get this spear from the king of Persia.

" The two steeds and the chariot belong to Dobar, king of Sigar.* The chariot exceeds all the chariots in the world for beauty of shape and goodliness of workmanship. The two noble steeds have no equal for strength and fleetness, and they travel with as much ease on sea as on land.

" The seven pigs I demand are the pigs of Asal, the king of the Golden Pillars. Whoever eats a part of them shall not suffer from ill health or disease; and even though they should be killed and eaten to-day, they will be alive and well to-morrow.

" The hound-whelp belongs to the king of Iroda,† and his name is Failinis. He shines as brightly as the sun in a summer sky; and every wild beast of the forest that sees him falls down to the earth powerless before him.

" The cooking-spit belongs to the warlike women of the island of Fincara. They are thrice fifty in number, and woe to the champion who approaches

* Sigar, i.e. Sicily.
† Iroda was the name given by the Irish to some country in the far north of Europe, probably Norway.

their house; for each of them is a match for three
good warriors in single combat; and they never yet
gave a cooking-spit to any one without being overcome in battle.

"The hill on which I require you to give three
shouts is the Hill of Midkena, in the north of Lochlann.[6]
Midkena and his sons are always guarding this hill,
for they are under gesa[12] not to allow any one to
shout on it. Moreover, it was they that instructed my
father in championship and feats of arms, and they
loved him very much; so that even if I should forgive
you his death they would not. And, though you
should be able to procure all the rest of the eric-fine,
you will not, I think, succeed in this, for they will
be sure to avenge on you my father's death.

"And this, ye sons of Turenn, is the eric-fine I
demand from you!"

———◆———

CHAPTER V.

THE SONS OF TURENN OBTAIN MANNANAN'S CANOE, "THE WAVE-SWEEPER."

THE sons of Turenn were so astounded on hearing
this eric-fine that they spoke not one word; but rising
up, they left the meeting, and repaired to the house
of their father Turenn.

He heard their story to the end, and then said, "Your tidings are bad, my sons, and I fear me you are doomed to meet your death in seeking what the Ildana asks. But the doom is a just one, for it was an evil thing to kill Kian. Now as to this eric-fine: it cannot be obtained by any living man without the help of either Luga himself or of Mannanan Mac Lir;[8] but if Luga wishes to aid you, ye shall be able to get it. Go ye now, therefore, and ask him to lend you Mannanan's steed, Enbarr of the Flowing Mane. If he wishes you to get the full eric-fine, he will lend you the steed; otherwise he will refuse, saying that she does not belong to him, and that he cannot lend what he himself has got on loan. Then, if ye obtain not the steed, ask him for the loan of Mannanan's canoe, the Wave-sweeper, which would be better for you than the steed; and he will lend you that, for he is forbidden to refuse a second request."

So the sons of Turenn returned to Luga, and having saluted him, they said—

"It is not in the power of any man to obtain this eric-fine without thy own aid, O Luga; we ask thee, therefore, to lend us Mannanan's steed, Enbarr of the Flowing Mane."

"That steed is not my own," said Luga; "and I cannot lend that which I have myself obtained on loan."

"If that be so," said Brian, "then I pray thee lend us Mannanan's canoe, the Wave-sweeper."

"I shall lend you that," replied Luga; "it lies at

Bruga of the Boyne;* and ye have my consent to take it."

So they came again to their father, and this time Ethnea, their sister, was with him; and they told them that Luga had given them the canoe.

"I have much fear," said Turenn, "that it will avail you little against the dangers of your quest. Nevertheless, Luga desires to obtain that part of the eric that will be useful to him at the battle of Moytura,[11] and so far he will help you. But in seeking that which is of no advantage to him, namely, the cooking-spit, and the three shouts on Midkena's Hill, therein he will give you no aid, and he will be glad if ye perish in your attempts to obtain it."

They then set out for Bruga of the Boyne, accompanied by their sister Ethnea, leaving Turenn lamenting after them. The canoe they found lying in the river; and Brian went into it and said—

"It seems to me that only one other person can sit here along with me;" and he began to complain very bitterly of its smallness. He ceased, however, at the bidding of Ethnea, who told him that the canoe would turn out large enough when they came to try it, and that it was under strict command not to let any one grumble at its smallness. And she went on to say—

"Alas, my beloved brothers, it was an evil deed

---

* Bruga of the Boyne, the palace of Angus, the great Dedannan magician, was situated on the north shore of the Boyne, not far from Slane. (See note 1 at end.)

to slay the father of Luga of the Long Arms! and I fear you will suffer much woe and hardship on account of it."

ETHNEA.

The deed was a dark one, a deed full of woe,
    Your brother Dedannan to slay;
And hard and relentless the heart of your foe,
The bright-faced Ildana, that forced you to go,
    This eric of vengeance to pay!

THE BROTHERS.

Oh, cease, sister Ethnea, cease thy sad wail :
    Why yield to this terror and gloom?
Long, long shall the poets remember the tale,
For our courage and valour and swords shall prevail,
    Or win us a glorious tomb!

ETHNEA.

Then search ye, my brothers, go search land and sea;
    Go search ye the isles of the East.—
Alas, that the cruel Ildana's decree
Has banished my three gentle brothers from me,
    On this fearful and perilous quest!

CHAPTER VI.

THE APPLES OF THE GARDEN OF HISBERNA.

AFTER this the three brothers entered the canoe, which they now found large enough to hold themselves and their arms, and whatsoever else they wished to bring; for this was one of its secret gifts. They then bade their sister farewell, and, leaving her weeping on the shore, they rowed swiftly till they had got beyond the beautiful shores and bright harbours of Erin, out on the open sea.

Then the two younger brothers said, "Now our quest begins: what course shall we take?"

Brian answered, "As the apples are the first part of the fine, we shall seek them first."

And then he spoke to the canoe, "Thou canoe of Mannanan, thou Sweeper of the waves, we ask thee and we command thee, that thou sail straightway to the Garden of Hisberna!"

The canoe was not unmindful of the voice of its master, and obeyed the command without delay, according to its wont. It took the shortest way across the deep sea-chasms, and, gliding over the green-sided waves more swiftly than the clear, cold wind of March, it stayed not in its course till it reached the harbour near the land of Hisberna.

Brian now spoke to his brothers, "Be sure that this quest is a perilous one, since we know that the best champions of the country, with the king at their head, are always guarding the apples. And now in what manner, think you, is it best for us to approach the garden?"

"It seems to us," answered his brothers, "that we had better go straight and attack these champions, and either bring away the apples, or fall fighting for them. For we cannot escape the dangers that lie before us; and if we are doomed to fall in one of these adventures, it may, perchance, be better for us to die here than to prolong our hardships."

But Brian answered, "Not so, my brothers; for it becomes a warrior to be prudent and wary as well as brave. We should now act so that the fame of our skill and valour may live after us, and that future men may not say, 'These sons of Turenn did not deserve to be called brave champions, for they were senseless and rash, and sought their own death by their folly.' In the present case, then, what I counsel is this: Let us take the shape of strong, swift hawks; and as we approach the garden, have ye care of the light, sharp lances of the guards, which they will certainly hurl at us: avoid them actively and cunningly, and when the men have thrown all, let us swoop down and bring away an apple each."

They approved this counsel; and Brian, striking his two brothers and himself with a druidical magic wand, all three were changed into three beautiful hawks. Then, flying swiftly to the garden, they began to descend in circles towards the tops of the trees; but the sharp-eyed guards perceived them, and with a great shout they threw showers of venomous darts at them. The hawks, however, mindful of Brian's warning, watched the spears with keen glances, and escaped them every one, until the guards had thrown all their light weapons. Then, swooping suddenly down on the trees, the two younger brothers carried off an apple each, and Brian two, one between his talons and the other in his beak; and the three rose again into the air without wound or hurt of any kind. Then, directing their course westward, they flew over the wide sea with the speed of an arrow.

The news spread quickly through the city, how three beautiful hawks had carried off the apples; and the king and his people were in great wrath. Now the king had three daughters, very skilful in magic and cunning in counsel; and they forthwith transformed themselves into three swift-winged, sharptaloned griffins, and pursued the hawks over the sea. But the hawks, when they saw they were pursued, increased their speed, and flew like the wind, and left their pursuers so far behind that they appeared to the griffins like three specks on the sky. Then the angry griffins let fly from their eyes, and from their open beaks, bright flashes of flame straight forward, which overtook and blinded the hawks, and scorched them, so that they could bear the heat no longer.

"Evil is our state now," said Ur and Urcar, "for these sheets of flame are burning us, and we shall perish if we do not get relief."

"I will try whether I cannot relieve you," said Brian; and with that he struck his brothers and himself with his golden druidical wand; and all three were instantly turned into swans. The swans dropped down on the sea; and when the griffins saw the hawks no longer straight before them, they gave up the chase. And the sons of Turenn went safely to their canoe, bringing the apples with them.

CHAPTER VII.

THE GIFTED SKIN OF THE PIG.

AFTER resting a little while, they held council as to their next journey; and what they resolved on was to go to Greece, to seek the skin of the pig, and to bring it away, either by consent or by force. So they went into the canoe, and Brian spoke—

"Thou canoe of Mannanan, thou Sweeper of the Waves, we ask thee and we command thee that thou sail with us straightway to Greece!"

And the canoe, obeying as before, glided swiftly and smoothly over the waves, till the sons of Turenn landed near the palace of the king of Greece.

"In what shape, think you, should we go to this court?" said Brian.

"We think it best," answered the others, "to go in our own shapes; that is to say, as three bold champions."

"Not so," said Brian. "It seems best to me that we should go in the guise of learned poets from Erin; for poets are held in much honour and respect by the great nobles of Greece."

"It is, indeed, hard for us to do that," answered his brothers, "for as to poems, we neither have any, nor do we know how to compose them."

However, as Brian would have it so, they consented, though unwillingly; and, tying up their hair after the manner of poets, they knocked at the door of the palace. The door-keeper asked who was there.

"We are skilful poets from Erin," said Brian, "and we have come to Greece with a poem for the king."

The door-keeper went and gave the message.

"Let them be brought in," said the king, "for it is to seek a good and bountiful master whom they may serve faithfully that they have come so far from Erin."

The sons of Turenn were accordingly led in to the banquet hall, where sat the king surrounded by his nobles; and, bowing low, they saluted him; and he saluted them in return, and welcomed them. They sat at the table among the company, and joined the feast at once, drinking and making merry like the others; and they thought they had never seen a banquet hall so grand, or a household so numerous and mirthful.

At the proper time the king's poets arose, according to custom, to recite their poems and their lays for the company. And when they had come to an end, Brian, speaking low, said to his brothers—

"As we have come here as poets, it is meet that we should practise the poetic art like the others; therefore now arise, and recite a poem for the king."

"We have no poems," they replied, "and we do not wish to practise any art except the art we have learned and practised from our youth, namely, to fight like brave champions, and to take by valour and force of arms that which we want, if we be stronger than our enemies, or to fall in battle if they be the stronger."

"That is not a pleasant way of making poetry," said Brian; and with that he arose and requested attention for his poem.   And when they sat listening, he said—

> To praise thee, O Tuis, we've come to this land :
> Like an oak among shrubs, over kings thou dost stand :
> Thy bounty, great monarch, shall gladden the bard ;
> And the *Imnocta-fessa* I claim as reward.
>
> Two neighbours shall war, with an O to an O ;
> A bard unrequited—how dreadful a foe !
> Thy bounty shall add to thy wealth and thy fame ;
> And the *Imnocta-fessa* is all that I claim.

"Your poem would doubtless be thought a very good one," said the king, "if we were able to judge of it; but it is unlike all other poems I have ever heard, for I do not in the least understand its sense."

"I will unfold its sense," said Brian.

> To praise thee, O Tuis, we've come to this land :
> Like an oak among shrubs, over kings thou dost stand :

"This means that as the oak excels all the other trees of the forest, so dost thou excel all the other kings of the world for greatness, nobility, and generosity.

"'*Imnocta-fessa*.' *Imnocta* means 'skin,' and *fessa* 'a pig.'   That is to say, thou hast, O king, the skin of a pig, which I desire to get from thee as a guerdon for my poetry.

> Two neighbours shall war, with an O to an O ;
> A bard unrequited—how dreadful a foe !

"*O* means 'an ear;' that is to say, thou and I shall

be ear to ear fighting with each other for the skin, if thou give it not of thy own free will.

"And that, O king, is the sense of my poem."

"Thy poem would have been a very good one," said the king, "and I would have given it due meed of praise if my pig's skin had not been mentioned in it. But it is a foolish request of thine, O ferdana,* to ask for that skin; for, even though all the poets and men of science of Erin, and all the nobles of the whole world were to demand it from me, I would refuse it. Nevertheless, thou shalt not pass unrewarded, for I will give thee thrice the full of the skin of red gold—one for thyself, and one for each of thy brothers."

"Thy ransom is a good one, O king," said Brian; "but I am a near-hearted and suspicious man, and I pray thee let me see with my eyes thy servants measure the gold, lest they deal unfairly with me."

The king agreed to this; so his servants went with the three sons of Turenn to the treasure-room, and one of them drew forth the skin from its place, to measure the gold. As soon as Brian caught sight of it, he sprang suddenly towards the servant, and, dashing him to the ground with his right hand, he snatched the skin with his left, and bound it hastily over his shoulders.

Then the three drew their keen swords, and rushed into the banquet hall. The king's nobles, seeing how matters stood, surrounded and attacked them; but the

---

* Ferdana, a poet; literally, " a man of verse."

sons of Turenn, nothing daunted by the number of
their foes, hewed down the foremost and scattered the
rest, so that scarce one of the whole party escaped
death or deadly wounds.

Then at last Brian and the king met face to face,
nor was either slow to answer the challenge of the
other. They fought as great champions fight, and it
was long doubtful which should prevail; but the end
of the combat was, that the king of Greece fell by the
overpowering valour of Brian, the son of Turenn.

After this victory, the three brothers rested in the
palace till they had regained their strength, and healed
up their wounds by means of the apples and the pig's
skin; and at the end of three days and three nights
they found themselves able to undertake the next
adventure.

CHAPTER VIII.

THE BLAZING SPEAR OF THE KING OF PERSIA.

So, after holding council, they resolved to go to seek
the spear of the king of Persia; and Brian reminded
his brothers that now, as they had the apples and the
skin to aid them, it would be all the easier to get
the spear, as well as the rest of the fine.

Leaving now the shores of Greece with all its blue
streams, they went on board the canoe, which, at

Brian's command, flew across the wide seas; and soon they made land near the palace of Pezar, king of Persia. And seeing how they had fared so well in their last undertaking, they resolved to put on the guise of poets this time also.

And so they put the poet's tie on their hair, and, passing through the outer gate, they knocked at the door of the palace. The door-keeper asked who they were, and from what country they had come.

"We are poets from Erin," answered Brian; "and we have brought a poem for the king."

So they were admitted and brought to the presence of the king, who seated them among the nobles of his household; and they joined in the drinking and the feasting and the revelry.

The king's poets now arose, and chanted their songs for the king and his guests. And when the applause had ceased, Brian, speaking softly, said to his brothers—

"Arise, now, and chant a poem for the king."

But they answered, "Ask us not to do that which we are unable to do; but if you wish us to exercise the art we have learned from our youth, we shall do so, namely, the art of fighting and overcoming our foes."

"That would be an unusual way of reciting poetry," said Brian; "but I have a poem for the king, and I shall now chant it for him."

So saying, he stood up; and when there was silence, he recited this poem—

In royal state may Pezar ever reign,
Like some vast yew tree, monarch of the plain ;
May Pezar's mystic javelin, long and bright,
Bring slaughter to his foes in every fight !

When Pezar fights and shakes his dreadful spear,
Whole armies fly and heroes quake with fear :
What shielded foe, what champion can withstand,
The blazing spear in mighty Pezar's hand !

"Your poem is a good one," said the king; "but one thing in it I do not understand, namely, why you make mention of my spear."

"Because," answered Brian, "I wish to get that spear as a reward for my poem."

"That is a very foolish request," said the king, "for no man ever escaped punishment who asked me for my spear. And as to your poetry, the highest reward I could now bestow on you, and the greatest favour these nobles could obtain for you, is that I should spare your life."

Thereupon Brian and his brothers started up in great wrath and drew their swords, and the king and his chiefs drew their swords in like manner; and they fought a deadly fight. But Brian at last, drawing forth one of his apples, and taking sure aim, cast it at the king and struck him on the forehead; so that Pezar fell, pierced through the brain.

After this Brian fought on more fiercely than before, dealing destruction everywhere around him; but when the chiefs saw that their king had fallen, they lost heart and fled through the doors, till at length none remained in the banquet hall but the three sons of Turenn.

Then they went to the room where the spear was kept; and they found it with its head down deep in a great caldron of water, which hissed and bubbled round it. And Brian, seizing it boldly in his hand, drew it forth; after which the three brothers left the palace and went to their canoe.

———————

CHAPTER IX.

THE CHARIOT AND STEEDS OF THE KING OF SIGAR.

RESTING now for some days from their toil, they resolved to seek the steeds and chariot of the king of Sigar; for this was the next part of the Ildana's eric-fine. So they commanded the canoe, and the canoe, obedient to their behest, glided swiftly and smoothly over the green waves till they landed in Sigar. Brian bore the great, heavy, venomed spear in his hand; and the three brothers were of good heart, seeing how they had succeeded in their last quest, and that they had now three parts of the fine.

"In what shape think you we should go to this court?" said Brian.

"How should we go," answered the others, "but in our own shapes, namely, as three hostile champions, who have come to get the chariot and steeds, either by force or by good will ? "

"That is not what seems best to me," said Brian. "My counsel is, that we go as soldiers from Erin, willing to serve for pay ; and should the king take us into his service, it is likely we shall find out where the chariot and steeds are kept."

His brothers having agreed to this, the three set out for the palace.

It happened that the king was holding a fair-meeting on the broad, level green before the palace ; and when the three warriors came near, the people made way for them. They bowed low to the king ; and he asked them who they were, and from what part of the world they had come.

"We are valiant soldiers from Erin," they answered, " seeking for service and pay among the great kings of the world."

"Do you wish to enter my service ? " asked the king : and they answered, " Yes." So they made a covenant with each other—the king to place them in a post of honour and trust, and they to serve him faithfully, and to name their own reward. Where-upon the brothers entered the ranks of the king's body-guard.

They remained in the palace for a month and a fortnight, looking round and carefully noting everything ; but they saw nothing of the chariot and steeds. At the end of that time Brian said to his brothers—

"It fares ill with us here, my brothers ; for we

know nothing of the chariot and steeds at this hour, more than when we first came hither."

The others said this was quite true, and asked if he meant to do anything in the matter.

"This is what I think we should do," answered Brian. "Let us put on our travelling array, and take our arms of valour in our hands; and in this fashion let us go before the king, and tell him that unless he shows us the chariot and steeds, we shall leave his service."

This they did without delay; and when they had come before the king, he asked them why they came to his presence so armed and in travelling gear.

"We will tell thee of that, O king," answered Brian. "We are valiant soldiers from Erin, and into whatsoever lands we have travelled, we have been trusted with the secret counsels of the kings who have taken us into their service; and we have been made the guardians of their rarest jewels and of all their gifted arms of victory. But as to thee, O king, thou hast not so treated us since we came hither; for thou hast a chariot and two steeds, which exceed all the chariots and steeds in the world, and yet we have never seen them."

"A small thing it is that has caused you to prepare for departure," said the king; "and there is, moreover, no need that you should leave my service; for I would have shown you those steeds the day you came, had I only known that you wished it. But ye shall see them now; for I have never had in my service soldiers from a distant land, in whom I and my people have placed greater trust than we have placed in you."

He then sent for the steeds, and had them yoked to the chariot—those steeds that were as fleet as the clear, cold wind of March, and which travelled with equal speed on land and on sea.

Brian, viewing them narrowly, said aloud, "Hear me, O king of Sicily.   We have served thee faithfully up to this time; and now we wish to name our own pay, according to the covenant thou hast made with us.   The guerdon we demand is yonder chariot and steeds; these we mean to have, and we shall ask for nothing more."

But the king, in great wrath, said, "Foolish and luckless men! Ye shall certainly die because you have dared to ask for my steeds!"

And the king and his warriors drew their swords, and rushed towards the sons of Turenn to seize them.

They, on the other hand, were not taken unaware; and a sore fight began.   And Brian, watching his opportunity, sprang with a sudden bound into the chariot, and, dashing the charioteer to the ground, he seized the reins in his left hand; then, raising the venomed spear of Pezar in his right, he smote the king with its fiery point in the breast, so that he fell dead.   And the three brothers dealt red slaughter among the king's guards, till those who were not slain scattered and fled in all directions.   So they fared in this undertaking.

CHAPTER X.

THE SEVEN PIGS OF THE KING OF THE GOLDEN PILLARS.

AFTER resting till their wounds were healed, Ur and Urcar asked where they should go next.

"We shall go," said Brian, "to Asal, the king of the Golden Pillars, to ask him for his seven pigs; for this is the next part of the Ildana's eric-fine."

So they set out; and the canoe brought them straightway to the land of the Golden Pillars, without delay and without mishap. As they drew nigh to the harbour, they saw the shore lined with men all armed. For the fame of the deeds of these great champions had begun to be noised through many lands; how they had been forced to leave Erin by the hard sentence of the Ildana; and how they were seeking and bearing away the most precious and gifted jewels of the world to pay the fine. Wherefore the king of the Golden Pillars had armed his people, and had sent them to guard the harbours.

The king himself came down to the beach to meet them. As soon as they had come within speaking distance, he bade them stay their course; and then he asked them, in an angry and chiding tone, if they were the three champions from Erin, who had overcome and slain so many kings.

Brian answered, "Be not displeased with us, O

king ; for in all this matter we are not to blame.   The
Ildana has demanded a fine which we perforce must
pay ; for we have promised, and the Dedannans are
our guarantee.   If the kings to whom he sent us had
given us peaceably the precious things we demanded,
we would gladly have departed in peace ; but as they
did not, we fought against them, unwillingly indeed
and overthrew them ; for no one has as yet been able
to withstand us."

"Tell me now," said the king, "what has brought
you to my country ? "

"We have come for thy seven pigs," answered
Brian ; "for they are a part of the fine."

"And in what manner do you think ye shall get
them ? " asked the king.

Brian answered, "Thou hast heard, O king, how
the Ildana has brought us to these straits, and we
must pay him the fine, every jot, or else we shall die
at the hands of our people.   Thou, perchance, wilt have
pity on our hardships, and give us these pigs in token
of kindness and friendship, and if so we shall be
thankful ; but if not, then we will fight for them, and
either bring them away by force, after slaying thee
and thy people, or fall ourselves in the attempt."

Hearing this, the king and his people went into
council ; and after debating the matter at full length,
they thought it best to give the pigs peaceably, seeing
that no king, however powerful, had as yet been able
to withstand the sons of Turenn.

The three champions wondered greatly when this

was told to them; for in no other country had they
been able to get any part of the fine without battle
and hardship, and without leaving much of their blood
behind them. So they were now very glad; and
thanked Asal and his people.

The king then brought them to his palace, and
gave them a kind welcome; and they were supplied
with food and drink to their hearts' desire, and slept
on soft, downy beds. So they rested after all their
weary journeys and toils.

When they arose next morning, they were brought
to the king's presence, and the pigs were given to
them; and Brian addressed the king in these words—

> The prizes we've brought to this land,
>   We have won them in conflict and blood;
> But the gift we have sought at thy hand,
>   That gift thou hast freely bestowed.
>
> The red spear rewarded our deeds,
>   When Pezar the mighty we slew;
> And the fight for the chariot and steeds,
>   Ah, long shall the Sigarites rue!
>
> Great Asal! in happier days,
>   When our deeds bring us glory and fame,
> Green Erin shall echo thy praise,
>   And her poets shall honour thy name!

CHAPTER XI.

THE HOUND-WHELP OF THE KING OF IRODA.

"Whither do you go next, ye sons of Turenn?" asked Asal.

"We go," answered Brian, "to Iroda, for Failinis, the king's hound-whelp."

"Then grant me this boon," said the king, "namely, that ye let me go with you to Iroda. For my daughter is the king's wife; and I will try to prevail on him that he give you the hound-whelp freely and without battle."

This they agreed to. But the king wished that they should go in his own ship; so it was got ready, and they went on board with all their wealth; and it is not told how they fared till they reached the borders of Iroda. The shores were covered with fierce, armed men, who were there by orders of the king to guard the harbour; and these men shouted at the crew, warning them to come no farther; for they knew the sons of Turenn, and well they knew what they came for.

Asal then requested the three champions to remain where they were for a time, while he went on shore to talk with his son-in-law. Accordingly he landed, and went to the king, who, after he had welcomed him, asked what had brought the sons of Turenn to his country.

"They have come for your hound-whelp," answered Asal.

And the king of Iroda said, "It was an evil counsel you followed, when you came with these men to my shores; for to no three champions in the world have the gods given such strength or such good luck as that they can get my hound-whelp, either by force or by my own free will."

"It will be unwise to refuse them," replied Asal. "They have overpowered and slain many great kings; for they have gifted arms that no warrior, however powerful, can withstand; and behold, I have come hither to tell you what manner of men these are, that you might be advised by me, and give them your hound-whelp in peace."

So he pressed him earnestly; but his words were only thrown away on the king of Iroda, who spoke scornfully of the sons of Turenn, and refused Asal's request with wrathful words.

Asal, much troubled at this, went and told the sons of Turenn how matters stood. And they, having without delay put on their battle-dress, and taken their arms in their hands, challenged the king of Iroda and his people. Then began a very fierce and bloody battle; for though nothing could stand before the sons of Turenn, yet the warriors of Iroda were many and very brave. So they fought till the two younger brothers became separated from Brian, and he was quite surrounded. But as he wielded the dreadful spear of Pezar, with its blazing, fiery point, his enemies fell back dismayed, and the ranks were broken before him, so that those who crossed his path stood in a gap of danger.

At length he espied the king of Iroda, where he fought hedged round by spears; and he rushed through the thick of the battle straight towards him, striking down spears and swords and men as he went. And now these two valiant warriors fought hand to hand a stout and watchful and fierce battle—for the others fell back by the king's command; and it was long before any advantage was gained on either side. But though to those who looked on, Brian seemed the more wrathful of the two, yet he held back his hand, so as not to slay his foe; and this it was, indeed, that prolonged the combat, for he sought to tire out the king. At length, watching his opportunity, Brian closed suddenly, and, seizing the king in his strong arms, he lifted him clean off the ground, and bore him to where Asal stood. Then, setting him down, he said—

"Behold thy son-in-law; it would have been easier to kill him three times over than to bring him to thee once!"

When the people saw their king a prisoner, they ceased fighting; and the end of all was that peace was made, and the hound-whelp was given over to the sons of Turenn. Then they took their leave, and left the shores of Iroda in friendship with the king and with Asal his father-in-law.

CHAPTER XII.

RETURN OF THE SONS OF TURENN, WITH PART OF THE ERIC-FINE.

Now we shall speak of Luga of the Long Arms. It was revealed to him that the sons of Turenn had obtained all those parts of the fine which he wanted for the battle of Moytura;[11] but that they had not yet got the cooking-spit, or given the three shouts on Midkena's Hill. So he sent after them a druidical spell, which, falling on them soon after they had left Iroda, caused them to forget the remaining part of the fine, and filled them with a longing desire to return to their native home. Accordingly they went on board their canoe, bringing with them every part of the fine they had gotten already; and the canoe glided swiftly over the waves to Erin.

At this time Luga was with the king at a fair-meeting on the plain before Tara; and it was made known to him secretly that the sons of Turenn had landed at Bruga of the Boyne. He left the assembly anon, telling no one; and he went direct to Caher-Crofinn * at Tara, and, closing the gates and doors after him, he put on his battle array, namely, the smooth Greek armour of Mannanan Mac Lir, and the enchanted mantle of the daughter of Flidas.

* Caher-Crofinn, otherwise called Rath-ree, the principal for-tress at Tara, the remains of which are still to be seen.

Soon after, the sons of Turenn were seen approaching; and as they came forward, the multitude flocked out to meet them, gazing with wonder at the many marvellous things they had brought. When the three champions had come to the royal tent, they were joyfully welcomed by the king and by the Dedannans in general; and then the king spoke kindly to them, and asked if they had brought the eric-fine.

"We have obtained it after much hardship and danger," they replied; "and now we wish to know where Luga is, that we may hand it over to him."

The king told them that Luga was at the assembly; but when they sent to search for him, he was nowhere to be found.

"I can tell where he is," said Brian. "It has been made known to him that we have arrived in Erin, bringing with us gifted arms that none can withstand; and he has gone to one of the strongholds of Tara, to avoid us, fearing we might use these venomed weapons against himself."

Messengers were then sent to Luga to tell him that the sons of Turenn had arrived, and to ask him to come forth to the meeting, that they might give him the fine.

But he answered, "I will not come to the meeting yet; but go ye back, and tell the sons of Turenn to give the fine to the king for me."

The messengers returned with this answer; and the sons of Turenn gave to the king for Luga all the wonderful things they had brought, keeping, however

their own arms; after which the whole company went
into the palace.

When Luga was told how matters stood, he came
to where the king and all the others were; and the
king gave him the fine. Then Luga, looking narrowly
at everything that had been given up to him, said—

"Here, indeed, is an eric enough to pay for any
one that ever yet was slain, or that shall be slain
to the end of time. But yet there is one kind of fine
that must be paid to the last farthing, namely, an
eric-fine; for of this it is not lawful to hold back
even the smallest part. And moreover, O king, thou
and the Dedannans whom I see here present, are
guarantees for the full payment of my eric-fine. Now
I see here the three apples, and the skin of the pig,
and the fiery-headed spear, and the chariot and
steeds, and the seven pigs, and the hound-whelp;
but where, ye sons of Turenn, is the cooking-spit
of the women of Fincara? And I have not heard
that ye have given the three shouts on Midkena's
Hill."

On hearing this, the sons of Turenn fell into a
faintness like the faintness before death. And when
they had recovered they answered not one word, but
left the assembly and went to their father's house.
To him and their sister Ethnea they told all that
had befallen them; and how they should set out on
another quest, as they had forgotten part of the eric-
fine through the spells of Luga.

At this Turenn was overwhelmed with grief; and

Ethnea wept in great fear and sorrow. And so they passed that night. Next day, they went down to the shore, and their father and sister went with them to their ship, and bade them farewell.

———✦———

CHAPTER XIII.

THE COOKING-SPIT OF THE WOMEN OF FINCARA.

THEN they went on board their ship—for they had Mannanan's canoe no longer—and they sailed forth on the green billowy sea to search for the Island of Fincara. For a whole quarter of a year they wandered hither and thither over the wide ocean, landing on many shores and inquiring of all they met; yet they were not able to get the least tidings of the island.

At last, they came across one very old man, who told them that he had heard of the Island of Fincara in the days of his youth; and that it lay not on the surface, but down deep in the waters, for it was sunk beneath the waves by a spell in times long past.[18]

Then Brian put on his water-dress, with his helmet of transparent crystal on his head, and, telling his brothers to await his return, he leaped over the side of the ship, and sank at once out of sight. He walked about for a fortnight down in the green salt sea, seeking for the Island of Fincara; and at last he found it.

There were many houses on the island; but one he saw larger and grander than the rest. To this he straightway bent his steps, and found it open. On entering, he saw in one large room a great number of beautiful ladies, busily employed at all sorts of embroidery and needlework; and in their midst was a long, bright cooking-spit lying on a table.

Without speaking a word, he walked straight to the table, and, seizing the spit in one hand, he turned round and walked towards the door. The women neither spoke nor moved, but each had her eyes fixed on him from the moment he entered, admiring his manly form, his beauty, and his fearlessness; but when they saw him about to walk off with the spit, they all burst out laughing; and one, who seemed chief among them, said—

"Thou hast attempted a bold deed, O son of Turenn! Know that there are thrice fifty warlike women here, and that the weakest among us would be able of herself to prevent thee taking this cooking-spit, even if thy two brothers were here to help thee. But thou art a brave and courageous champion, else thou wouldst not have attempted, unaided, to take it by force, knowing the danger. And for thy boldness and valour, and for the comeliness of thy person, we will let thee take this one, for we have many others besides."

So Brian, after thanking them, brought away the spit joyfully, and sought his ship.

Ur and Urcar waited for Brian in the same spot the whole time, and when he came not, they began to fear that he would return no more. With these thoughts they were at last about to leave the place, when they saw the glitter of his crystal helmet down deep in the water, and immediately after he came to the surface with the cooking-spit in his hand. They brought him on board, and now all felt very joyful and courageous of heart.

CHAPTER XIV.

THE THREE SHOUTS ON MIDKENA'S HILL.

THE three brothers next sailed away towards the north of Lochlann, and never abated speed till they moored their vessel near the Hill of Midkena, which rose smooth and green over the sea-shore. When Midkena saw them approaching, he knew them at once, and, coming towards them armed for battle, he addressed them aloud—

"You it was that slew Kian, my friend and pupil; and now come forth and fight, for you shall not leave these shores till you answer for his death."

Brian, in no degree daunted by the fierce look and threatening speech of Midkena, sprang ashore, and the two heroes attacked each other with great fury.

When the three sons of Midkena heard the clash of arms, they came forth, and, seeing how matters stood, they rushed down to aid their father ; but just as they arrived at the shore, Midkena fell dead, cloven through helmet and head by the heavy sword of Brian.

And now a fight began, three on each side ; and if men were afar off, even in the land of Hisberna, in the east of the world, they would willingly come the whole way to see this battle, so fierce and haughty were the minds of those mighty champions, so skilful and active were they in the use of their weapons, so numerous and heavy were their blows, and so long did they continue to fight without either party giving way. The three sons of Turenn were at last dreadfully wounded—wounded almost to death. But neither fear nor weakness did this cause them, for their valour and their fury arose all the more for their wounds, and with one mighty onset they drove their spears through the bodies of their foes ; and the sons of Midkena fell before them into the long sleep of death.

But now that the fight was ended, and the battlefury of the victors had passed off—now it was that they began to feel the effects of their wounds. They threw themselves full length on the blood-stained sward, and long they remained without moving or speaking a word, as if they were dead ; and a heavy curtain of darkness fell over their eyes.

At last Brian, raising his head, spoke to his brothers to know if they lived, and when they answered him feebly, he said—

"My dear brothers, let us now arise and give the three shouts on the hill while there is time, for I feel the signs of death."

But they were not able to rise.

Then Brian, gathering all his remaining strength, stood up and lifted one with each hand, while his own blood flowed plentifully; and then they raised three feeble shouts on Midkena's Hill.

CHAPTER XV.

RETURN AND DEATH OF THE SONS OF TURENN.

MAKING no further delay, he led them to their ship, and they set sail for Erin. While they were yet far off, Brian, gazing over the sea towards the west, suddenly cried out—

"Lo, I see Ben Edar * yonder, rising over the waters; and I see also Dun Turenn farther towards the north."

And Ur answered from where he reclined with Urcar on the deck, "If we could but get one sight of Ben Edar methinks we should regain our health and strength; and as thou lovest us, and as thou lovest

* Ben Edar, now Howth Hill, near Dublin. Dun Turenn, the fortress of their father Turenn.

thy own renown, my brother, come and raise our
heads and rest them on thy breast, that we may see
Erin once more.   After that, we shall welcome either
life or death."

UR.

O brother, torch of valour, strong of hand,
   Come, place our weary heads upon thy breast;
And let us look upon our native land,
   Before we sink to everlasting rest!

BRIAN.

Belovèd sons of Turenn, woe is me!
   My wounds are deep, my day of strength is past;
Yet not for this I grieve, but that I see
   Your lives, my noble brothers, ebbing fast!

UR.

Would we could give our lives to purchase thine;
   Ah, gladly would we die to ease thy pain!
For art thou not the pride of Turenn's line,
   The noblest champion of green Erin's plain?

BRIAN.

That mighty Dannan healer, Dianket; *
   Or Midac, who excelled his sire in skill;
The maiden-leech, Armedda, mightier yet,
   Who knew the herbs to cure, the herbs to kill:

Oh, were they here; or had we now at hand
   Those gifted apples from the distant East;
Then might we hope to reach our native land,
   And live again in joy and peace and rest!

---

  * Dianket, the great Dedannan physician.   His son Midac and
his daughter Armedda were still more skilful than their father.   (See
note 1 at the end.)

Ur.

Brother, methinks could we but see once more
  Ben Edar's slopes, or Bregia's * dewy plain,
Tailltenn,† or Bruga's ‡ mystic mansion hoar,
  Our blood would course in health and strength again.

Or let us once behold our father's home,
  Or winding Liffey down by Ahaclee,§
Old Frevan's hill,‖ or Tara's ¶ regal dome ;
  Then welcome death or life, whiche'er may be!

So Brian raised their heads and rested them on his
breast, and they gazed on the rocky cliffs and green
slopes of Ben Edar while the ship wafted slowly
towards land.

Soon after this they landed on the north side of
Ben Edar, from which they made their way slowly
to Dun Turenn. And when they had reached the
green in front of the house, Brian cried out—

"Father, dear father, come forth to thy children!"

Turenn came forth and saw his sons all wounded
and pale and feeble.

---

* Bregia, the plain lying between the Liffey and the Boyne.

† Tailltenn, now Teltown, on the Blackwater, about midway between Navan and Kells, in Meath. Here annual meetings were held
from the most ancient times, on the first of August, and for some
days before and after, at which games were celebrated, like the
Olympic games of Greece.

‡ Bruga on the Boyne, where Angus or Mac Indoc, the great
Dedannan enchanter, had his "mystic mansion hoar." (See note 1 at
the end.)

§ Ahaclee, the old name of Dublin.

‖ Frevan, now the hill of Frewen, rising over Lough Owel, near
Mullingar, where the ancient Irish kings had one of their palaces.

¶ Tara, in Meath, the chief seat of the Irish kings.

And Brian said, " Go, beloved father—go quick to
Tara, and quickly return. Bring this cooking-spit
to Luga, and tell him that we have given the three
shouts on Midkena's Hill. Say that we have now paid
the full eric-fine, and bring back from him the apples
of the Garden of Hisberna, to heal our wounds, else
we die."

BRIAN.

Father, our wounds are deadly ; nought can save
   Thy children's lives but Luga's friendly hand :
Go, seek him, father—fare thee fast—and crave
   The healing apples from Hisberna's land!

TURENN.

In vain, my sons, ye seek to fly your doom ;
   The stern Ildana's mind too well I know :
Alas! far liefer would he see your tomb,
   Than all the treasures all this world could show!

BRIAN.

But he is just ; and though his sire we slew,
   Have we not paid full eric for the deed ?
The great Ildana is our kinsman too,
   And will relent in this our time of need.

Then go, my father, thou art swift and strong ;
   Speed like the wind—why linger here to mourn?
Go straight to Luga's home, nor tarry long ;
   Or, father, we shall die ere thou return!

Turenn set out and travelled like the wind till he
reached Tara, where he found Luga.

He gave him the cooking-spit, and said, "Behold,
my three sons have now paid thee the full eric-fine,
for they have given the three shouts on Midkena's
Hill. But they are wounded even unto death ; and

now give me, I pray thee, the apples from the Garden of Hisberna, to cure them, else they die."

But Luga refused, and turned away from Turenn.

Turenn hastened back to his sons with a sorrowful heart, and told them that he had failed to get the apples.

Then Brian said, "Take me with thee to Tara. I will see him, and perchance he may have pity on us, and give us the apples."

And it was done so. But when Brian begged for the apples, Luga said—

"I will not give them to thee. If thou shouldst offer me the full of the whole earth of gold, I would not give them to thee. Thou and thy brothers committed a wicked and pitiless deed when you slew my father. For that deed you must suffer, and with nothing short of your death shall I be content."

> For the blood that you spilled,
>   For the hero you killed—
> The deed is avenged, and your doom is fulfilled!

Brian turned away and went back to his brothers, and, lying down between them, his life departed; and his brothers died at the same moment.

Then their father and their sister stood hand in hand over their bodies, lamenting. And Turenn spoke this lay—

> Oh, pulseless is my heart this woful hour,
>   My strength is gone, my joy for ever fled;
> Three noble champions, Erin's pride and power,
>   My three fair youths, my children, cold and dead!

Mild Ur, the fair-haired; Urcar, straight and tall;
  The kings of Banba * worthy both to be;
And Brian, bravest, noblest, best of all,
  Who conquered many lands beyond the sea:

Lo, I am Turenn, your unhappy sire,
  Mourning with feeble voice above your grave;
No life, no wealth, no honours I desire;
  A place beside my sons is all I crave!

After this Turenn and Ethnea fell on the bodies of the three young heroes and died.

And they were all buried in one grave.

This is the story of the Fate of the Children of Turenn.

* Banba, one of the ancient names of Ireland.

THE

OVERFLOWING OF LOUGH NEAGH,

AND THE

STORY OF LIBAN THE MERMAID.

In the days of old a good king ruled over Muman,* whose name was Marid Mac Carido. He had two sons, Ecca and Rib. Ecca was restless and unruly, and in many ways displeased the king; and he told his brother Rib that he had made up his mind to leave his home, and win lands for himself in some far off part of the country. Rib tried hard to dissuade him; but though this delayed his departure for a while, he was none the less bent on going.

At last Ecca, being wrought upon by his stepmother Ebliu (from whom Slieve Eblinne † was afterwards named), did a grievous wrong to his father, and fled from Muman with all his people; and his brother Rib and his stepmother Ebliu went with him. Ten hundred men they were in all,

---

* Muman, *i.e.* Munster.

† Slieve Eblinne, now Slieve Eelim or Slieve Phelim, in Tipperary, sometimes called the Twelve Hills of Evlinn. "Eblinne" is the genitive of "Ebliu,"

besides women and children; and they turned their faces towards the north.

After they had travelled for some time, their druids [3] told them that it was not fated for them to settle in the same place; and accordingly, when they had come to the Pass of the two Pillar Stones, they parted.

Rib and his people turned to the west, and they journeyed till they came to the plain of Arbthenn. And there the water of a fountain burst forth over the land, and drowned them all; and a great lake was formed, which to this day is called the Lake of Rib.*

Ecca continued his journey northwards; and he and his people fared slowly on till they came near to Bruga† of the Boyne, the palace of Mac Indoc, where they were fain to rest. No sooner had they halted, than a tall man came forth from the palace, namely, Angus Mac Indoc of the Bruga, son of the Dagda, and commanded them to leave the place without delay. But they, being spent with the toil of travel, heeded not his words, and, pitching their tents, they rested on the plain before the palace. Whereupon Angus, being wroth that his commands were unheeded, killed all their horses that night.

Next day, he came forth again, and he said to them, " Your horses I slew last night; and now, unless ye depart from this place, I will slay your people to-night."

* Now Lough Ree, on the Shannon.
* See note, page 62; see also note 1 at the end of the book.

And Ecca said to him, "Much evil hast thou done to us already, for thou hast killed all our horses. And now we cannot go, even though we desire it, for without horses we cannot travel."

Then Angus brought to them a very large horse in full harness, and they put all their goods on him. And when they were about to go, he said to them—

"Beware that ye keep this great steed walking continually; not even a moment's rest shall ye give him, otherwise he will certainly be the cause of your death." [14]

After this they set out again, on a Sunday in the mid-month of autumn, and travelled on till they reached the Plain of the Grey Copse,* where they intended to abide. They gathered then round the great steed to take their luggage off him, and each was busy seeing after his own property, so that they forgot to keep the horse moving. And the moment he stood still, a magic well sprang up beneath his feet. [14]

Now Ecca, when he saw the well spring up, was troubled, remembering Angus's warning. And he caused a house to be built round it, and near it he built his palace, for the better security. And he chose a woman to take care of the well, charging her strictly to keep the door locked, except when the people of the palace came for water.

After that the King of Ulad,† that is to say, Muri-

* The Plain of the Grey Copse, according to the legend, was the name of the plain now covered by Lough Neagh.

† Ulad, *i.e.* Ulster.

dach, the son of Fiaca Findamnas (who was grandson of
Conal Carna of the Red Branch [15]) came against Ecca
to drive him forth from Ulad.   But Ecca made a stout
fight, so that he won the lordship of half of Ulad from
Muridach.   And after that his people settled down on
the Plain of the Grey Copse.

Now Ecca had two daughters, Ariu and Liban,
of whom Ariu was the wife of Curnan the Simpleton.
And Curnan went about among the people, foretelling
that a lake would flow over them from the well, and
urging them earnestly to make ready their boats .

Come forth, come forth, ye valiant men; build boats, and build ye
    fast !
I see the water surging out, a torrent deep and vast ;
I see our chief and all his host o'erwhelmed beneath the wave ;
And Ariu, too, my best beloved, alas ! I cannot save.
       But Liban east and west shall swim
       Long ages on the ocean's rim,
       By mystic shores and islets dim,
          And down in the deep sea cave !

And he ceased not to warn all he met, repeating
this verse continually; but the people gave no heed to
the words of the Simpleton.

Now the woman who had charge of the well, on a
certain occasion forgot to close the door, so that the
spell was free to work evil.   And immediately the
water burst forth over the plain, and formed a great
lake, namely the Lake of the Copse.   And Ecca and
all his family and all his folk were drowned, save only
his daughter Liban, and Conang, and Curnan the
Simpleton.   And they buried Ariu, and raised a
mound over her, which is called from her Carn-Arenn.

Of Conang nothing more is told. But as to Curnan, he died of grief after his wife Ariu; and he was buried in a mound, which is called Carn-Curnan to this day in memory of him.

And thus the great Lake of the Copse was formed, which is now called Lough Necca,* in memory of Ecca, the son of Marid. And it was the overflow of this lake which, more than all other causes, scattered the Ultonians over Erin.

Now as to Liban. She also was swept away like the others; but she was not drowned. She lived for a whole year with her lap-dog, in her chamber beneath the lake, and God protected her from the water. At the end of the year she was weary; and when she saw the speckled salmon swimming and playing all round her, she prayed and said—

"O my Lord, I wish I were a salmon, that I might swim with the others through the clear green sea!"

And at the words she took the shape of a salmon, except her face and breast, which did not change. And her lap-dog was changed to an otter, and attended her afterwards whithersoever she went, as long as she lived in the sea.

And so she remained swimming about from sea to sea for three hundred years; that is to say, from the time of Ecca, the son of Marid, to the time of Comgall of Bangor. [16]

Now on one occasion, Comgall sent Beoc, the son

* Lough Necca, now Lough Neagh.

of Indli, from Bangor to Rome, to talk with Gregory [*] concerning some matters of order and rule.   And when Beoc's curragh [17] was sailing over the sea, he and his crew heard sweet singing in the waters beneath them, as it were the chanting of angels.

And Beoc, having listened for a while, looked down into the water, and asked what the chant was for, and who it was that sang.

And Liban answered, "I am Liban, the daughter of Ecca, son of Marid; and it is I who sang the chant thou hast heard."

"Why art thou here?" asked Beoc.

And she replied, "Lo, I have lived for three hundred years beneath the sea; and I have come hither to fix a day and a place of meeting with thee.   I shall now go westward; and I beseech thee, for the sake of the holy men of Dalaradia,[†] to come to Inver Ollarba [‡] to meet me, on this same day at the end of a year.   Say also to Comgall and to the other holy men of Bangor, all that I say to thee.   Come with thy boats and thy fishing-nets, and thou shalt take me from the waters in which I have lived."

"I shall not grant thee the boon thou askest," said Beoc, "unless thou give me a reward."

"What reward dost thou seek?" asked Liban.

---

[*] Gregory, *i.e.* Pope Gregory.

[†] Dalaradia, the old name of a territory which included the southern half of the county Antrim and a part of Down.

[‡] Inver Ollarba, *i.e.* the *inver*, or mouth of the river Ollarba, which was the ancient name of the Larne Water, in Antrim.

"That thou be buried in one grave with me in my own monastery," answered Beoc.

"That shall be granted to thee," said Liban.

Beoc then went on his way to Rome. And when he had returned, he related to Comgall and to the other saints of the monastery at Bangor, the story of the mermaid. And now the end of the year was nigh.

Then they made ready their nets, and on the day appointed they went in their boats to Inver Ollarba, a goodly company of the saints of Erin. And Liban was caught in the net of Fergus of Miluc :* and her head and shoulders were those of a maiden, but she had the body of a fish.

Now the boat in which she was brought to land was kept half full of sea water, in which she remained swimming about. And many came to see her ; and all were filled with wonder when they saw her strange shape and heard her story.

Among the rest came the chief of the tribe of Hua-Conang, wearing a purple cloak; and she kept gazing at him earnestly. The young chief, seeing this, said to her—

"Dost thou wish to have this cloak ? If so, I will give it to thee willingly."

But she answered, "Not so: I desire not thy cloak. But it brings to my mind my father Ecca;

* Miluc, or Meelick, the name of an ancient ecclesiastical establishment in the county Antrim. See " Ecclesiastical Antiquities of Down, Connor. and Dromore " (page 3), by the Rev. William Reeves, M.B., M.R.I.A.

for on the day he was drowned, he wore a cloak of purple like thine. But may good luck be on thee for thy gentleness, and on him who shall come after thee in thy place; and in every assembly where thy successor sits, may he be known to all without inquiry."

After that there came up a large-bodied, dark-visaged, fierce hero, and killed her lap-dog. Whereupon she was grieved; and she told him that the heroism of himself and his tribe should be stained by the baseness of their minds, and that they should not be able to defend themselves against injuries till they should do penance, by fasting, for her sake.

Then the warrior repented what he had done, and humbled himself before her.

And now there arose a contention about her, as to whom she should belong. Comgall said she was his, forasmuch as she was caught in his territory. But Fergus urged that she belonged to him by right, as it was in his net she was taken. And Beoc said he had the best right of all to her, on account of the promise she had made to him.

And as no one could settle the dispute, these three saints fasted and prayed that God would give a judgment between them, to show who should own Liban.

And an angel said to one of the company, "Two wild oxen will come hither to-morrow from Carn-Arenn, that is to say, from the grave-mound of Liban's sister, Ariu. Yoke a chariot to them, and place the mermaid in it; and into whatsoever territory they shall bring her, she shall remain with the owner thereof."

The oxen came on the morrow, as the angel had foretold. And when they were yoked, and when Liban was placed in the chariot, they brought her straightway to Beoc's church, namely to Tec-Da-Beoc.

Then the saints gave her a choice—either to die immediately after baptism, and go to heaven ; or to live on earth as long as she had lived in the sea, and then to go to heaven after these long ages. And the choice she took was to die immediately. Whereupon Comgall baptised her ; and he gave her the name of Murgen, that is, "Sea-born," or Murgelt, that is "Mermaid."

And she is counted among the holy virgins, and held in honour and reverence, as God ordained for her in heaven ; and wonders and miracles are performed through her means at Tec-Da-Beoc.

CONNLA OF THE GOLDEN HAIR,
AND THE FAIRY MAIDEN.

CONNLA of the Golden Hair was the son of Conn the Hundred-fighter.[18]   One day as he stood with his father on the royal Hill of Usna,* he saw a lady a little way off, very beautiful, and dressed in strange attire. She approached the spot where he stood; and when she was near, he spoke to her, and asked who she was, and from what place she had come.

The lady replied, "I have come from the Land of the Living[19]—a land where there is neither death nor old age, nor any breach of law. The inhabitants of earth call us Aes-shee,[19] for we have our dwellings within large, pleasant, green hills. We pass our time very pleasantly in feasting and harmless amusements, never growing old; and we have no quarrels or contentions."

The king and his company marvelled very much; for though they heard this conversation, no one saw the lady except Connla alone.

"Who is this thou art talking to, my son?" said the king.

* Hill of Usna.   (See note, page 37.)

And anon she answered for the youth, "Connla is speaking with a lovely, noble-born young lady, who will never die, and who will never grow old. I love Connla of the Golden Hair, and I have come to bring him with me to Moy-mell,[19] the plain of never-ending pleasure. On the day that he comes with me he shall be made king; and he shall reign for ever in Fairyland, without weeping and without sorrow. Come with me, O gentle Connla of the ruddy cheek, the fair, freckled neck, and the golden hair! Come with me, beloved Connla, and thou shalt retain the comeliness and dignity of thy form, free from the wrinkles of old age, till the awful day of judgment!"

> Thy flowing golden hair, thy comely face,
> Thy tall majestic form of peerless grace,
> That show thee sprung from Conn's exalted race.

King Conn the Hundred-fighter, being much troubled, called then on his druid,[3] Coran, to put forth his power against the witchery of the banshee [19]—

"O Coran of the mystic arts and of the mighty incantations, here is a contest such as I have never been engaged in since I was made king at Tara— a contest with an invisible lady, who is beguiling my son to Fairyland by her baleful charms. Her cunning is beyond my skill, and I am not able to withstand her power; and if thou, Coran, help not, my son will be taken away from me by the wiles and witchery of a woman from the fairy hills."

Coran, the aiuid, then came forward, and began to chant against the voice of the lady. And his power was greater than hers for that time, so that she was forced to retire.

As she was going away she threw an apple to Connla, who straightway lost sight of her; and the king and his people no longer heard her voice.

The king and the prince returned with their company to the palace; and Connla remained for a whole month without tasting food or drink, except the apple. And though he ate of it each day, it was never lessened, but was as whole and perfect in the end as at the beginning. Moreover, when they offered him aught else to eat or drink, he refused it; for while he had his apple he did not deem any other food worthy to be tasted. And he began to be very moody and sorrowful, thinking of the lovely fairy maiden.

At the end of the month, as Connla stood by his father's side among the nobles, on the Plain of Arcomin, he saw the same lady approaching him from the west. And when she had come near, she addressed him in this manner—

"A glorious seat, indeed, has Connla among wretched, short-lived mortals, awaiting the dreadful stroke of death! But now, the ever-youthful people of Moy-mell, who never feel old age, and who fear not death, seeing thee day by day among thy friends, in the assemblies of thy Fatherland, love thee with a strange love; and they will make thee king over them if thou wilt come with me."

When the king heard the words of the lady, he commanded his people to call the druid again to him, saying—

"Bring my druid, Coran, to me; for I see that the fairy lady has this day regained the power of her voice."

At this the lady said, "Valiant Conn, fighter of a hundred, the faith of the druids has come to little honour among the upright, mighty, numberless people of this land. When the righteous law shall be restored, it will seal up the lips of the false, black demon; and his druids shall no longer have power to work their guileful spells."

Now the king observed, and marvelled greatly, that whenever the lady was present, his son never spoke one word to any one, nay, even though they addressed him many times. And when the lady had ceased to speak, the king said—

"Connla, my son, has thy mind been moved by the words of the lady?"

Connla spoke then, and replied, "Father, I am very unhappy; for though I love my people beyond all, yet I am filled with sadness on account of this lady!"

When Connla had said this, the maiden again addressed him, and chanted these words in a very sweet voice—

THE CHANT OF THE FAIRY MAIDEN TO CONNLA OF THE GOLDEN HAIR.

I.

A land of youth, a land of rest,
    A land from sorrow free;
It lies far off in the golden west,
    On the verge of the azure sea.
A swift canoe of crystal bright,
    That never met mortal view—
We shall reach the land ere fall of night,
    In that strong and swift canoe:
        We shall reach the strand
        Of that sunny land,
    From druids and demons free;
        The land of rest,
        In the golden west,
    On the verge of the azure sea!

II.

A pleasant land of winding vales, bright streams, and verdurous
    plains,
Where summer all the live-long year, in changeless splendour reigns;
A peaceful land of calm delight, of everlasting bloom;
Old age and death we never know, no sickness, care, or gloom;
        The land of youth,
        Of love and truth,
    From pain and sorrow free;
        The land of rest,
        In the golden west,
    On the verge of the azure sea!

III.

There are strange delights for mortal men in that island of the
    west;
The sun comes down each evening in its lovely vales to rest:
        And though far and dim
        On the ocean's rim

It seems to mortal view,
 We shall reach its halls
 Ere the evening falls,
In my strong and swift canoe :
 And ever more
 That verdant shore
Our happy home shall be ;
 The land of rest,
 In the golden west,
On the verge of the azure sea '

IV.

It will guard thee, gentle Connla of the flowing golden hair,
It will guard thee from the druids, from the demons of the air ;
My crystal boat will guard thee, till we reach that western shore,
Where thou and I in joy and love shall live for evermore :
 From the druid's incantation,
  From his black and deadly snare,
 From the withering imprecation
  Of the demon of the air,
It will guard thee, gentle Connla of the flowing golden hair :
My crystal boat will guard thee, till we reach that silver strand
Where thou shalt reign in endless joy, the king of the Fairy-land ! *

When the maiden had ended her chant, Connla suddenly walked away from his father's side, and sprang into the curragh, the gleaming, straight-gliding, strong, crystal canoe. The king and his people saw them afar off and dimly, moving away over the bright sea towards the sunset. They gazed sadly after them, till they lost sight of the canoe over the utmost verge ; and no one can tell whither they went, for Connla was never again seen in his native land.

---

* This is an expansion, rather than a translation, of the original, which is very short, and in some places very obscure.

THE VOYAGE OF MAILDUN.

AN ACCOUNT
OF THE ADVENTURES OF MAILDUN AND HIS CREW,
AND OF THE WONDERFUL THINGS THEY SAW DURING THEIR VOYAGE
OF THREE YEARS AND SEVEN MONTHS, IN THEIR CURRAGH, [17]
ON THE WESTERN SEA.

————◆◇◆————

CHAPTER I.

MAILDUN'S CHILDHOOD AND YOUTH. HE BEGINS HIS VOYAGE IN QUEST OF THE PLUNDERERS WHO SLEW HIS FATHER.

THERE was once an illustrious man of the tribe of Owenaght* of Ninus, Allil Ocar Aga by name, a goodly hero, and lord of his own tribe and territory. One time, when he was in his house unguarded, a fleet of plunderers landed on the coast, and spoiled his territory. The chief fled for refuge to the church of Dooclone; but the spoilers followed him thither, slew him, and burned the church over his head.

---

* There were several tribes named Owenaght in the south of Ireland. This particular tribe were called, as in the text, the Owenaght of Ninus, and also, according to an interlined gloss in the "Book of the Dun Cow," the Owenaght of the Aras, i.e. of the Aran Islands. Their territory was situated in the north-west of the county Clare, opposite the Islands of Aran.

Not long after Allil's death, a son was born to him. The child's mother gave him the name of Maildun ; and, wishing to conceal his birth, she brought him to the queen of that country, who was her dear friend. The queen took him to her, and gave out that he was her own child, and he was brought up with the king's sons, slept in the same cradle with them, and was fed from the same breast and from the same cup. He was a very lovely child; and the people who saw him thought it doubtful if there was any other child living at the time equally beautiful.

As he grew up to be a young man, the noble qualities of his mind gradually unfolded themselves. He was high-spirited and generous, and he loved all sorts of manly exercises. In ball-playing, in running and leaping, in throwing the stone, in chess-playing, in rowing, and in horse-racing, he surpassed all the youths that came to the king's palace, and won the palm in every contest.

One day, when the young men were at their games, a certain youth among them grew envious of Maildun ; and he said, in an angry and haughty tone of voice—

" It is a cause of much shame to us that we have to yield in every game, whether of skill or of strength, whether on land or on water, to an obscure youth, of whom no one can tell who is his father or his mother, or what race or tribe he belongs to."

On hearing this, Maildun ceased at once from play; for until that moment he believed that he was the son of the king of the Owenaght, and of the queen who had nursed him. And going anon to the queen, he told her what had happened; and he said to her—

"If I am not thy son, I will neither eat nor drink till thou tell me who my father and mother are."

She tried to soothe him, and said, "Why do you worry yourself searching after this matter? Give no heed to the words of this envious youth. Am I not a mother to you? And in all this country, is there any mother who loves her son better than I love you?"

He answered, "All this is quite true; yet I pray thee let me know who my parents are."

The queen then, seeing that he would not be put off, brought him to his mother, and put him into her hands. And when he had spoken with her, he asked her to tell him who his father was.

"You are bent on a foolish quest, my child,' she said; "for even if you knew all about your father, the knowledge would bring neither advantage nor happiness to you; for he died before you were born."

"Even so," he replied, "I wish to know who he was."

So his mother told him the truth, saying, "Your father was Allil Ocar Aga, of the tribe of Owenaght of Ninus."

Maildun then set out for his father's territory; and his three foster brothers, namely, the king's three sons, who were noble and handsome youths like himself, went with him. When the people of his tribe found out that the strange youth was the son of their chief, whom the plunderers had slain years before, and when they were told that the three others were the king's sons, they gave them all a joyful welcome, feasting them, and showing them much honour; so that Maildun was made quite happy, and soon forgot all the abasement and trouble he had undergone.

Some time after this, it happened that a number of young people were in the churchyard of Dooclone— the same church in which Maildun's father had been slain—exercising themselves in casting a hand-stone. The game was to throw the stone clear over the charred roof of the church that had been burned; and Maildun was there contending among the others. A foul-tongued fellow named Brickna, a servant of the people who owned the church, was standing by; and he said to Maildun—

"It would better become you to avenge the man who was burned to death here, than to be amusing yourself casting a stone over his bare, burnt bones."

"Who was he?" inquired Maildun.

"Allil Ocar Aga, your father," replied the other.

"Who slew him?" asked Maildun.

"Plunderers from a fleet slew him and burned him in this church," replied Brickna; "and the same plunderers are still sailing in the same fleet."

Maildun was disturbed and sad after hearing this. He dropped the stone that he held in his hand, folded his cloak round him, and buckled on his shield. And he left the company, and began to inquire of all he met, the road to the plunderers' ships. For a long time he could get no tidings of them; but at last some persons, who knew where the fleet lay, told him that it was a long way off, and that there was no reaching it except by sea.

Now Maildun was resolved to find out these plunderers, and to avenge on them the death of his father. So he went without delay into Corcomroe,* to the druid[3] Nuca, to seek his advice about building a curragh, and to ask also for a charm to protect him, both while building it, and while sailing on the sea afterwards.

The druid gave him full instructions. He told him the day he should begin to build his curragh, and the exact day on which he was to set out on his voyage; and he was very particular about the number of the crew, which, he said, was to be sixty chosen men, neither more nor less.

So Maildun built a large triple-hide curragh,[17] following the druid's directions in every particular, chose his crew of sixty, among whom were his two friends, Germane and Diuran Lekerd; and on the day appointed put out to sea.

---

* Corcomroe, an ancient territory, now a barony in the north-west of the county Clare. (For the meaning and history of this name, see the author's "Origin and History of Irish Names of Places," Series I. Part i. Chapter ii.)

When he had got only a very little way from the land, he saw his three foster brothers running down to the shore, signalling and calling out to him to return and take them on board; for they said they wished to go with him.

"We shall not turn back," said Maildun; "and you cannot come with us; for we have already got our exact number."

"We will swim after you in the sea till we are drowned, if you do not return for us," replied they; and so saying, the three plunged in and swam after the curragh.

When Maildun saw this, he turned his vessel towards them, and took them on board rather than let them be drowned.

----••----

CHAPTER II.

THE FIRST ISLAND. TIDINGS OF THE PLUNDERERS.

THEY sailed that day and night, as well as the whole of next day, till darkness came on again; and at midnight they saw two small bare islands, with two great houses on them near the shore. When they drew near, they heard the sounds of merriment and laughter, and the shouts of revellers intermingled with the loud voices of warriors boasting of their deeds. And listening to catch the conversation, they heard one warrior say to another—

"Stand off from me, for I am a better warrior than thou; it was I who slew Allil Ocar Aga, and burned Dooclone over his head; and no one has ever dared to avenge it on me. Thou hast never done a great deed like that!"

"Now surely," said Germane and Diuran to Maildun, "Heaven has guided our ship to this place! Here is an easy victory. Let us now sack this house, since God has revealed our enemies to us, and delivered them into our hands!"

While they were yet speaking, the wind arose, and a great tempest suddenly broke on them. And they were driven violently before the storm, all that night and a part of next day, into the great and boundless ocean; so that they saw neither the islands they had left nor any other land; and they knew not whither they were going.

Then Maildun said, "Take down your sail and put by your oars, and let the curragh drift before the wind in whatsoever direction it pleases God to lead us;" which was done.

He then turned to his foster brothers, and said to them, "This evil has befallen us because we took you into the curragh, thereby violating the druid's directions; for he forbade me to go to sea with more than sixty men for my crew, and we had that number before you joined us. Of a surety more evil will come of it."

His foster brothers answered nothing to this, but remained silent.

CHAPTER III.

THE ISLAND OF THE MONSTROUS ANTS.

For three days and three nights they saw no land. On the morning of the fourth day, while it was yet dark, they heard a sound to the north-east; and Germane said—

"This is the voice of the waves breaking on the shore."

As soon as it was light they saw land and made towards it. While they were casting lots to know who should go and explore the country, they saw great flocks of ants coming down to the beach, each of them as large as a foal. The people judged by their numbers, and by their eager and hungry look, that they were bent on eating both ship and crew; so they turned their vessel round and sailed quickly away.

Their multitudes countless, prodigious their size;
  Were never such ants seen or heard of before.
They struggled and tumbled and plunged for the prize,
And fiercely the famine-fire blazed from their eyes,
  As they ground with their teeth the red sand of the shore!

CHAPTER IV.

THE TERRACED ISLE OF BIRDS.

AGAIN for three days and three nights they saw no
land. But on the morning of the fourth day they
heard the murmur of the waves on the beach; and as
the day dawned, they saw a large high island, with
terraces all round it, rising one behind another. On
the terraces grew rows of tall trees, on which were
perched great numbers of large, bright-coloured birds.

When the crew were about to hold council as to
who should visit the island and see whether the
birds were tame, Maildun himself offered to go. So
he went with a few companions; and they viewed
the island warily, but found nothing to hurt or
alarm them; after which they caught great numbers
of the birds and brought them to their ship.

> A shield-shaped island, with terraces crowned,
> And great trees circling round and round:
> From the summit down to the wave-washed rocks,
> There are bright-coloured birds in myriad flocks—
> Their plumes are radiant; but hunger is keen;
>   So the birds are killed,
>   Till the curragh is filled,
> And the sailors embark on the ocean green!

CHAPTER V.

A MONSTER.

THEY sailed from this, and on the fourth day discovered a large, sandy island, on which, when they came near, they saw a huge, fearful animal standing on the beach, and looking at them very attentively. He was somewhat like a horse in shape; but his legs were like the legs of a dog; and he had great, sharp claws of a blue colour.

Maildun, having viewed this monster for some time, liked not his look; and, telling his companions to watch him closely, for that he seemed bent on mischief, he bade the oarsmen row very slowly towards land.

The monster seemed much delighted when the ship drew nigh the shore, and gambolled and pranced about with joy on the beach, before the eyes of the voyagers; for he intended to eat the whole of them the moment they landed.

"He seems not at all sorry to see us coming," said Maildun; "but we must avoid him and put back from the shore."

This was done. And when the animal observed them drawing off, he ran down in a great rage to the very water's edge, and digging up large, round pebbles with his sharp claws, he began to fling them at the vessel; but the crew soon got beyond his reach, and sailed into the open sea.

A horrible monster, with blazing eyes,
In shape like a horse and tremendous in size.
Awaiting the curragh, they saw;
With big bony jaws
And murderous claws,
That filled them with terror and awe:
How gleeful he dances,
And bellows and prances,
As near to the island they draw;
Expecting a feast—
The bloodthirsty beast—
With his teeth like edge of a saw:
Then he ran to the shore,
With a deafening roar,
Intending to swallow them raw:
But the crew, with a shout,
Put their vessel about,
And escaped from his ravenous maw! ·

CHAPTER VI.

THE DEMON HORSE-RACE.

AFTER sailing a long distance, they came in view of
a broad, flat island. It fell to the lot of Germane to go
and examine it, and he did not think the task a
pleasant one. Then his friend Diuran said to him—

"I will go with you this time; and when next it
falls to my lot to visit an island, you shall come with
me." So both went together.

They found the island very large; and some distance from the shore they came to a broad green

* See note, page 128.

race-course, in which they saw immense hoof-marks, the size of a ship's sail, or of a large dining-table. They found nut-shells, as large as helmets, scattered about; and although they could see no one, they observed all the marks and tokens that people of huge size were lately employed there at sundry kinds of work.

Seeing these strange signs, they became alarmed, and went and called their companions from the boat to view them. But the others, when they had seen them, were also struck with fear, and all quickly retired from the place and went on board their curragh.

When they had got a little way from the land, they saw dimly, as it were through a mist, a vast multitude of people on the sea, of gigantic size and demoniac look, rushing along the crests of the waves with great outcry. As soon as this shadowy host had landed, they went to the green, where they arranged a horse-race.

The horses were swifter than the wind; and as they pressed forward in the race, the multitudes raised a mighty shout like thunder, which reached the crew as if it were beside them. Maildun and his men, as they sat in their curragh, heard the strokes of the whips and the cries of the riders; and though the race was far off, they could distinguish the eager words of the spectators:—"Observe the grey horse!" "See that chestnut horse!" "Watch the horse with the white spots!" "My horse leaps better than yours!"

After seeing and hearing these things, the crew sailed away from the island as quickly as they were

able, into the open ocean, for they felt quite sure that
the multitude they saw was a gathering of demons.

A spacious isle of meadowy plains, with a broad aı. 1 sandy shore :
Two bold and trusty spies are sent, its wonders to explore.
Mysterious signs, strange, awful sights, now meet the wanderers'
    eyes :
Vast hoof-marks, and the traces dire of men of monstrous size :
And lo ! on the sea, in countless hosts, their shadowy forms expand ;
They pass the affrighted sailors by, and like demons they rush to
    land ;
They mount their steeds, and the race is run, in the midst of hell'·
    uproar :
Then the wanderers quickly raise their sails, and leave the accursèi
    shore.

————••————

CHAPTER VII.

THE PALACE OF SOLITUDE.

THEY suffered much from hunger and thirst this
time, for they sailed a whole week without making
land ; but at the end of that time they came in sight of
a high island, with a large and very splendid house
on the beach near the water's edge.   There were two
doors—one turned inland, and the other facing the sea ;
and the door that looked towards the sea was closed
with a great flat stone.   In this stone was an opening,
through which the waves, as they beat against the
door every day, threw numbers of salmon into the
house.

The voyagers landed, and went through the whole
house without meeting any one.   But they saw in one

large room an ornamented couch, intended for the head of the house, and in each of the other rooms was a larger one for three members of the family : and there was a cup of crystal on a little table before each couch. They found abundance of food and ale, and they ate and drank till they were satisfied, thanking God for having relieved them from hunger and thirst.

> Aloft, high towering o'er the ocean's foam,
> The spacious mansion rears its glittering dome.
> Each day the billows, through the marble door,
> Shoot living salmon floundering on the floor.
> Couches that lure the sailors to recline,
> Abundant food, brown ale, and sparkling wine ;
> Tables and chairs in order duly placed,
> With crystal cups and golden goblets graced.
> But not a living soul the wanderers found ;
> 'Twas silence all and solitude profound.
> They eat and drink, give thanks, then hoist their sail,
> And skim the deep once more, obedient to the gale.

CHAPTER VIII.

THE ISLAND OF THE WONDERFUL APPLE TREE.

AFTER leaving this, they suffered again from hunger, till they came to an island with a high hill round it on every side. A single apple tree grew in the middle, very tall and slender, and all its branches were in like manner exceedingly slender, and of wonderful length, so that they grew over the hill and down to the sea.

When the ship came near the island, Maildun

caught one of the branches in his hand. For three days and three nights the ship coasted the island, and during all this time he held the branch, letting it slide through his hand, till on the third day he found a cluster of seven apples on the very end. Each of these apples supplied the travellers with food and drink for forty days and forty nights.

———◆———

CHAPTER IX.

THE ISLAND OF BLOODTHIRSTY QUADRUPEDS.

A BEAUTIFUL island next came in view, in which they saw, at a distance, multitudes of large animals shaped like horses. The voyagers, as they drew near, viewed them attentively, and soon observed that one of them opened his mouth and bit a great piece out of the side of the animal that stood next him, bringing away skin and flesh. Immediately after, another did the same to the nearest of his fellows. And, in short, the voyagers saw that all the animals in the island kept worrying and tearing each other from time to time in this manner; so that the ground was covered far and wide with the blood that streamed from their sides.

> In needless strife they oft contend,
>   A cruel, mutual-mangling brood;
> Their flesh with gory tusks they rend,
>   And crimson all the isle with blood.

CHAPTER X.

AN EXTRAORDINARY MONSTER.

THE next island had a wall all round it. When they came near the shore, an animal of vast size, with a thick, rough skin, started up inside the wall, and ran round the island with the swiftness of the wind. When he had ended his race, he went to a high point, and standing on a large, flat stone, began to exercise himself according to his daily custom, in the following manner. He kept turning himself completely round and round in his skin, the bones and flesh moving, while the skin remained at rest.

When he was tired of this exercise, he rested a little; and he then began turning his skin continually round his body, down at one side and up at the other like a mill-wheel; but the bones and flesh did not move.

After spending some time at this sort of work, he started and ran round the island as at first, as if to refresh himself. He then went back to the same spot, and this time, while the skin that covered the lower part of his body remained without motion, he whirled the skin of the upper part round and round like the movement of a flat-lying millstone. And it was in this manner that he spent most of his time on the island.

Maildun and his people, after they had seen

these strange doings, thought it better not to venture
nearer. So they put out to sea in great haste. The
monster, observing them about to fly, ran down to the
beach to seize the ship; but finding that they had got
out of his reach, he began to fling round stones at
them with great force and an excellent aim. One of
them struck Maildun's shield and went quite through
it, lodging in the keel of the curragh; after which the
voyagers got beyond his range and sailed away.

In a wall-circled isle a big monster they found,
  With a hide like an elephant, leathery and bare;
He threw up his heels with a wonderful bound,
  And ran round the isle with the speed of a hare.

But a feat more astounding has yet to be told:
  He turned round and round in his leathery skin;
His bones and his flesh and his sinews he rolled—
  He was resting outside while he twisted within!

Then, changing his practice with marvellous skill,
  His carcase stood rigid and round went his hide;
It whirled round his bones like the wheel of a mill—
  He was resting within while he twisted outside!

Next, standing quite near on a green little hill,
  After galloping round in the very same track,
While the skin of his belly stood perfectly still,
  Like a millstone he twisted the skin of his back!

But Maildun and his men put to sea in their boat,
  For they saw his two eyes looking over the wall;
And they knew by the way that he opened his throat,
  He intended to swallow them, curragh and all! *

---

* The verse in the original is quite serious; but I could not resist
the temptation to give it a humorous turn. The same observation
applies to the verse at page 122.

CHAPTER XI.

THE ISLE OF RED-HOT ANIMALS.

NOT daring to land on this island, they turned away hurriedly, much disheartened, not knowing whither to turn or where to find a resting-place. They sailed for a long time, suffering much from hunger and thirst, and praying fervently to be relieved from their distress. At last, when they were beginning to sink into a state of despondency, being quite worn out with toil and hardship of every kind, they sighted land.

It was a large and beautiful island, with innumerable fruit trees scattered over its surface, bearing abundance of gold-coloured apples. Under the trees they saw herds of short, stout animals, of a bright red colour, shaped somewhat like pigs ; but coming nearer, and looking more closely, they perceived with astonishment that the animals were all fiery, and that their bright colour was caused by the red flames which penetrated and lighted up their bodies.

The voyagers now observed several of them approach one of the trees in a body, and striking the trunk all together with their hind legs, they shook down some of the apples and ate them. In this manner the animals employed themselves every day, from early morning till the setting of the sun when they retired into deep caves, and were seen no more till next morning.

Numerous flocks of birds were swimming on the sea, all round the island. From morning till noon, they continued to swim away from the land, farther and farther out to sea; but at noon they turned round, and from that to sunset they swam back towards the shore. A little after sunset, when the animals had retired to their caves, the birds flocked in on the island, and spread themselves over it, plucking the apples from the trees and eating them.

Maildun proposed that they should land on the island, and gather some of the fruit, saying that it was not harder or more dangerous for them than for the birds; so two of the men were sent beforehand to examine the place. They found the ground hot under their feet, for the fiery animals, as they lay at rest, heated the earth all around and above their caves; but the two scouts persevered notwithstanding, and brought away some of the apples.

When morning dawned, the birds left the island and swam out to sea; and the fiery animals, coming forth from their caves, went among the trees as usual, and ate the apples till evening. The crew remained in their curragh all day; and as soon as the animals had gone into their caves for the night, and the birds had taken their place, Maildun landed with all his men. And they plucked the apples till morning, and brought them on board, till they had gathered as much as they could stow into their vessel.

CHAPTER XII.

THE PALACE OF THE LITTLE CAT.

AFTER rowing for a long time, their store of apples failed them, and they had nothing to eat or drink; so that they suffered sorely under a hot sun, and their mouths and nostrils were filled with the briny smell of the sea. At last they came in sight of land—a little island with a large palace on it. Around the palace was a wall, white all over, without stain or flaw, as if it had been built of burnt lime, or carved out of one unbroken rock of chalk; and where it looked towards the sea it was so lofty that it seemed almost to reach the clouds.

The gate of this outer wall was open, and a number of fine houses, all snowy white, were ranged round on the inside, enclosing a level court in the middle, on which all the houses opened. Maildun and his people entered the largest of them, and walked through several rooms without meeting with any one. But on reaching the principal apartment, they saw in it a small cat, playing among a number of low, square, marble pillars, which stood ranged in a row; and his play was, leaping continually from the top of one pillar to the top of another. When the men entered the room, the cat looked at them for a moment, but returned to his play anon, and took no turther notice of them.

Looking now to the room itself, they saw three rows of precious jewels ranged round the wall from one door-jamb to the other. The first was a row of brooches of gold and silver, with their pins fixed in the wall, and their heads outwards; the second, a row of torques of gold and silver; and the third, a row of great swords, with hilts of gold and silver.

Round the room were arranged a number of couches, all pure white and richly ornamented. Abundant food of various kinds was spread on tables, among which they observed a boiled ox and a roast hog; and there were many large drinking-horns, full of good, intoxicating ale.

"Is it for us that this food has been prepared?" said Maildun to the cat.

The cat, on hearing the question, ceased from playing, and looked at him; but he recommenced his play immediately. Whereupon Maildun told his people that the dinner was meant for them; and they all sat down, and ate and drank till they were satisfied, after which they rested and slept on the couches.

When they awoke, they poured what was left of the ale into one vessel; and they gathered the remnants of the food to bring them away. As they were about to go, Maildun's eldest foster brother asked him—

"Shall I bring one of those large torques away with me?"

"By no means," said Maildun; "it is well that

we have got food and rest. Bring nothing away, for it is certain that this house is not left without some one to guard it."

The young man, however, disregarding Maildun's advice, took down one of the torques and brought it away. But the cat followed him, and overtook him in the middle of the court, and, springing on him like a blazing, fiery arrow, he went through his body, and reduced it in a moment to a heap of ashes. He then returned to the room, and, leaping up on one of the pillars, sat upon it.

Maildun turned back, bringing the torque with him, and, approaching the cat, spoke some soothing words; after which he put the torque back to the place from which it had been taken. Having done this, he collected the ashes of his foster brother, and, bringing them to the shore, cast them into the sea. They all then went on board the curragh, and continued their voyage, grieving for their lost companion, but thanking God for His many mercies to them.

CHAPTER XIII.

AN ISLAND THAT DYED BLACK AND WHITE.

ON the morning of the third day, they came to another island, which was divided into two parts by a wall of brass running across the middle. They saw two

great flocks of sheep, one on each side of the wall;
and all those at one side were black, while those at
the other side were white.

A very large man was employed in dividing and
arranging the sheep; and he often took up a sheep
and threw it with much ease over the wall from one
side to the other. When he threw over a white sheep
among the black ones, it became black immediately;
and in like manner, when he threw a black sheep
over, it was instantly changed to white.

The travellers were very much alarmed on witnessing these doings; and Maildun said—

"It is very well that we know so far. Let us now
throw something on shore, to see whether it also will
change colour; if it does, we shall avoid the island."

So they took a branch with black-coloured bark
and threw it towards the white sheep, and no sooner
did it touch the ground than it became white. They
then threw a white-coloured branch on the side of the
black sheep, and in a moment it turned black.

"It is very lucky for us," said Maildun, "that we
did not land on the island, for doubtless our colour
would have changed like the colour of the branches."

So they put about with much fear, and sailed
away.

CHAPTER XIV.

THE ISLAND OF THE BURNING RIVER.

ON the third day, they came in view of a large, broad island, on which they saw a herd of gracefully shaped swine; and they killed one small porkling for food. Towards the centre rose a high mountain, which they resolved to ascend, in order to view the island; and Germane and Diuran Lekerd were chosen for this task.

When they had advanced some distance towards the mountain, they came to a broad, shallow river; and sitting down on the bank to rest, Germane dipped the point of his lance into the water, which instantly burned off the top, as if the lance had been thrust into a furnace. So they went no farther.

On the opposite side of the river, they saw a herd of animals like great hornless oxen, all lying down; and a man of gigantic size near them: and Germane began to strike his spear against his shield, in order to rouse the cattle.

"Why are you frightening the poor young calves in that manner?" demanded the big shepherd, in a tremendous voice.

Germane, astonished to find that such large animals were nothing more than calves, instead of answering the question, asked the big man where the mothers of those calves were.

"They are on the side of yonder mountain," he replied.

Germane and Diuran waited to hear no more; but, returning to their companions, told them all they had seen and heard; after which the crew embarked and left the island.

———————

CHAPTER XV.

THE MILLER OF HELL.

THE next island they came to, which was not far off from the last, had a large mill on it; and near the door stood the miller, a huge-bodied, strong, burly man. They saw numberless crowds of men and horses laden with corn, coming towards the mill; and when their corn was ground they went away towards the west. Great herds of all kinds of cattle covered the plain as far as the eye could reach, and among them many wagons laden with every kind of wealth that is produced on the ridge of the world. All these the miller put into the mouth of his mill to be ground; and all, as they came forth, went westwards.

Maildun and his people now spoke to the miller, and asked him the name of the mill, and the meaning of all they had seen on the island. And he, turning quickly towards them, replied in few words—

"This mill is called the Mill of Inver-tre-Kenand, and I am the miller of hell. All the corn and all the riches of the world that men are dissatisfied with, or which they complain of in any way, are sent here to be ground; and also every precious article, and every kind of wealth, which men try to conceal from God. All these I grind in the Mill of Inver-tre-Kenand, and send them afterwards away to the west."

He spoke no more, but turned round and busied himself again with his mill. And the voyagers, with much wonder and awe in their hearts, went to their curragh and sailed away.*

————◆————

CHAPTER XVI.

THE ISLE OF WEEPING.

AFTER leaving this, they had not been long sailing when they discovered another large island, with a great multitude of people on it. They were all black, both skin and clothes, with black head-dresses also; and they kept walking about, sighing and weeping and wringing their hands, without the least pause or rest.

It fell to the lot of Maildun's second foster brother to go and examine the island. And when he went among the people, he also grew sorrowful, and fell to weeping and wringing his hands, with the others.

---

* The incident of the big miller occurs in the Voyage of the Sons of O'Corra, as well as in the Voyage of Maildun. The two accounts are somewhat different; and I have combined both here.

Two of the crew were sent to bring him back; but they were unable to find him among the mourners; and, what was worse, in a little time they joined the crowd, and began to weep and lament like all the rest.

Maildun then chose four men to go and bring back the others by force, and he put arms in their hands, and gave them these directions—

"When you land on the island, fold your mantles round your faces, so as to cover your mouths and noses, that you may not breathe the air of the country; and look neither to the right nor to the left, neither at the earth nor at the sky, but fix your eyes on your own men till you have laid hands on them."

They did exactly as they were told, and having come up with their two companions, namely, those who had been sent after Maildun's foster brother, they seized them and brought them back by force. But the other they could not find. When these two were asked what they had seen on the island, and why they began to weep, their only reply was—

"We cannot tell; we only know that we did what we saw the others doing."

And after this the voyagers sailed away from the island, leaving Maildun's second foster brother behind.

CHAPTER XVII.

THE ISLE OF THE FOUR PRECIOUS WALLS.

THE next was a high island, divided into four parts by four walls meeting in the centre. The first was a wall of gold ; the second, a wall of silver ; the third, a wall of copper ; and the fourth, a wall of crystal. In the first of the four divisions were kings ; in the second, queens ; in the third, youths ; and in the fourth, young maidens.

When the voyagers landed, one of the maidens came to meet them, and leading them forward to a house, gave them food. This food, which she dealt out to them from a small vessel, looked like cheese, and whatever taste pleased each person best, that was the taste he found on it. And after they had eaten till they were satisfied, they slept in a sweet sleep, as if gently intoxicated, for three days and three nights. When they awoke on the third day, they found themselves in their curragh on the open sea; and there was no appearance in any direction either of the maiden or of the island.

———◆◆———

CHAPTER XVIII.

THE PALACE OF THE CRYSTAL BRIDGE.

THEY came now to a small island, with a palace on it, having a copper chain in front, hung all over with a number of little silver bells. Straight before the door there was a fountain, spanned by a bridge of crystal, which led to the palace. They walked towards the bridge, meaning to cross it, but every time they stepped on it they fell backwards flat on the ground.

After some time, they saw a very beautiful young woman coming out of the palace, with a pail in her hand; and she lifted a crystal slab from the bridge, and, having filled her vessel from the fountain, she went back into the palace.

"This woman has been sent to keep house for Maildun," said Germane.

"Maildun indeed!" said she, as she shut the door after her.

After this they began to shake the copper chain, and the tinkling of the silver bells was so soft and melodious that the voyagers gradually fell into a gentle, tranquil sleep, and slept so till next morning. When they awoke, they saw the same young woman coming forth from the palace, with the pail in her hand; and she lifted the crystal slab as before, filled her vessel, and returned into the palace.

"This woman has certainly been sent to keep house for Maildun," said Germane.

"Wonderful arc the powers of Maildun!" said she, as she shut the door of the court behind her.

They stayed in this place for three days and three nights, and each morning the maiden came forth in the same manner, and filled her pail. On the fourth day, she came towards them, splendidly and beautifully dressed, with her bright yellow hair bound by a circlet of gold, and wearing silver-work shoes on her small, white feet. She had a white mantle over her shoulders, which was fastened in front by a silver brooch studded with gold; and under all, next her soft, snow-white skin, was a garment of fine white silk.

" My love to you, Maildun, and to your companions," she said; and she mentioned them all, one after another, calling each by his own proper name. " My love to you," said she. " We knew well that you were coming to our island, for your arrival has long been foretold to us."

Then she led them to a large house standing by the sea, and she caused the curragh to be drawn high up on the beach. They found in the house a number of couches, one of which was intended for Maildun alone, and each of the others for three of his people. The woman then gave them, from one vessel, food which was like cheese; first of all ministering to Maildun, and then giving a triple share to every three of his companions; and whatever taste each man wished for, that was the taste he found on it. She then lifted the crystal slab at the bridge, filled her pail, and dealt out drink to them; and she knew exactly how much to give, both of food and of drink, so that each had enough and no more.

"This woman would make a fit wife for Maildun," said his people. But while they spoke, she went from them with her pail in her hand.

When she was gone, Maildun's companions said

to him, "Shall we ask this maiden to become thy wife?"

He answered, "What advantage will it be to you to ask her?"

She came next morning, and they said to her, "Why dost thou not stay here with us? Wilt thou make friendship with Maildun; and wilt thou take him for thy husband?"

She replied that she and all those that lived on the island were forbidden to marry with the sons of men; and she told them that she could not disobey, as she knew not what sin or transgression was.

She then went from them to her house; and on the next morning, when she returned, and after she had ministered to them as usual, till they were satisfied with food and drink, and were become cheerful, they spoke the same words to her.

"To-morrow," she replied, "you will get an answer to your question;" and so saying, she walked towards her house, and they went to sleep on their couches.

When they awoke next morning, they found themselves lying in their curragh on the sea, beside a great high rock; and when they looked about, they saw neither the woman, nor the palace of the crystal bridge, nor any trace of the island where they had been sojourning.

CHAPTER XIX.

THE ISLE OF SPEAKING BIRDS.

ONE night, soon after leaving this, they heard in the distance, towards the north-east, a confused murmur of voices, as if from a great number of persons singing psalms. They followed the direction of the sound, in order to learn from what it proceeded; and at noon the next day, they came in view of an island, very hilly and lofty. It was full of birds, some black, some brown, and some speckled, who were all shouting and speaking with human voices; and it was from them that the great clamour came.

CHAPTER XX.

THE AGED HERMIT, AND THE HUMAN SOULS.

AT a little distance from this they found another small island, with many trees on it, some standing singly, and some in clusters, on which were perched great numbers of birds. They also saw an aged man on the island, who was covered thickly all over with long, white hair, and wore no other dress. And when they landed, they spoke to him, and asked him who he was and what race he belonged to.

"I am one of the men of Erin," he replied. "On

a certain day, a long, long time ago, I embarked in a
small curragh, and put out to sea on a pilgrimage;
but I had got only a little way from shore, when my
curragh became very unsteady, as if it were about
to overturn. So I returned to land, and, in order
to steady my boat, I placed under my feet at the
bottom, a number of green surface sods, cut from one
of the grassy fields of my own country, and began my
voyage anew.   Under the guidance of God, I arrived
at this spot; and He fixed the sods in the sea for me,
so that they formed a little island.   At first I had
barely room to stand; but every year, from that time
to the present, the Lord has added one foot to the
length and breadth of my island, till in the long
lapse of ages it has grown to its present size.   And
on one day in each year, He has caused a single tree
to spring up, till the island has become covered with
trees.   Moreover, I am so old that my body, as you
see, has become covered with long, white hair, so that
I need no other dress.

   "And the birds that ye see on the trees," he
continued, " these are the souls of my children, and
of all my descendants, both men and women, who
are sent to this little island to abide with me according
as they die in Erin.   God has caused a well of ale
to spring up for us on the island : and every morning
the angels bring me half a cake, a slice of fish, and a
cup of ale from the well ; and in the evening the same
allowance of food and ale is dealt out to each man
and woman of my people.   And it is in this manner

that we live, and shall continue to live till the end of the world; for we are all awaiting here the day of judgment."

Maildun and his companions were treated hospitably on the island by the old pilgrim for three days and three nights; and when they were taking leave of him, he told them that they should all reach their own country except one man.

CHAPTER XXI.

THE ISLAND OF THE BIG BLACKSMITHS.

WHEN they had been for a long time tossed about on the waters, they saw land in the distance. On approaching the shore, they heard the roaring of a great bellows, and the thundering sound of smiths' hammers striking a large glowing mass of iron on an anvil; and every blow seemed to Maildun as loud as if a dozen men had brought down their sledges all together.

When they had come a little nearer, they heard the big voices of the smiths in eager talk.

" Are they near ? " asked one.

" Hush ! silence ! " says another.

" Who are they that you say are coming ? " inquired a third.

" Little fellows, that are rowing towards our shore in a pigmy boat," says the first.

When Maildun heard this, he hastily addressed the crew—

" Put back at once, but do not turn the curragh: reverse the sweep of your oars, and let her move stern forward, so that those giants may not perceive that we are flying!"

The crew at once obey, and the boat begins to move away from the shore, stern forward, as he had commanded.

The first smith again spoke. " Are they near enough to the shore?" said he to the man who was watching.

" They seem to be at rest," answered the other; " for I cannot perceive that they are coming closer, and they have not turned their little boat to go back."

In a short time the first smith asks again, " What are they doing now?"

" I think," said the watcher, " they are flying; for it seems to me that they are now farther off than they were a while ago."

At this the first smith rushed out of the forge— a huge, burly giant—holding, in the tongs which he grasped in his right hand, a vast mass of iron sparkling and glowing from the furnace; and, running down to the shore with long, heavy strides, he flung the red-hot mass with all his might after the curragh. It fell a little short, and plunged down just near the prow, causing the whole sea to hiss and boil and heave up around the boat. But they plied their oars, so that they quickly got beyond his reach, and sailed out into the open ocean.

CHAPTER XXII.

THE CRYSTAL SEA.

AFTER a time, they came to a sea like green crystal. It was so calm and transparent that they could see the sand at the bottom quite clearly, sparkling in the sunlight. And in this sea they saw neither monsters, nor ugly animals, nor rough rocks; nothing but the clear water and the sunshine and the bright sand. For a whole day they sailed over it, admiring its splendour and beauty.

CHAPTER XXIII.

A LOVELY COUNTRY BENEATH THE WAVES.

AFTER leaving this they entered on another sea, which seemed like a clear, thin cloud; and it was so transparent, and appeared so light, that they thought at first it would not bear up the weight of the curragh.

Looking down, they could see, beneath the clear water, a beautiful country, with many mansions surrounded by groves and woods. In one place was a single tree; and, standing on its branches, they saw an animal fierce and terrible to look upon.

Round about the tree was a great herd of oxen grazing, and a man stood near to guard them, armed

with shield and spear and sword; but when he looked
up and saw the animal on the tree, he turned anon
and fled with the utmost speed. Then the monster
stretched forth his neck, and, darting his head
downward, plunged his fangs into the back of the
largest ox of the whole herd, lifted him off the ground
into the tree, and swallowed him down in the twinkling
of an eye; whereupon the whole herd took to flight.

When Maildun and his people saw this, they were
seized with great terror; for they feared they should
not be able to cross the sea over the monster, on
account of the extreme mist-like thinness of the
water; but after much difficulty and danger they got
across it safely.

CHAPTER XXIV.

AN ISLAND GUARDED BY A WALL OF WATER.

WHEN they came to the next island, they observed
with astonishment that the sea rose up over it on
every side, steep and high, standing, as it were, like a
wall all round it. When the people of the island saw
the voyagers, they rushed hither and thither, shouting,
"There they are, surely! There they come again for
another spoil!"

Then Maildun's people saw great numbers of men
and women, all shouting and driving vast herds of
horses, cows, and sheep. A woman began to pelt the

crew from below with large nuts; she flung them so
that they alighted on the waves round the boat,
where they remained floating; and the crew gathered
great quantities of them and kept them for eating.

When they turned to go away, the shouting ceased;
and they heard one man calling aloud, "Where are
they now?" and another answering him, "They are
gone away!"

From what Maildun saw and heard at this island,
it is likely that it had been foretold to the people that
their country should some day be spoiled by certain
marauders; and that they thought Maildun and his
men were the enemies they expected.

CHAPTER XXV.

A WATER-ARCH IN THE AIR.

ON the next island they saw a very wonderful thing,
namely, a great stream of water which, gushing up out
of the strand, rose into the air in the form of a rain-
bow, till it crossed the whole island and came down
on the strand at the other side. They walked under
it without getting wet; and they hooked down from
it many large salmon. Great quantities of salmon of
a very great size fell also out of the water over their
heads down on the ground; so that the whole island
smelled of fish, and it became troublesome to gather
them on account of their abundance.

From the evening of Sunday till the evening of Monday, the stream never ceased to flow, and never changed its place, but remained spanning the island like a solid arch of water. Then the voyagers gathered the largest of the salmon, till they had as much as the curragh would hold; after which they sailed out into the great sea.

CHAPTER XXVI.

THE SILVER PILLAR OF THE SEA.

THE next thing they found after this was an immense silver pillar standing in the sea. It had eight sides, each of which was the width of an oar-stroke of the curragh, so that its whole circumference was eight oar-strokes. It rose out of the sea without any land or earth about it, nothing but the boundless ocean; and they could not see its base deep down in the water, neither were they able to see the top on account of its vast height.

A silver net hung from the top down to the very water, extending far out at one side of the pillar; and the meshes were so large that the curragh in full sail went through one of them. When they were passing through it, Diuran struck the mesh with the edge of his spear, and with the blow cut a large piece off it.

"Do not destroy the net," said Maildun; "for what we see is the work of great men."

"What I have done," answered Diuran, "is for the honour of my God, and in order that the story of our adventures may be more readily believed; and I shall lay this silver as an offering on the altar of Armagh, if I ever reach Erin."

That piece of silver weighed two ounces and a half, as it was reckoned afterwards by the people of the church of Armagh.

After this they heard some one speaking on the top of the pillar, in a loud, clear, glad voice; but they knew neither what he said, nor in what language he spoke.

CHAPTER XXVII.

AN ISLAND STANDING ON ONE PILLAR.

THE island they saw after this was named Encos;* and it was so called because it was supported by a single pillar in the middle. They rowed all round it, seeking how they might get into it; but could find no landing-place. At the foot of the pillar, however, down deep in the water, they saw a door securely closed and locked, and they judged that this was the way into the island. They called aloud, to find out if any persons were living there; but they got no reply. So they left it, and put out to sea once more.

* Encos means "one foot."

CHAPTER XXVIII.

THE ISLAND QUEEN DETAINS THEM WITH HER MAGIC
THREAD-CLEW.

THE next island they reached was very large. On one side rose a lofty, smooth, heath-clad mountain, and all the rest of the island was a grassy plain. Near the sea-shore stood a great high palace, adorned with carvings and precious stones, and strongly fortified with a high rampart all round. After landing, they went towards the palace, and sat to rest on the bench before the gateway leading through the outer rampart; and, looking in through the open door, they saw a number of beautiful young maidens in the court.

After they had sat for some time, a rider appeared at a distance, coming swiftly towards the palace; and on a near approach, the travellers perceived that it was a lady, young and beautiful and richly dressed. She wore a blue, rustling silk head-dress; a silver-fringed purple cloak hung from her shoulders; her gloves were embroidered with gold thread; and her feet were laced becomingly in close-fitting scarlet sandals. One of the maidens came out and held her horse, while she dismounted and entered the palace; and soon after she had gone in, another of the maidens came towards Maildun and his companions and said—

"You are welcome to this island. Come into the

palace; the queen has sent me to invite you, and is waiting to receive you."

They followed the maiden into the palace; and the queen bade them welcome, and received them kindly. Then, leading them into a large hall in which a plentiful dinner was laid out, she bade them sit down and eat. A dish of choice food and a crystal goblet of wine were placed before Maildun; while a single dish and a single drinking-bowl, with a triple quantity of meat and drink, were laid before each three of his companions. And having eaten and drunk till they were satisfied, they went to sleep on soft couches till morning.

Next day, the queen addressed Maildun and his companions—

"Stay now in this country, and do not go a-wandering any longer over the wide ocean from island to island. Old age or sickness shall never come upon you; but you shall be always as young as you are at present, and you shall live for ever a life of ease and pleasure."

"Tell us," said Maildun, "how you pass your life here."

"That is no hard matter," answered the queen. "The good king who formerly ruled over this island was my husband, and these fair young maidens that you see are our children. He died after a long reign, and as he left no son, I now reign, the sole ruler of the island. And every day I go to the Great Plain, to administer justice and to decide causes among my people."

"Wilt thou go from us to-day?" asked Maildun.

"I must needs go even now," she replied, "to give judgments among the people; but as to you, you will all stay in this house till I return in the evening, and you need not trouble yourselves with any labour or care."

They remained in that island during the three months of winter. And these three months appeared to Maildun's companions as long as three years, for they began to have an earnest desire to return to their native land. At the end of that time, one of them said to Maildun—

"We have been a long time here; why do we not return to our own country?"

"What you say is neither good nor sensible," answered Maildun, "for we shall not find in our own country anything better than we have here."

But this did not satisfy his companions, and they began to murmur loudly. "It is quite clear," said they, "that Maildun loves the queen of this island; and as this is so, let him stay here; but as for us, we will return to our own country."

Maildun, however, would not consent to remain after them, and he told them that he would go away with them.

Now, on a certain day, not long after this conversation, as soon as the queen had gone to the Great Plain to administer justice, according to her daily custom, they got their curragh ready and put out to sea. They had not gone very far from land when the queen came riding towards the shore; and, seeing how matters stood, she went into the palace and soon returned with a ball of thread in her hand.

Walking down to the water's edge, she flung the ball after the curragh, but held the end of the thread in her hand. Maildun caught the ball as it was passing, and it clung to his hand; and the queen, gently pulling the thread towards her, drew back the curragh to the very spot from which they had started in the little harbour. And when they had landed, she made them promise that if ever this happened again, some one should always stand up in the boat and catch the ball.

The voyagers abode on the island, much against their will, for nine months longer. For every time they attempted to escape, the queen brought them back by means of the clew, as she had done at first, Maildun always catching the ball.

At the end of the nine months, the men held council, and this is what they said—

"We know now that Maildun does not wish to leave the island; for he loves this queen very much, and he catches the ball whenever we try to escape, in order that we may be brought back to the palace."

Maildun replied, "Let some one else attend to the ball next time, and let us try whether it will cling to his hand."

They agreed to this, and, watching their opportunity, they again put off towards the open sea. The queen arrived, as usual, before they had gone very far

and flung the ball after them as before. Another man
of the crew caught it, and it clung as firmly to his
hand as to Maildun's; and the queen began to draw
the curragh towards the shore. But Diuran, drawing
his sword, cut off the man's hand, which fell with the
ball into the sea; and the men gladly plying their oars,
the curragh resumed her outward voyage.

When the queen saw this, she began to weep and
lament, wringing her hands and tearing her hair with
grief; and her maidens also began to weep and cry
aloud and clap their hands, so that the whole palace
was full of grief and lamentation. But none the
less did the men bend to their oars, and the curragh
sailed away; and it was in this manner that the
voyagers made their escape from the island.

CHAPTER XXIX.

THE ISLE OF INTOXICATING WINE-FRUITS.

THEY were now a long time tossed about on the great
billows, when at length they came in view of an island
with many trees on it. These trees were somewhat
like hazels, and they were laden with a kind of fruit
which the voyagers had not seen before, extremely
large, and not very different in appearance from
apples, except that they had a rough, berry-like rind.

After the crew had plucked all the fruit off one small tree, they cast lots who should try them, and the lot fell on Maildun. So he took some of them, and, squeezing the juice into a vessel, drank it. It threw him into a sleep of intoxication so deep that he seemed to be in a trance rather than in a natural slumber, without breath or motion, and with the red foam on his lips. And from that hour till the same hour next day, no one could tell whether he was living or dead.

When he awoke next day, he bade his people to gather as much of the fruit as they could bring away with them; for the world, as he told them, never produced anything of such surpassing goodness. They pressed out the juice of the fruit till they had filled all their vessels; and so powerful was it to produce intoxication and sleep, that, before drinking it, they had to mix a large quantity of water with it to moderate its strength.

CHAPTER XXX.

THE ISLE OF THE MYSTIC LAKE.

THE island they came to next was larger than most of those they had seen. On one side grew a wood of yew trees and great oaks; and on the other side was a grassy plain, with one small lake in the midst. A noble-looking house stood on the near part of the plain, with a small church not far off; and numerous flocks of sheep browsed over the whole island.

The travellers went to the church, and found in it a hermit, with snow-white beard and hair, and all the other marks of great old age. Maildun asked who he was, and whence he had come.

He replied, "I am one of the fifteen people, who, following the example of our master, Brendan of Birra,[20] sailed on a pilgrimage out into the great ocean. After many wanderings, we settled on this island, where we lived for a long time; but my companions died one after another, and of all who came hither, I alone am left."

The old pilgrim then showed them Brendan's satchel,[21] which he and his companions had brought with them on their pilgrimage; and Maildun kissed it, and all bowed down in veneration before it. And he told them that as long as they remained there, they might eat of the sheep and of the other food of the island; but to waste nothing.

One day, as they were seated on a hill, gazing out over the sea, they saw what they took to be a black cloud coming towards them from the south-west. They continued to view it very closely as it came nearer and nearer; and at last they perceived with amazement that it was an immense bird, for they saw quite plainly the slow, heavy flapping of his wings. When he reached the island, he alighted on a little hillock over the lake; and they felt no small alarm, for they thought, on account of his vast size, that if he saw them, he might seize them in his talons, and carry them off over the sea. So they hid themselves under trees and in the crannies of rocks; but they never lost sight of the bird, for they were bent on watching his movements.

He appeared very old, and he held in one claw a branch of a tree, which he had brought with him over the sea, larger and heavier than the largest full-grown oak. It was covered with fresh, green leaves, and was heavily laden with clusters of fruit, red and rich-looking like grapes, but much larger.

He remained resting for a time on the hill, being much wearied after his flight, and at last he began to eat the fruit off the branch. After watching him for some time longer, Maildun ventured warily towards the hillock, to see whether he was inclined to mischief; but the bird showed no disposition to harm him. This emboldened the others, and they all followed their chief.

The whole crew now marched in a body round the bird, headed by Maildun, with their shields raised; and as he still made no stir, one of the men, by Maildun's directions, went straight in front of him, and brought away some of the fruit from the branch which he still held in his talons. But the bird went on plucking and eating his fruit, and never took the least notice.

On the evening of that same day, as the men sat looking over the sea to the south-west, where the great

bird first appeared to them, they saw in the distance
two others, quite as large, coming slowly towards them
from the very same point.   On they came, flying at a
vast height, nearer and nearer, till at last they swooped
down and alighted on the hillock in front of the first
bird, one on each side.

Although they were plainly much younger than the
other, they seemed very tired, and took a long rest.
Then, shaking their wings, they began picking the old
bird all over, body, wings, and head, plucking out the
old feathers and the decayed quill points, and smoothing down his plumage with their great beaks.   After
this had gone on for some time, the three began
plucking the fruit off the branch, and they ate till
they were satisfied.

Next morning, the two birds began at the very
same work, picking and arranging the feathers of the
old bird as before; and at midday they ceased, and
began again to eat the fruit, throwing the stones and
what they did not eat of the pulp, into the lake, till the
water became red like wine.   After this the old bird
plunged into the lake and remained in it, washing
himself, till evening, when he again flew up on the
hillock, but perched on a different part of it, to avoid
touching and defiling himself with the old feathers
and the other traces of age and decay, which the
younger birds had removed from him.

On the morning of the third day, the two younger
birds set about arranging his feathers for the third
time; and on this occasion they applied themselves to

their task in a manner much more careful and particular than before, smoothing the plumes with the nicest touches, and arranging them in beautiful lines and glossy tufts and ridges. And so they continued without the least pause till midday, when they ceased. Then, after resting for a little while, they opened their great wings, rose into the air, and flew away swiftly towards the south-west, till the men lost sight of them in the distance.

Meantime the old bird, after the others had left, continued to smooth and plume his feathers till evening; then, shaking his wings, he rose up, and flew three times round the island, as if to try his strength. And now the men observed that he had lost all the appearances of old age: his feathers were thick and glossy, his head was erect and his eye bright, and he flew with quite as much power and swiftness as the others. Alighting for the last time on the hillock, after resting a little, he rose again, and turning his flight after the other two, to the point from which he had come, he was soon lost to view, and the voyagers saw no more of him.

It now appeared very clear to Maildun and his companions that this bird had undergone a renewal of youth from old age, according to the word of the prophet, which says, " Thy youth shall be renewed as the eagle." Diuran, seeing this great wonder, said to his companions—

" Let us also bathe in the lake, and we shall obtain a renewal of youth like the bird."

But they said, "Not so, for the bird has left the poison of his old age and decay in the water."

Diuran, however, would have his own way; and he told them he was resolved to try the virtue of the water, and that they might follow his example or not, whichever they pleased. So he plunged in and swam about for some time, after which he took a little of the water and mixed it in his mouth; and in the end he swallowed a small quantity. He then came out perfectly sound and whole; and he remained so ever after, for as long as he lived he never lost a tooth or had a grey hair, and he suffered not from disease or bodily weakness of any kind. But none of the others ventured in.

The voyagers, having remained long enough on this island, stored in their curragh a large quantity of the flesh of the sheep; and after bidding farewell to the ancient cleric, they sought the ocean once more.

> Now once again, when winds and tide combine,
> The flying curragh cleaves the crested brine.
> Far to the west an island rose to view,
> With verdant plains, clear streams, and mountains blue.
> An aged hermit, bred in Erin's land,
> Welcomed and blessed the chieftain and his band;
> Brought food and drink, and bade them rest awhile,
> And view the wonders of that lovely isle.
> Lo, from the sea, three birds of monstrous size,
> With vast wings slowly moving, cleave the skies;
> And as they nearer drew, the sailors saw
> One held a fruit branch firmly in his claw.
> Down by the clear, mysterious lake they light,
> Eat from the branch, and rest them from their flight.

The aged bird, with plumes decayed and thin,
Paused on the brink awhile, then, plunging in,
He bath'd and smooth'd his feathers o'er and o'er,
Shook his great wings and rested on the shore.
  Now while the other two his plumes arrange,
Through all his frame appears a wondrous change :
His eyes grow bright, his head erect and bold,
His glossy plumage shines like burnished gold ;
Free from old age, his glorious form expands ;
In radiant youth and beauty proud he stands !
  Such was the gift that lake of wonder gave ;
Such was the virtue of its mystic wave.

CHAPTER XXXI.

THE ISLE OF LAUGHING.

THEY next came to an island with a great plain extending over its whole surface. They saw a vast multitude of people on it, engaged in sundry youthful games, and all continually laughing. The voyagers cast lots who should go to examine the island; and the lot fell upon Maildun's third foster brother.

The moment he landed he went among the others and joined in their pastimes and in their laughter, as if he had been among them all his life. His companions waited for him a very long time, but were afraid to venture to land after him; and at last, as there seemed no chance of his returning, they left him and sailed away.

CHAPTER XXXII.

THE ISLE OF THE BLEST.

THEY came now to a small island with a high wall of fire all round it, and there was a large open door in the wall at one side near the sea. They sailed backward and forward many times, and always paused before the door; for whenever they came right in front of it, they could see almost the whole island through it.

And this is what they saw: A great number of people, beautiful and glorious-looking, wearing rich garments adorned and radiant all over, feasting joyously, and drinking from embossed vessels of red gold which they held in their hands. The voyagers heard also their cheerful, festive songs; and they marvelled greatly, and their hearts were full of gladness at all the happiness they saw and heard. But they did not venture to land.

CHAPTER XXXIII.

THE HERMIT OF THE SEA-ROCK.

A LITTLE time after leaving this, they saw something a long way off towards the south, which at first they took to be a large white bird floating on the sea, and rising and falling with the waves; but on turning their curragh towards it for a nearer view, they found that it was a man. He was very old, so old that he was covered all over with long, white hair, which grew from his body; and he was standing on a broad, bare rock, and kept continually throwing himself on his knees, and never ceased praying.

When they saw that he was a holy man, they asked and received his blessing; after which they began to converse with him; and they inquired who he was, and how he had come to that rock. Then the old man gave them the following account:—

"I was born and bred in the island of Tory.* When I grew up to be a man, I was cook to the brotherhood of the monastery; and a wicked cook I was; for every day I sold part of the food intrusted to me, and secretly bought many choice and rare things with the money. Worse even than this I did; I made secret passages underground into the church and into the houses belonging to it, and I stole from time to time great quantities of golden vestments, book-covers adorned with brass and gold, and other holy and precious things.

" I soon became very rich, and had my rooms filled with costly couches, with clothes of every colour, both linen and woollen, with brazen pitchers and caldrons, and with brooches and armlets of gold. Nothing was wanting in my house, of furniture and ornament, that a person in a high rank of life might be expected to have; and I became very proud and overbearing.

* Tory Island, off the coast of Donegal, where there was a monastery dedicated to St. Columkille.

" One day, I was sent to dig a grave for the body
of a rustic that had been brought from the mainland
to be buried on the island. I went and fixed on a
spot in the little graveyard; but as soon as I had
set to work, I heard a voice speaking down deep in
the earth beneath my feet—

" ' Do not dig this grave ! '

" I paused for a moment, startled; but, recovering
myself, I gave no further heed to the mysterious
words, and again I began to dig. The moment I did
so, I heard the same voice, even more plainly than
before—

" ' Do not dig this grave ! I am a devout and holy
person, and my body is lean and light; do not put
the heavy, pampered body of that sinner down upon
me ! '

" But I answered, in the excess of my pride and
obstinacy, ' I will certainly dig this grave; and I will
bury this body down on you ! '

" ' If you put that body down on me, the flesh will
fall off your bones, and you will die, and be sent to
the infernal pit at the end of three days; and, moreover, the body will not remain where you put it.'

" ' What will you give me,' I asked, ' if I do not
bury the corpse on you ? '

" ' Everlasting life in heaven,' replied the voice.

" ' How do you know this; and how am I to be
sure of it ? ' I inquired.

" And the voice answered me, ' The grave you are
digging is clay. Observe now whether it will remain

so, and then you will know the truth of what I tell
you. And you will see that what I say will come to
pass, and that you cannot bury that man on me, even
if you should try to do so.'

"These words were scarce ended, when the grave
was turned into a mass of white sand before my face.
And when I saw this, I brought the body away, and
buried it elsewhere.

"It happened, some time after, that I got a new
curragh made, with the hides painted red all over; and
I went to sea in it. As I sailed by the shores and
islands, I was so pleased with the view of the land
and sea from my curragh that I resolved to live
altogether in it for some time; and I brought on board
all my treasures—silver cups, gold bracelets, and ornamented drinking-horns, and everything else, from the
largest to the smallest article.

"I enjoyed myself for a time, while the air was
clear and the sea calm and smooth. But one day, the
winds suddenly arose and a storm burst upon me,
which carried me out to sea, so that I quite lost sight
of land, and I knew not in what direction the curragh
was drifting. After a time, the wind abated to a
gentle gale, the sea became smooth, and the curragh
sailed on as before, with a quiet, pleasant movement.

"But suddenly, though the breeze continued to
blow, I thought I could perceive that the curragh
ceased moving, and, standing up to find out the cause,
I saw with great surprise an old man not far off,
sitting on the crest of a wave.

"He spoke to me; and, as soon as I heard his voice, I knew it at once, but I could not at the moment call to mind where I had heard it before. And I became greatly troubled, and began to tremble, I knew not why.

"'Whither art thou going?' he asked.

"'I know not,' I replied; 'but this I know, I am pleased with the smooth, gentle motion of my curragh over the waves.'

"'You would not be pleased,' replied the old man, 'if you could see the troops that are at this moment around you.'

"'What troops do you speak of?' I asked. And he answered—

"'All the space round about you, as far as your view reaches over the sea, and upwards to the clouds, is one great towering mass of demons, on account of your avarice, your thefts, your pride, and your other crimes and vices.'

"He then asked, 'Do you know why your curragh has stopped?'

"I answered, 'No;' and he said, 'It has been stopped by me; and it will never move from that spot till you promise me to do what I shall ask of you.'

"I replied that perhaps it was not in my power to grant his demand.

"'It is in your power,' he answered; 'and if you refuse me, the torments of hell shall be your doom.'

"He then came close to the curragh, and, laying

his hands on me, he made me swear to do what he demanded.

"'What I ask is this,' said he; 'that you throw into the sea this moment all the ill-gotten treasures you have in the curragh.'

"This grieved me very much, and I replied, 'It is a pity that all these costly things should be lost.'

"To which he answered, 'They will not go to loss; a person will be sent to take charge of them. Now do as I say.'

"So, greatly against my wishes, I threw all the beautiful precious articles overboard, keeping only a small wooden cup to drink from.

"'You will now continue your voyage,' he said; 'and the first solid ground your curragh reaches, there you are to stay.'

"He then gave me seven cakes and a cup of watery whey as food for my voyage; after which the curragh moved on, and I soon lost sight of him. And now I all at once recollected that the old man's voice was the same as the voice that I had heard come from the ground, when I was about to dig the grave for the body of the rustic. I was so astonished and troubled at this discovery, and so disturbed at the loss of all my wealth, that I threw aside my oars, and gave myself up altogether to the winds and currents, not caring whither I went; and for a long time I was tossed about on the waves, I knew not in what direction.

"At last it seemed to me that my curragh ceased to move; but I was not sure about it, for I could see

no sign of land. Mindful, however, of what the old
man had told me, that I was to stay wherever my
curragh stopped, I looked round more carefully; and
at last I saw, very near me, a small rock level with
the surface, over which the waves were gently laughing and tumbling. I stepped on to the rock; and the
moment I did so, the waves seemed to spring back,
and the rock rose high over the level of the water;
while the curragh drifted by and quickly disappeared,
so that I never saw it after. This rock has been my
abode from that time to the present day.

"For the first seven years, I lived on the seven
cakes and the cup of whey given me by the man who
had sent me to the rock. At the end of that time
the cakes were all gone; and for three days I fasted,
with nothing but the whey to wet my mouth. Late
in the evening of the third day, an otter brought me
a salmon out of the sea; but though I suffered much
from hunger, I could not bring myself to eat the fish
raw, and it was washed back again into the waves.

"I remained without food for three days longer;
and in the afternoon of the third day, the otter
returned with the salmon. And I saw another otter
bring firewood; and when he had piled it up on the
rock, he blew it with his breath till it took fire and
lighted up. And then I broiled the salmon and ate
till I had satisfied my hunger.

"The otter continued to bring me a salmon every
day, and in this manner I lived for seven years longer.
The rock also grew larger and larger daily, till it

became the size you now see it. At the end of seven years, the otter ceased to bring me my salmon, and I fasted for three days. But at the end of the third day, I was sent half a cake of fine wheaten flour and a slice of fish; and on the same day my cup of watery whey fell into the sea, and a cup of the same size, filled with good ale, was placed on the rock for me.

"And so I have lived, praying and doing penance for my sins to this hour. Each day my drinking-vessel is filled with ale, and I am sent half a wheat-flour cake and a slice of fish; and neither rain nor wind, nor heat, nor cold, is allowed to molest me on this rock."

This was the end of the old man's history. In the evening of that day, each man of the crew received the same quantity of food that was sent to the old hermit himself, namely, half a cake and a slice of fish; and they found in the vessel as much good ale as served them all.

The next morning he said to them, "You shall all reach your own country in safety. And you, Maildun, you shall find in an island on your way, the very man that slew your father; but you are neither to kill him nor take revenge on him in any way. As God has delivered you from the many dangers you have passed through, though you were very guilty, and well deserved death at His hands; so you forgive your enemy the crime he committed against you."

After this they took leave of the old man and sailed away.

THE OLD HERMIT'S STORY.

The storms may roar and the seas may rage,
  But here, on this bare, brown rock,
I pray and repent and I tell my beads,
  Secure from the hurricane's shock.

For the good, kind God, in pity to me,
  Holds out His protecting hand;
And cold nor heat nor storm nor sleet,
  Can molest me where I stand.

I robbed the churches and wronged the poor,
  And grew richer day by day;
But now on this bare, brown ocean rock,
  A heavy penance I pay.

A bloated sinner died unshrived,
  And they brought his corse to me—
" Go, dig the grave and bury the dead,
  And pray for the soul set free."

I dug the grave, but my hands were stayed
  By a solemn and fearful sound,
For the feeble tones of a dead man's voice
  Came up from the hollow ground!

The dead monk speaks up from the grave—

Place not that pampered corse on mine,
  For my bones are weak and thin;
I cannot bear the heavy weight
  Of a body defiled by sin.

I was a meek and holy man;
  I fasted and watched and prayed;
A sinner's corse would defile the clay
  Where my wasted body is laid

The old hermit continues his story—

> The voice then ceased, and I heard no more
> Its hollow, beseeching tone;
> Then I closed the grave, and left the old monk
> To rest in his coffin alone.
>
> My curragh sailed on the western main,
> And I saw, as I viewed the sea,
> A withered old man upon a wave;
> And he fixed his eyes on me.
>
> He spoke, and his voice my heart's blood froze,
> And I shook with horror and fear:
> 'Twas the very voice of the dead old monk
> That sounded in mine ear!

The dead monk speaks again—

> Far from my grave the sinner's corse
> In unhallowed clay lies deep;
> And now in my coffin, undefiled,
> For ever in peace I sleep.
>
> Go, live and pray on the bare, brown rock,
> Far out in the stormy sea;
> A heavy penance for heavy crimes,
> And heaven at last for thee!

The old hermit ends his story—

> And here I live from age to age;
> I pray and repent and fast;
> An otter brings me food each day,
> And I hope for heaven at last.
>
> The tempests roar and the billows rage,
> But God holds forth His hand,
> And cold nor heat nor storm nor sleet,
> Can harm me where I stand.

CHAPTER XXXIV.

SIGNS OF HOME.

Soon after they saw a beautiful verdant island, with herds of oxen, cows, and sheep browsing all over its hills and valleys; but no houses nor inhabitants were to be seen. And they rested for some time on this island, and ate the flesh of the cows and sheep.

One day, while they were standing on a hill, a large falcon flew by; and two of the crew, who happened to look closely at him, cried out, in the hearing of Maildun—

"See that falcon! he is surely like the falcons of Erin!"

"Watch him closely," cried Maildun; "and observe exactly in what direction he is flying!"

And they saw that he flew to the south-east, without turning or wavering.

They went on board at once; and, having unmoored, they sailed to the south-east after the falcon. After rowing the whole day, they sighted land in the dusk of the evening, which seemed to them like the land of Erin.

CHAPTER XXXV.

MAILDUN MEETS HIS ENEMY, AND ARRIVES HOME.

ON a near approach, they found it was a small island; and now they recognised it as the very same island they had seen in the beginning of their voyage, in which they had heard the man in the great house boast that he had slain Maildun's father, and from which the storm had driven them out into the great ocean.

They turned the prow of their vessel to the shore, landed, and went towards the house. It happened that at this very time the people of the house were seated at their evening meal; and Maildun and his companions, as they stood outside, heard a part of their conversation.

Said one to another, " It would not be well for us if we were now to see Maildun."

"As to Maildun," answered another, "it is very well known that he was drowned long ago in the great ocean."

"Do not be sure," observed a third; " perchance he is the very man that may waken you up some morning from your sleep."

"Supposing he came now," asks another, " what should we do ? "

The head of the house now spoke in reply to

the last question; and Maildun at once knew his voice—

"I can easily answer that," said he. "Maildun has been for a long time suffering great afflictions and hardships; and if he were to come now, though we were enemies once, I should certainly give him a welcome and a kind reception."

When Maildun heard this he knocked at the door, and the door-keeper asked who was there; to which Maildun made answer—

"It is I, Maildun, returned safely from all my wanderings."

The chief of the house then ordered the door to be opened; and he went to meet Maildun, and brought himself and his companions into the house. They were joyfully welcomed by the whole household; new garments were given to them; and they feasted and rested, till they forgot their weariness and their hardships.

They related all the wonders God had revealed to them in the course of their voyage, according to the word of the sage who says, "It will be a source of pleasure to remember these things at a future time."

After they had remained here for some days, Maildun returned to his own country. And Diuran Lekerd took the five half-ounces of silver he had cut down from the great net at the Silver Pillar, and laid it, according to his promise, on the high altar of Armagh.

THE FAIRY PALACE OF THE QUICKEN TREES.*

———◦◇◦———

CHAPTER I.

COLGA, KING OF LOCHLANN, INVADES ERIN, AND IS SLAIN.

ONCE upon a time, a noble, warlike king ruled over Lochlann,[6] whose name was Colga of the Hard Weapons. On a certain occasion, this king held a meeting of his chief people, on the broad, green plain before his palace of Berva.[6] And when they were all gathered together, he spoke to them in a loud, clear voice, from where he sat high on his throne; and he asked them whether they found any fault with the manner in which he ruled them, and whether they knew of anything deserving of blame in him as their sovereign lord and king. They replied, as if with the voice of one man, that they found no fault of any kind.

* The quicken tree, or quickbeam, or mountain ash, or roan-tree; Gaelic, *caerthainn*. Many mystic virtues were anciently attributed to this tree.

Then the king spoke again and said, "You see not as I see. Do you not know that I am called King of the Four Tribes of Lochlann, and of the Islands of the Sea? And yet there is one island which acknowledges not my rule."

And when they had asked which of the islands he meant, he said—

"That island is Erin of the green hills. My forefathers, indeed, held sway over it, and many of our brave warriors died there in fight. There fell the great king, Balor of the Mighty Blows;[9] his son Bres[9] also; and his queen, Kethlenda of the Crooked Teeth;[9] there, too, fell Irann and Slana, sisters of the king; and many others that I do not name. But though our hosts at last subdued the land and laid it under tribute, yet they held it not long; for the men of Erin arose and expelled our army, regaining their ancient freedom.

"And now it is my desire that we once more sail to Erin with a fleet and an army, to bring it under my power, and take, either by consent or by force, the tributes that are due to me by right. And we shall thereafter hold the island in subjection till the end of the world."

The chiefs approved the counsel of the king, and the meeting broke up.

Then the king made proclamation, and sent his swift scouts and couriers all over the land, to muster his fighting men, till he had assembled a mighty army in one place.

And when they had made ready their curve-sided, white-sailed ships, and their strong, swift-gliding boats, the army embarked. And they raised their sails and plied their oars; and they cleft the billowy, briny sea; and the clear, cold winds whistled through their sails; and they made neither stop nor stay, till they landed on the shore of the province of Ulad.*

The King of Ireland at that time was Cormac Mac Art,[22] the grandson of Conn the Hundred-fighter.[18] And when Cormac heard that a great fleet had come to Erin, and landed an army of foreigners, he straightway sent tidings of the invasion to Allen † of the green hill-slopes, where lived Finn,[23] and the noble Fena[23] of the Gaels.

When the king's messengers had told their tale, Finn despatched his trusty, swift-footed couriers to every part of Erin where he knew the Fena dwelt; and he bade them to say that all should meet him at a certain place, near that part of the coast where the Lochlann army lay encamped. And he himself led the Fena of Leinster northwards to join the muster.

They attacked the foreigners, and the foreigners were not slow to meet their onset; and the Fena were sore pressed in that battle, so that at one time the Lochlanns were like to prevail.

Oscar, the son of Oisin,[23] when he saw his friends falling all round him, was grieved to the heart;

* Ulad, *i.e.* Ulster.
† The Hill of Allen, in the county Kildare, where Finn had his palace. (See note 23 at the end.)

and he rested for a space to gather his wrath and
his strength. Then, renewing the fight, he rushed
with fury towards the standard of Colga, the Lochlann king, dealing havoc and slaughter among those
foreigners that stood in his track. The king saw
Oscar approach, and met him; and they fought a
deadly battle hand-to-hand. Soon their shields were
rent, their hard helmets were dinted with sword-
blows, their armour was pierced in many places, and
their flesh was torn with deep wounds. And the end
of the fight was, that the king of the foreigners was
slain by Oscar, the son of Oisin.

When the Lochlanns saw their king fall, they
lost heart, and the battle went against them. But
they fought on nevertheless, till evening, when their
army entirely gave way, and fled from the field.
And of all the nobles and princes and mighty chiefs
who sailed to Erin on that expedition, not one was
left alive, except the youngest son of the king, whose
name was Midac. Him Finn spared on account of
his youth; with intent to bring him up in his own
household.

After the Fena had rested for a time, and buried
their dead, they turned their faces southward, and
marched slowly towards Allen, bringing their sick
and wounded companions. And Finn placed Midac
among the household of Allen, treating him honour-
ably, and giving him servants and tutors. Moreover,
he enlisted him in the Fena, and gave him a high
post as befitted a prince.

CHAPTER II.

MIDAC, THE SON OF COLGA, MEDITATES REVENGE.

AFTER this things went on as before, while Midac grew up towards manhood, and hunted and feasted with the Fena, and fought with them when they fought. But he never lost an opportunity of making himself acquainted with all their haunts and hunting-grounds, their palaces and fortresses, and in particular with their manner of carrying on war.

It happened one day that Finn and some of his leading chiefs were in council, considering sundry matters, especially the state and condition of the Fena; and each chief was commanded by Finn to speak, and give his opinion or advice on anything that he deemed weighty enough to be debated by the meeting.

And after many had spoken, Conan Mail, the son of Morna, stood up and said—

"It seems to me, O king, that you and I and the Fena in general are now in great danger. For you have in your house, and mixing with your people, a young man who has good cause of enmity towards you; that is to say, Midac, the son of the king of Lochlann. For was it not by you that his father and brothers and many of his friends were slain? Now I notice that this young prince is silent and distant, and talks little to those around him. Moreover, I see that day after day he takes much pains to know all matters relating to the Fena; and as he has friends in Lochlann, mighty men with armies and ships, I fear me the day may come when this prince will use his knowledge to our destruction."

The king said that all this was quite true, and he asked Conan to give his opinion as to what should be done.

" What I advise in the matter is this," said Conan, " that Midac be not allowed to abide any longer in the palace of Allen.   But as it is meet that he should be treated in a manner becoming a prince, let him be given a tract of land for himself in some other part of Erin, with a home and a household of his own.   Then shall we be freed from his presence, and he can no longer listen to our counsels, and learn all our secrets and all our plans."

This speech seemed to Finn and the other chiefs reasonable and prudent, and they agreed to follow the advice of Conan Mail.

Accordingly Finn sent for the prince, and said to him—

" Thou knowest, Midac, that thou hast been brought up from boyhood in my household, and that thou hast been dealt with in every way as becomes a prince. Now thou art a man, and standest in no further need of instruction, for thou hast learned everything needful for a prince and for a champion of the Fena; and it is not meet that thou shouldst abide longer in the house of another.   Choose, therefore, the two cantreds

that please thee best in all Erin, and they shall be
given to thee and to thy descendants for ever as a
patrimony. There thou shalt build houses and a homestead for thyself, and I will help thee with men and
with cattle and with all things else necessary."

Midac listened in silence; and when the king had
done speaking, he replied in a cold and distant manner
and in few words, that the proposal was reasonable
and proper, and pleased him well. And thereupon he
chose the rich cantred of Kenri on the Shannon, and
the cantred of the Islands lying next to it on the
north, at the other side of the river.*

Now Midac had good reasons for choosing these
two territories beyond all others in Erin. For the
river opens out between them like a great sea, in
which are many islands and sheltered harbours, where
ships might anchor in safety; and he hoped to bring a
fleet and an army into Erin some day, to avenge on
Finn and the Fena the defeats they had inflicted on his
countrymen, and above all, the death of his father and
brothers. And being bent on treachery, he could not
have chosen in all Erin a territory better suited for
carrying out his secret designs.

So these two cantreds were bestowed on Midac.
Finn gave him also much cattle and wealth of all
kinds; so that when his houses were built, and when

* The cantreds of Kenri and Islands are now two baronies : the
former the barony of Kenry, in Limerick, a little below the city ;
the latter the barony of Islands, in Clare, on the opposite side of
the Shannon, including the mouth of the river Fergus, with its
numerous *islands,* from which the barony has its name.

he was settled in his new territory, with his servants
and his cattle and his wealth all round him, there
was no brugaid* in Erin richer or more prosperous
than he.

For fourteen years Midac lived in his new home,
growing richer every year.   But the Fena knew
nothing of his way of life, for he kept himself apart,
and none of his old acquaintances visited him.   And
though he was enrolled in the ranks of the Fena, he
never, during all that time, invited one of them to his
house, or offered them food or drink or entertainment
of any kind.

One day, Finn and the Fena went to hunt in the
district of Fermorc,† and over the plains of Hy Conall
Gavra.†   And when all was arranged and the chase
about to begin, Finn himself, and a few of his companions, went to the top of the hill of Knockfierna ‡ to
see the sport; while the main body of the Fena scattered themselves over the plain with their dogs and
attendants, to start the deer and the wild boars and
all the other game of the forest.

Then Finn's people pitched their tents, and made
soft couches of rushes and heather, and dug cooking-places [24]; for they intended the hill to be the

---

* Brugaid, a sort of local officer, who was allowed a tract of land
free, on condition that he maintained a large establishment as a house
of public hospitality.   Many of the brugaids were very rich.

† Fermorc and Hy Conall Gavra are now the baronies of Upper
and Lower Connello, in the county Limerick.

‡ Knockfierna, a conspicuous hill, celebrated for its fairy lore,
near Croom, in the county Limerick; very near Kenri, Midac's
territory.

resting-place of all who chose to rest, till the chase was ended.

After Finn and his companions had sat for some time on the hill, they saw a tall warrior coming towards them, armed in full battle array. He wore a splendid coat of mail of Lochlann workmanship, and over it a mantle of fine satin dyed in divers colours. A broad shield hung on his left shoulder, and his helmet glittered in the morning sun like polished silver. At his left side hung a long sword, with golden hilt and enamelled sheath; and he held in his right hand his two long, polished, death-dealing spears. His figure and gait were wonderfully majestic, and as he came near, he saluted the king in stately and courteous words.

Finn returned the salutation, and spoke with him for a while; and at length he asked him whence he had come, and if he had brought any tidings.

" As to the place I came from," he answered, " that need not be spoken of; and for news, I have nothing to tell except that I am a ferdana,* and that I have come to thee, O king of the Fena, with a poem."

" Methinks, indeed," replied Finn, " that conflict and battle are the poetry you profess; for never have I seen a hero more noble in mien and feature."

" I am a ferdana nevertheless," answered the stranger; " and if thou dost not forbid me, I will prove it by reciting a poem I have brought for thee."

" A mountain-top is not the place for poetry," said

* Ferdana, a poet.

Finn ; "and moreover, there is now no opportunity
either for reciting or listening. For I and these few
companions of mine have come to sit here that we may
view the chase, and listen to the eager shouts of the
men, and the sweet cry of the hounds.

" But if you are, as you say," continued Finn, " a
ferdana, remain here with us till the chase is ended ;
and then you shall come with me to one of our
palaces, where I shall listen to your poem, and bestow
on you such gifts as are meet for a poet of your
rank."

But the strange champion answered, "It is not
my wish to go to your palace ; and I now put you
under gesa,[12] which true heroes do not suffer, that you
listen to my poem, and that you find out and explain
its meaning."

"Well then," said Finn, "let there be no further
delay ; repeat your poem."

So the hero recited the following verse :—

> I saw a house by a river's shore,
> Famed through Erin in days of yore,
> Radiant with sparkling gems all o'er,
> Its lord deep skilled in magical lore ;
> No conqueror ever defiled its floor ;
> No spoiler can rive its golden store ;
> Fire cannot burn its battlements hoar ;
> Safe it stands when the torrents pour ;
> Feasting and joy for evermore,
> To all who enter its open door !
> > Now if thou hast learned a champion's lore,
> > Tell me the name of that mansion hoar,
> > With roof of crystal and marble floor—
> > The mansion I saw by the river's shore.

"I can explain that poem," said Finn. "The mansion you saw is Bruga of the Boyne,* the fairy palace of Angus, the Dedannan prince, son of the Dagda, which is open to all who wish to partake of its feasts and its enjoyments. It cannot be burned by fire, or drowned by water, or spoiled by robbers, on account of the great power of its lord and master; for there is not now, and there never was, and there never shall be, in Erin, a man more skilled in magic arts than Angus of the Bruga."

"That is the sense of my poem," said the stranger; "and now listen to this other, and explain it to me if thou canst"—

> I saw to the south a bright-faced queen,
> With couch of crystal and robe of green;
> A numerous offspring, sprightly and small,
> Plain through her skin you can see them all;
> Slowly she moves, and yet her speed
> Exceeds the pace of the swiftest steed!
>> Now tell me the name of that wondrous queen,
>> With her couch of crystal and robe of green.†

"I understand the sense of that poem also," said Finn. "The queen you saw is the river Boyne, which flows by the south side of the palace of Bruga. Her couch of crystal is the sandy bed of the river; and her robe of green the grassy plain of Bregia, ‡ through

---

* Bruga of the Boyne. (See note, page 62.)

† The poets were much given to proposing poetical puzzles of this kind; and it was considered a mark of superior education, and of great acuteness in a champion to be able to explain them. (For another example, see the enigmatical verse about the skin of the pig, in the story of "The Children of Turenn," page 69.)

‡ Bregia or Magh Breagh, the ancient name of the plain extending from the Liffey northwards to the borders of the county Louth. (For

which it flows.   Her children, which you can see
through her skin, are the speckled salmon, the lively,
pretty trout, and all the other fish that swim in the
clear water of the river.   The river flows slowly indeed ;
but its waters traverse the whole world in seven years,
which is more than the swiftest steed can do."

"These are my poems," said the champion ; "and
thou hast truly explained their meaning."

"And now," said Finn, "as I have listened to thy
poetry and explained it, tell us, I pray thee, who thou
art and whence thou hast come ; for I marvel much
that so noble a champion should live in any of the five
provinces of Erin without being known to me and my
companions."

Then Conan Mail spoke.   "Thou art, O king, the
wisest and most far-seeing of the Fena, and thou hast
unravelled and explained the hard poetical puzzles of
this champion.   Yet, on the present occasion, thou
knowest not a friend from a foe ; for this man is
Midac, whom thou didst bring up with much honour
in thine own house, and afterwards made rich, but
who is now thy bitter enemy, and the enemy of all
the Fena.   Here he has lived for fourteen years,
without fellowship or communication with his former
companions.   And though he is enrolled in the order
of the Fena, he has never, during all that time, invited
thee to a banquet, or come to see any of his old
friends, or given food or entertainment to any of the
Fena, either master or man."

this name, see the author's "Irish Names of Places," Series II.
Part IV. chap. II.

Midac answered, " If Finn and the Fena have
not feasted with me, that is none of my fault; for my
house has never been without a banquet fit for either
king or chief; but you never came to partake of it.
I did not, indeed, send you an invitation; but that you
should not have waited for, seeing that I was one of
the Fena, and that I was brought up in your own
household.   Howbeit, let that pass.   I have now a
feast ready, in all respects worthy of a king; and I
put you under gesa that you and the chiefs that are
here with you, come this night to partake of it.   I
have two palaces, and in each there is a banquet.   One
is the Palace of the Island, which stands on the sea;
and the other is the Palace of the Quicken Trees, which
is a little way off from this hill; and it is to this that
I wish you to come."

Finn consented; and Midac, after he had pointed
out the way to the Palace of the Quicken Trees, left
them, saying he would go before, that he might have
things in readiness when they should arrive.

CHAPTER III.

FINN IS ENTRAPPED BY MIDAC, AND HELD BY ENCHANT-
MENT IN THE PALACE OF THE QUICKEN TREES.

FINN now held council with his companions, and they
agreed that the king's son, Oisin, and five other chiefs,
with their followers, should tarry on the hill till the

hunting party returned, while Finn went to the palace with the rest.

And it was arranged that Finn should send back word immediately to the party on the hill, how he fared; and that Oisin and the others were to follow him to the palace when the hunting party had returned.

Those that remained with Oisin were Dermat O'Dyna; Fatha Conan, the son of the son of Conn; Kylta Mac Ronan; Ficna, the son of Finn; and Innsa, the son of Swena Selga.

And of those who went with Finn to the Palace of the Quicken Trees, the chief were Gaul Mac Morna; Dathkeen the Strong-limbed; Mac Luga of the Red Hand; Glas Mac Encarda from Beara; the two sons of Aed the Lesser, son of Finn; Racad and Dalgus, the two kings of Leinster; Angus Mac Bresal Bola; and the two leaders of the Connaught Fena, namely, Mac-na-Corra and Corr the Swift-footed.

As Finn and his party came nigh to the palace, they were amazed at its size and splendour; and they wondered greatly that they had never seen it before. It stood on a level green, which was surrounded by a light plantation of quicken trees, all covered with clusters of scarlet berries. At one side of the little plain, very near the palace, was a broad river, with a rocky bank at the near side, and a steep pathway leading down to a ford.

But what surprised them most was that all was lonely and silent—not a living soul could they see in any direction; and Finn, fearing some foul play, would have turned back, only that he bethought him of his gesa and his promise. The great door was wide open, and Conan went in before the others; and after viewing the banqueting hall, he came out quite enraptured with what he had seen. He praised the beauty and perfect arrangement of everything, and told his companions that no other king or chief in all Erin had a banqueting hall to match the hall of Midac, the son of Colga. They all now entered, but they found no one—neither host nor guests nor attendants.

As they gazed around, they thought they had never seen a banquet hall so splendid. A great fire burned brightly in the middle, without any smoke, and sent forth a sweet perfume, which filled the whole room with fragrance, and cheered and delighted the heroes. Couches were placed all round, with rich coverlets and rugs, and soft, glossy furs. The curved walls were of wood,* close-jointed and polished like ivory; and each board was painted differently from those above and below; so that the sides of the room, from floor to roof, were all radiant with a wonderful variety of colours.

Still seeing no one, they seated themselves on the couches and rugs. Presently a door opened, and Midac walked into the room. He stood for a few moments before the heroes, and looked at them one

* The houses of the ancient Irish were circular, and generally made of wood.

after another, but never spoke one word; then, turning round, he went out and shut the great door behind him.

Finn and his friends were much surprised at this; however, they said nothing, but remained resting as they were for some time, expecting Midac's return. Still no one came, and at length Finn spoke—

"We have been invited here, my friends, to a banquet; and it seems to me very strange that we should be left so long without attendance, and without either food or drink. Perhaps, indeed, Midac's attendants have made some mistake, and that the feast intended for this palace has been prepared in the Palace of the Island. But I wonder greatly that such a thing should have happened."

"I see something more wonderful than that," said Gaul Mac Morna; "for lo, the fire, which was clear and smokeless when we first saw it, and which smelled more sweetly than the flowers of the plain, now fills the hall with a foul stench, and sends up a great cloud of black, sooty smoke!"

"I see something more wonderful than that," said Glas Mac Encarda; "for the boards in the walls of this banquet hall, which were smooth and close-jointed and glorious all over with bright colours when we came, are now nothing but rough planks, clumsily fastened together with tough quicken tree withes, and as rude and unshapen as if they had been hacked and hewed with a blunt axe!"

"I see something more wonderful than that," said

Foilan, the son of Aed the Lesser; "for this palace, which had seven great doors when we came in, all wide open, and looking pleasantly towards the sunshine, has now only one small, narrow door, close fastened, and facing straight to the north!"

"I see something more wonderful than that," said Conan Mail; "for the rich rugs and furs and the soft couches, which were under us when we sat here first, are all gone, not as much as a fragment or a thread remaining; and we are now sitting on the bare, damp earth, which feels as cold as the snow of one night!"*

Then Finn again spoke. "You know, my friends, that I never tarry in a house having only one door. Let one of you then, arise, and break open that narrow door, so that we may go forth from this foul, smoky den!"

"That shall be done," cried Conan; and, so saying, he seized his long spear, and, planting it on the floor, point downwards, he attempted to spring to his feet. But he found that he was not able to move, and turning to his companions, he cried out with a groan of anguish—

"Alas, my friends! I see now something more wonderful than all; for I am firmly fixed by some druidical spell to the cold clay floor of the Palace of the Quicken Trees!"

---

* "As cold as the snow of one night;" "As white as the snow of one night," are usual comparisons in Gaelic. The first night's snow seems particularly cold and white when you see it in the morning on account of the contrast with the green fields of the day before.

And immediately all the others found themselves, in like manner, fixed where they sat. And they were silent for a time, being quite confounded and overwhelmed with fear and anguish.

At length Gaul spoke, and said, "It seems clear, O king, that Midac has planned this treachery, and that danger lies before us. I wish, then, that you would place your thumb under your tooth of knowledge,[25] and let us know the truth; so that we may at once consider as to the best means of escaping from this strait."

Whereupon Finn placed his thumb under his tooth of knowledge, and mused for a little while. Then suddenly withdrawing his thumb, he sank back in his seat and groaned aloud.

"May it be the will of the gods," said Gaul, "that it is the pain of thy thumb that has caused thee to utter that groan!"

"Alas! not so," replied Finn. "I grieve that my death is near, and the death of these dear companions! For fourteen years has Midac, the son of the king of Lochlann, been plotting against us; and now at last he has caught us in this treacherous snare, from which I can see no escape.

"For in the Palace of the Island there is, at this moment, an army of foreigners, whom Midac has brought hither for our destruction. Chief over all is Sinsar of the Battles, from Greece, the Monarch of the World, who has under his command sixteen warlike princes, with many others of lesser note. Next to Sinsar is his son, Borba the Haughty, who commands also a number of fierce and hardy knights.

"There are, besides, the three kings of the Island of the Torrent, large-bodied and bloodthirsty, like three furious dragons, who have never yet yielded to an enemy on the field of battle. It is these who, by their sorcery, have fixed us here; for this cold clay that we sit on is part of the soil of the enchanted Island of the Torrent, which they brought hither, and placed here with foul spells. Moreover, the enchantment that binds us to this floor can never be broken unless the blood of these kings be sprinkled on the clay. And very soon some of Sinsar's warriors will come over from the Palace of the Island, to slay us all, while we are fixed here helpless, and unable to raise a hand in our own defence."

Full of alarm and anguish were the heroes when they heard these tidings. And some began to shed bitter tears in silence, and some lamented aloud. But Finn again spoke and said—

"It becomes us not, my friends, being heroes, to weep and wail like women, even though we are in danger of death; for tears and lamentations will avail us nothing. Let us rather sound the Dord-Fian,* sweetly and plaintively, according to our wont, that it may be a comfort to us before we die."

So they ceased weeping, and, joining all together, they sounded the Dord-Fian in a slow, sad strain.

* Dord-Fian, or Dord-Fiansa, a sort of musical war-cry, usually performed by several persons in chorus.

CHAPTER IV.

INNSA, FINN'S FOSTER SON, DEFENDS THE FORD LEADING TO THE PALACE OF THE QUICKEN TREES.

Now let us speak of Oisin, and the party who tarried with him on the hill of Knockfierna. When he found that his father Finn had not sent back a messenger as he had promised, though the night was now drawing nigh, he began to fear that something was wrong; and he said to his companions—

"I marvel much that we have got no news from the king, how he and his companions have fared in the Palace of the Quicken Trees. It is clear to me that he would have fulfilled his promise to send us word, if he had not been hindered by some unforeseen difficulty. Now, therefore, I wish to know who will go to the palace and bring me back tidings."

Ficna, the son of Finn, stood forth and offered to go; and Finn's foster son, Innsa, the son of Swena Selga, said he would go with him.

They both set out at once, and as they travelled with speed, they soon reached the plain on which stood the Palace of the Quicken Trees; and now the night was darkening around them. As they came near to the palace, they marvelled to hear the loud, slow strains of the Dord-Fian; and Innsa exclaimed joyfully—

"Things go well with our friends, seeing that they are amusing themselves with the Dord-Fian!"

But Ficna, who guessed more truly how things really stood, replied—

"It is my opinion, friend, that matters are not so pleasant with them as you think; for it is only in time of trouble or danger that Finn is wont to have the Dord-Fian sounded in a manner so slow and sad."

While they talked in this wise, it chanced that the Dord-Fian ceased for a little space; and Finn hearing the low hum of conversation outside, asked was that the voice of Ficna. And when Ficna answered, "Yes," Finn said to him—

"Come not nearer, my son; for this place teems with dangerous spells. We have been decoyed hither by Midac, and we are all held here by the foul sorcery of the three kings of the Island of the Torrent."

And thereupon Finn told him the whole story of the treachery that had been wrought on them, from beginning to end; and he told him also that nothing could free them but the blood of those three kings sprinkled on the clay.

Then he asked who the second man was whom he had heard conversing with Ficna; and when he was told that it was Innsa, the son of Swena Selga, he addressed Ficna earnestly—

"Fly, my son, from this fatal place! Fly, and save my foster child from the treacherous swords of the foreigners; for they are already on their way hither!"

But Innsa quickly answered, "That I will never do. It would, indeed, be an ungrateful return to a kind foster father, to leave thee now in deadly strait, and seek my own safety."

And Ficna spoke in a like strain.

Then Finn said, "Be it so, my sons; but a sore trial awaits you. Those who come hither from the Palace of the Island must needs pass the ford under the shadow of these walls. Now this ford is rugged and hard to be crossed; and one good man, standing in the steep, narrow entrance at the hither side, might dispute the passage for a time against many. Go now, and defend this ford; and haply some help may come in time."

So both went to the ford. And when they had viewed it carefully, Ficna, seeing that one man might defend it for a short time almost as well as two, said to Innsa—

"Stay thou here to guard the ford for a little time, while I go to the Palace of the Island to see how the foreigners might be attacked. Haply, too, I may meet with the party coming hither, and decoy them on some other track."

And Innsa consented; and Ficna set out straightway for the Palace of the Island.

Now as to the Palace of the Island. When Midac returned in the morning, and told how Finn and his people were held safe in the Palace of the Quicken Trees, the foreigners were in great joy. And they feasted and drank and were merry till evening; when an Irla * of the King of the World spoke in secret to his brother, and said—

" I will go now to the Palace of the Quicken Trees, and I will bring hither the head of Finn the son of Cumal; and I shall gain thereby much renown, and shall be honoured by the King of the World."

So he went, bringing with him a goodly number of his own knights; and nothing is told of what befell them till they arrived at the brink of the ford under the Palace of the Quicken Trees. Looking across through the darkness, the Irla thought he saw a warrior standing at the other brink; and he called aloud to ask who was there, and whether he belonged to the noble or the ignoble races of the world.

And when Innsa answered that he belonged to the household of Finn, the son of Cumal, the Irla said—

" Lo, we are going to the Palace of the Quicken Trees, to bring Finn's head to the King of the World; and thou shalt come with us and lead us to the door."

" That, indeed," replied Innsa, " would be a strange way for a champion to act who has been sent hither by Finn to guard this ford. I will not allow any foe to pass—of that be sure; and I warn you that you come not to my side of the ford ! "

At this the Irla said to his knights, " Force the ford: then shall we see if yonder hero can fight as well as he threatens."

And at the word, they rushed through the water,

* Irla, *i.e.* an earl, a chief.

as many as could find room. But only one or two at a time could attack; and the young champion struck them down right and left as fast as they came up, till the ford became encumbered with their bodies.

And when the conflict had lasted for a long time, and when they found that they could not dislodge him, the few that remained retired across the ford; and Innsa was fain to rest after his long combat.

But the Irla, seeing so many of his knights slain, was mad with wrath; and, snatching up his sword and shield, he attacked Innsa; and they fought a long and bloody fight.

Now the Irla was fresh and strong, while Innsa was weary and sore wounded; and at length the young hero fell in the ford, and the Irla beheaded him, and, exulting in his victory, brought the head away.

Finn and his companions, as they sat in miserable plight in the Palace of the Quicken Trees, heard the clash of arms at the ford, and the shouts and groans of warriors; and after a time all was still again; and they knew not how the fight had ended.

And now the Irla, thinking over the matter, deemed it unsafe to go to the Palace of the Quicken Trees without a larger body of knights; so he returned towards the Palace of the Island, intending to bring Innsa's head to the King of the World. When he had come within a little distance of the palace, he met Ficna, who was then on his way back to the ford; and seeing that he was coming from the Palace of the Island, he deemed that he was one of the knights of the King of the World.

Ficna spoke to him, and asked whither he had come.

"I come," replied the Irla, "from the ford of the Palace of the Quicken Trees. There, indeed, on oui way to the palace, to slay Finn the son of Cumal, we were met by a young champion, who defended the ford and slew my knights. But he fell at length beneath my sword; and, lo, I have brought his head for a triumph to the King of the World!"

Ficna took the head tenderly, and kissed the cheek thrice, and said, sorrowing—

"Alas, dear youth! only this morning I saw the light of valour in those dim eyes, and the bloom of youth on that faded cheek!"

Then turning wrathfully to the Irla, he asked—

"Knowest thou to whom thou hast given the young warrior's head?"

And the Irla replied, "Hast thou not come from the Palace of the Island, and dost thou not belong to the host of the King of the World?"

"I am not one of his knights," answered Ficna; "and neither shalt thou be, after this hour!"

Whereupon they drew their swords, and fought where they stood; and the foreign Irla fell by the avenging sword of Ficna, the son of Finn. Ficna beheaded him and returned to the ford, bringing the head, and also the head of Innsa. And when he had come to the ford, he made a grave of green sods cn the bank, in which he laid the body and the head of Innsa, sometimes grieving for the youth, and sometimes rejoicing that his death had been avenged.

Then he went on to the Palace of the Quicken Trees, bringing the Irla's head; and when he had come nigh the door, he called aloud to Finn, who, impatient and full of anxious thoughts, asked—

"Tell us, Ficna, who fought the battle at the ford, and how it has ended."

"Thine own. foster son, Innsa, defended the ford against many foes, whose bodies now encumber the stream."

"And how is it now with my foster son?" asked Finn.

"He died where he fought," replied Ficna; "for at the end, when he was weary and sore wounded, the foreign Irla attacked him, and slew him."

"And thou, my son, didst thou stand by and see my nursling slain?"

"Truly I did not," answered Ficna. "Would that I had been there, and I would have defended and saved him! And even now he is well avenged; for I met the Irla soon after, and lo, I have brought thee his head. Moreover, I buried thy nursling tenderly in a grave of green sods by the ford."

And Finn wept and said, "Victory and blessings be with thee, my son! Never were children better than mine. Before I saw them, few were my possessions and small my consideration in Erin; but since they have grown up around me, I have been great and prosperous, till I fell by treachery into this evil plight. And now, Ficna, return and guard the ford, and peradventure our friends may send help in time."

So Ficna went and sat on the brink of the ford.

CHAPTER V.

FICNA, THE SON OF FINN, DEFENDS THE FORD.

Now at the Palace of the Island, another Irla, whose name was Kironn, brother to him who had been slain by Ficna, spoke to some of his own followers—

"It is long since my brother left for the Palace of the Quicken Trees; I fear me that he and his people have fared ill in their quest. And now I will go to seek for them."

And he went, bringing a company of knights well armed; and when they had come to the ford, they saw Ficna at the far side. Kironn called out and asked who he was, and asked also who had made such a slaughter in the ford.

Ficna answered, "I am one of the household champions of Finn the son of Cumal, and he has sent me here to guard this ford. As to the slaughter of yonder knights, your question stirs my mind to wrath, and I warn you, if you come to this side of the ford, you will get a reply, not in words, but in deeds."

Then Kironn and his men rushed through the water, blind with rage, and struck wildly at Ficna. But the young hero watchfully parried their strokes and thrusts; and one after another they fell beneath his blows, till only a single man was left, who ran back with all speed to the Palace of the Island to tell the tale. And Ficna sat down on the brink, covered all over with wounds, and weary from the toil of battle.

When these tidings were brought to the palace, Midac was very wroth, and he said, "These men should not have gone to force the ford without my knowledge; for they were far too few in number, and neither were they bold and hardy enough to meet Finn's valiant champions. I know these Fena well, and it is not to me a matter of surprise that the Irla and his people fell by them.

"But I will now go with a choice party of my own brave men; and I will cross the ford despite their guards, and slay Finn and all his companions in the Palace of the Quicken Trees.

"Moreover, there is one man among them, namely, Conan Mail,[23] who of all the men of Erin has the largest appetite, and is fondest of choice eating and drinking. To him will I bring savoury food and delicious drink, not, indeed, to delight him with eating and drinking, but that I may torment him with the sight and smell of what he cannot taste."

So, having got the food, he set out with a chosen band; and when he had arrived at the ford, he saw a warrior at the far side. He asked who he was, and finding that it was Ficna, he spoke guilefully to him.

"Dear art thou to me, Ficna, dearer even than all the rest of Finn's household; for during the time I lived among the Fena, you never used me ill, or lifted a hand to either man or dog belonging to me."

But Ficna spurned his smooth words, and replied, "While you lived among the Fena, there was not a man among them that had less to do with you than I. But this I know, that you were treated kindly by all, especially by my father Finn, and you have repaid him by ingratitude and treachery."

When Midac heard this speech he was filled with wrath, and no longer hiding his evil mind, he ordered Ficna with threats to leave the ford. But Ficna laughed with scorn, and replied—

"The task is easy, friend Midac, to dislodge a single champion; and surely it is a small matter to you whether I stand in this narrow pass or abandon my post. Come forward, then, you and your knights; but here I will remain to receive you. I only regret you did not come sooner, while my blood was hot, and before my wounds grew stiff, when you would have got a better welcome!"

Then Midac ordered forward his knights, and they ran eagerly across the ford. But Ficna overthrew them with a mighty onset, like a hawk among a flight of small birds, or like a wolf among a flock of sheep. When Midac saw this, he buckled on his shield and took his sword. Then, treading warily over the rough rocks, and over the dead bodies of his knights, he confronted Ficna, and they attacked each other with deadly hate and fury.

We shall now speak of those who remained on Knockfierna. When Oisin found that the two heroes did not return as soon as he expected, he thus addressed his companions—

"It seems to me a long time, my friends, since Ficna and Innsa went to the Palace of the Quicken Trees; methinks if they have sped successfully they should have long since come back with tidings of Finn and the others."

And one of his companions answered, "It is plain that they have gone to partake of the feast, and it fares so well with them that they are in no haste to leave the palace."

But Dermat O'Dyna of the Bright Face spoke and said, "It may be as you say, friend, but I should like to know the truth of the matter. And now I will go and find out why they tarry, for my mind misgives me that some evil thing has happened."

And Fatha Conan said he would go with him.

So the two heroes set out for the Palace of the Quicken Trees; and when they were yet a good way off from the ford they heard the clash of arms. They paused for a moment, breathless, to listen, and then Dermat exclaimed—

"It is the sound of single combat, the combat of mighty heroes; it is Ficna fighting with the foreigners, for I know his war-shout. I hear the clash of swords and the groans of warriors; I hear the shrieks of the ravens over the fairy-mansions, and the howls of the wild men of the glens! Hasten, Fatha, hasten, for Ficna is in sore strait, and his shout is a shout for help!"

And so they ran like the wind till they reached the hill-brow over the river; and, looking across in the dim moonlight, they saw the whole ford heaped with the bodies of the slain, and the two heroes fighting to the death at the far side. And at the first glance they observed that Ficna, being sore wounded, was yielding and sheltering behind his shield, and scarce able to ward off the blows of Midac.

Then Fatha cried out, "Fly, Dermat, fly! Save our dear companion! Save the king's son from death."

And Dermat, pausing for a moment, said, as if communing with himself—

"This is surely an evil plight: for if I run to the other side, the foreigner, being the more enraged for seeing me, will strike with greater fury, and I may not overtake the prince alive; and if I cast my spear, I may strike the wrong man!"

But Fatha, overhearing him, said, "Fear not, Dermat, for you never yet threw an erring cast of a spear!"

Then Dermat, putting his finger in the silken loop of his spear, threw a deadly cast with unerring aim, and struck Midac, so that the iron spear-head went right through his body, and the length of a warrior's hand beyond.

"Woe to the man," exclaimed Midac—"woe to him whom that spear reaches: for it is the spear of Dermat O'Dyna!"

And now his wrath increased, and he struck at Ficna more fiercely than before.

Dermat shouted to him to hold his hand and not slay the king's son; and as he spoke he rushed down the slope and across the ford, to save the young hero.   But Midac, still pressing on with unabated strength and fury, replied—

"Had you wished to save the prince's life, you should have spared mine: now that I have been wounded to death by your spear, Finn shall never see his son alive!"

Even as he spoke, he raised his sword for a mighty blow; and just as Dermat, shouting earnestly, was closing on them, he struck the prince lifeless to the earth, but fell down himself immediately after.

Dermat came up on the instant, and looked sadly at his friend lying dead.   Then, addressing Midac, he said—

"If I had found thee dead, I would have passed thee untouched; but now that I have overtaken thee alive, I must needs behead thee, for thy head will be to Finn a worthy eric [10] for his son."

And so saying, he struck off Midac's head with one sweep of his heavy sword.

Dermat now repaired to the Palace of the Quicken Trees, leaving Fatha to watch the ford till his return. And when he had come near, he called aloud and struck the door with his heavy spear, for his wrath had not yet left him; but the door yielded not.

Finn knew the voice, and called out impatiently, "Do not try to enter here, Dermat, for this place is full of foul spells. But tell us first, I pray thee, who fought that long and bitter fight; for we heard the clash of arms and the shouts of warriors, but we know nothing more."

"Thy noble son, Ficna," returned Dermat, "fought single-handed against the foreigners."

"And how fares it with my son after that battle?"

"He is dead," answered Dermat; "first sore wounded by many foes whom he slaughtered, and afterwards slain by Midac, the son of Colga. But thy son is avenged; for though I came to the ford indeed too late to save him, I have slain Midac, and here I have brought thee his head as an eric."

And for a long time Dermat heard no more.

At last Finn spoke again and said—

"Victory and blessings be with you, Dermat, for often before did you relieve the Fena from sore straits. But never have we been in such plight as this. For here we sit spell-bound, and only one thing can release us, the blood of the three fierce kings of the Island of the Torrent sprinkled on this clay. Meantime, unless the for be well defended, the foreigners will come and slay us. In you, Dermat, we trust, and unless you aid us well and faithfully now, we shall of a certainty perish. Guard the ford till the rising of the sun, for then I know the Fena will come to aid you."

"I and Fatha will of a certainty keep the enemy at bay," replied Dermat; and he bade them farewell for a time, and was about to return to the ford: but Conan Mail, with a groan, said—

"Miserable was the hour when I came to this palace, and cold and comfortless is the clay on which I sit—the clay of the Island of the Torrent. But worst of all to be without food and drink so long. And while I sit here, tormented with hunger and thirst, there is great plenty of ale and wine and of rich, savoury food yonder in the Palace of the Island. I am not able to bear this any longer; and now, Dermat, I beseech you to bring me from the palace as much food as I can eat and a drinking-horn of wine."

"Cursed be the tongue that spoke these selfish words!" said Dermat. "A host of foreigners are now seeking to compass your death, with only Fatha and myself to defend you. Surely this is work enough for two good men! And now it seems I must abandon my post, and undertake a task of much danger, to get food for the gluttonous Conan Mail!"

"Alas, Dermat-na-man!"[23] replied Conan, "if it were a lovely maiden, with bright eyes and golden hair, who made this little request, quickly and eagerly you would fly to please her, little recking of danger or trouble. But now you refuse me, and the reason is not hard to see. For you formerly crossed me four times in my courtships; and now it likes you well to see me die of hunger in this dungeon!"

"Well, then," said Dermat, "cease your upbraiding,

and I will try to bring you food; for it is better to face danger than to suffer the revilings of your foul tongue."

So saying, he went back to the ford to Fatha, where he stood watching; and after he had told him how matters stood, he said to him—

"I must needs go to the Palace of the Island, to get food for Conan Mail; and you shall guard the ford till I return."

But Fatha told him that there was food and drink enough at the other side of the ford, which Midac had brought from the palace, and urged him to bring a good meal of this to Conan.

"Not so," said Dermat. "He would taunt me with bringing him food taken from the hands of dead men; and though one may recover from his blow, it is not so easy to recover from the venom of his tongue." *

So he left Fatha at the ford, and repaired to the Palace of the Island.

As he drew nigh, he heard the noise of feasting and revelry, and the loud talk and laughter of men deep in drink. Walking tiptoe, he peered warily through the open door, and saw the chiefs and the knights sitting at the tables; with Sinsar of the Battles and his son Borba high seated over all. He saw also many attendants serving them with food and drink, each holding in his hand a large ornamented drinking-horn, filled with wine.

Dermat entered the outer door softly, and stood

* A satirical allusion to Conan's well-known cowardice.

in a dark part of the passage near the door, silent and stern, with sword drawn, watching his opportunity. And after a time one of the attendants, unsuspecting, passed close to him; when Dermat, with a swift, sure blow, struck off his head. And he snatched the drinking-horn from the man's hand before he fell, so that not a drop of the wine was spilled.

Then, laying the drinking-horn aside for a moment, he walked straight into the hall, and taking up one of the dishes near where the king sat, he went out through the open door, bringing with him both dish and drinking-horn. And amidst the great crowd, and the drinking, and the noise, no one took the least notice of him, so that he got off without hindrance or harm of any kind.

When he reached the ford, he found Fatha lying fast asleep on the bank. He wondered very much that he could sleep in the midst of such a slaughter; but knowing that the young warrior was worn out with watching and toil, he left him lying asleep, and went to the Palace of the Quicken Trees with the food for Conan.

When he had come to the door, he called aloud to Conan and said—

"I have here a goodly meal of choice food: how am I to give it to thee?"

Conan said, "Throw it towards me through yonder little opening."

Dermat did so; and as fast as he threw the food, Conan caught it in his large hands, and ate it up

ravenously. And when it was all gone, Dermat
said —

"I have here a large drinking-horn of good wine :
how am I to give it to thee ?"

Conan answered, "There is a place behind the
palace where, from a rock, you may reach the lower
parapet with a light, airy bound. Come from that
straight over me, and break a hole in the roof with
your spear, through which you can pour the wine
down to me."

Dermat did so; and as he poured down the wine,
Conan, with upturned face, opened his great mouth
and caught it, and swallowed it every drop.

After this Dermat came down and returned to the
ford, where he found Fatha still asleep; and he sat
beside him, but did not awaken him.

———————— ⚬ ————————

CHAPTER VI.

DERMAT O'DYNA SLAYS THE THREE KINGS OF THE
ISLAND OF THE TORRENT, BREAKS THE SPELL
WITH THEIR BLOOD, AND FREES FINN.

TIDINGS were brought to the Palace of the Island that
Midac and all whom he led were slain at the ford;
and the three kings of the Island of the Torrent said—

"The young king of Lochlann did wrong to make
this attempt without asking our counsel; and had we
known of the thing we would have hindered him.

For to us belongs the right to behead Finn and his
companions, since it is the spell-venom of the clay
which we brought from the Island of the Torrent that
holds them bound in the Palace of the Quicken Trees.
And now, indeed, we will go and slay them all."

So they set out with a strong party, and soon
reached the ford. Looking across in the dim light,
they saw Dermat, and called aloud to ask who he was.

"I am Dermat O'Dyna," he replied, "one of Finn's
champions. He has sent me to guard this ford, and
whoever you are, I warn you not to cross!"

Then they sought to beguile Dermat, and to win
him over by smooth words; and they replied—

"It is a pleasure to us to meet you, Dermat; for
we are old friends of yours. We are the three kings
of the Island of the Torrent, your fellow-pupils in
valour and all heroic feats. For you and we lived
with the same tutors from the beginning; and you
never learned a feat of arms that we did not learn
in like manner. Leave the ford, then, that we may
pass on to the Palace of the Quicken Trees."

But Dermat answered in few words, "Finn and
his companions are under my protection till morning;
and I will defend the ford as long as I am alive!"

And he stood up straight and tall like a pillar, and
scowled across the ford.

A number of the foreigners now rushed towards
Dermat, and raging in a confused crowd, assailed him.
But the strong hero met them as a rock meets the
waves, and slew them with ease as they came within

the range of his sword. Yet still they pressed on, others succeeding those that fell; and in the midst of the rage of battle, Fatha started up from his sleep, awakened by the crashing of weapons and the riving of shields.

He gazed for a moment, bewildered, at the combatants, and, seeing how matters stood, he was wroth with Dermat for not awakening him; so that he ran at him fiercely with drawn sword. But Dermat stepped aside, and, being angry, thus addressed him—

" Slake thy vengeance on our foes for the present: for me, the swords of the foreigners are enough, methinks, without thine to aid them!"

Then Fatha turned and attacked the foe, and his onset was even more deadly than that of Dermat; so that they fell before him to the right and left on the ford.

And now at last the three kings, seeing so many of their men falling, advanced slowly towards Dermat; and Dermat, unterrified, stood in his place to meet them. And their weapons clashed and tore through their shields, and the fight was long and furious; till at last the champion-pride and the battle-fury of Dermat arose, so that the three dragon-like kings fell slain one by one before him, on that ford of red slaughter.

And now, though smarting with wounds, and breathless, and weary, Dermat and Fatha remembered Finn and the Fena; and Dermat called to mind what Finn had told him as to how the spell was to be broken. So he struck off the heads of the three kings, and, followed by Fatha, he ran with them, all gory as they were, to the Palace of the Quicken Trees.

As they drew nigh to the door, Finn, knowing their voices and their footsteps, called aloud anxiously to ask how it fared with the combatants at the ford; "For," said he, "the crashing and the din of that battle exceeded all we have yet heard, and we know not how it has ended."

Dermat answered, "King of the Fena, Fatha and I have slain the three kings of the Island of the Torrent; and lo, here we have their heads all bloody; but how am I to bring them to thee?"

"Victory and blessings be with you, Dermat; you and Fatha have fought a valiant fight, worthy of the Fena of Erin! Now sprinkle the door with the blood."

Dermat did so, and in a moment the door flew wide open with a crash. And inside they saw the heroes in sore plight, all pale and faint, seated on the cold clay round the wall. Dermat and Fatha, holding the gory heads by the hair, sprinkled the earth under each with the blood, beginning with Finn, and freed them one by one; and the heroes, as they found the spell broken, sprang to their feet with exulting cries. And they thanked the gods for having relieved them from that perilous strait, and they and the two heroes joyfully embraced each other.

But danger still threatened, and they now took counsel what they should do; and Finn, addressing Dermat and Fatha, said—

"The venom of these foul spells has withered our

strength, so that we are not able to fight; but at sunrise they will lose their power, and we shall be strong again.   It is necessary, therefore, that you still guard the ford, and at the rising of the sun we shall relieve you."

So the two heroes went to the ford, and Fatha returned with food and drink for Finn and the others.

After the last battle at the ford, a few who had escaped brought back tidings to the King of the World and his people, that the three kings of the Island of the Torrent had fallen by the hands of Dermat and Fatha.   But they knew not that Finn and the others had been released.

Then arose the king's son, Borba the Haughty, who, next to the king himself, was mightiest in battle of all the foreign host.   And he said—

"Feeble warriors were they who tried to cross this ford.   I will go now and avenge the death of our people on these Fena, and I will bring hither the head of Finn the son of Cumal, and place it at my father's feet."

So he marched forth without delay, with a large body of chosen warriors, till he reached the edge of the ford.   And although Dermat and Fatha never trembled before a foe, yet when they saw the dark mass drawing nigh, and heard the heavy tread and clank of arms, they dreaded that they might be dislodged and overpowered by repeated attacks, leaving Finn and the rest helpless and unprotected.   And each in his heart longed for the dawn of morning.

No parley was held this time, but the foreigners came straight across the ford—as many abreast as could find footing. And as they drew near, Dermat spoke to Fatha—

"Fight warily, my friend: ward the blows of the foremost, and be not too eager to slay, but rather look to thy own safety. It behoves us to nurse our strength and prolong the fight, for the day is dawning, and sunrise is not far off!"

The foreigners came on, many abreast; but their numbers availed them naught, for the pass was narrow; and the two heroes, one taking the advancing party to the right, and the other to the left, sometimes parried and sometimes slew, but never yielded an inch from where they stood.

And now at last the sun rose up over the broad plain of Kenri; and suddenly the withering spell went forth from the bones and sinews of the heroes who sat at the Palace of the Quicken Trees, listening with anxious hearts to the clash of battle at the ford. Joyfully they started to their feet, and, snatching up their arms, hastened down to the ford with Finn at their head; but one they sent, the swiftest among them, to Knockfierna, to take the news to Oisin.

Dermat and Fatha, fighting eagerly, heeded not that the sun had risen, though it was now indeed glittering before their eyes on the helmets and arms of their foes. But as they fought, there rose a great shout behind them; and Finn and Gaul and the rest ran down the slope to attack the foreigners.

The foreigners, not in the least dismayed, answered the attack; and the fight went on, till Gaul Mac Morna and Borba the Haughty met face to face in the middle of the ford, and they fought a hard and deadly combat. The battle-fury of Gaul at length arose, so that nothing could stand before him, and, with one mighty blow, he cleft the head from the body of Borba.

And now the foreigners began to yield: but they still continued to fight, till a swift messenger sped to the Palace of the Island, and told the great king, Sinsar of the Battles, that his son was dead, slain by Gaul; and that his army was sore pressed by the Fena, with Finn at their head.

When the people heard these tidings, they raised a long and sorrowful cry of lamentation for the king's son; but the king himself, though sorrow filled his heart, showed it not. And he arose and summoned his whole host; and, having arranged them in their battalions and in their companies under their princes and chiefs, he marched towards the battle-field, desiring vengeance on the Fena more than the glory of victory.

CHAPTER VII.

THE FIGHT AT THE FORD, WITH THE FOREIGN ARMY.

ALL the Fena who had gone to the chase from Knock-fierna had returned, and were now with Oisin, the son of Finn. And the messenger came slowly up the hill-side, and told them, though with much difficulty, for he was weary and breathless, the whole story from beginning to end, of Finn's enchantment, and of the battles at the ford, and how their companions at that moment stood much in need of aid against the foreigners.

Instantly the whole body marched straight towards the Palace of the Quicken Trees, and arrived on the hill-brow over the ford, just as the King of the World and his army were approaching from the opposite direction.

And now the fight at the ford ceased for a time, while the two armies were put in battle array; and on neither side was there any cowardice or any desire to avoid the combat.

The Fena were divided into four battalions. The active, bright-eyed Clann Baskin marched in front of the first battalion; the fierce, champion-like Clann Morna led the second; the strong, sanguinary Mic-an-Smoil brought up the third; and the fourth was led forward by the fearless, venomous Clann O'Navnan.

And they marched forward, with their silken banners, each banner-staff in the hand of a tall, trusty hero; their helmets glittering with precious gems; their broad, beautiful shields on their left shoulders; with their long, straight, deadly lances in their hands; and their heavy, keen-edged swords hanging at the left side of each. Onward they marched; and woe to those who crossed the path of that host of active, high-minded champions, who never turned their backs on an enemy in battle!

And now at last the fight began with showers of light, venomous missiles; and many a hero fell even before the combatants met face to face. Then they drew their long, broad-bladed swords, and the ranks closed and mingled in deadly strife. It would be vain to attempt a description of that battle, for it was hard to distinguish friend from foe. Many a high-souled hero fell wounded and helpless, and neither sigh nor groan of pain escaped them; but they died, encouraging their friends to vengeance with voice and gesture. And the first thought of each champion was to take the life of his foe rather than to save his own.

The great king Finn himself moved tall and stately from battalion to battalion, now fighting in the foremost ranks, and now encouraging his friends and companions, his mighty voice rising clear over the clash of arms and the shouts of the combatants. And wherever he moved, there the courage of the Fena rose high, and their valour and their daring increased, so that the ranks of their foes fell back thinned and scattered before them.

Oscar, resting for a moment from the toil of battle, looked round, and espied the standard of the King of the World, where he stood guarded by his best warriors, to protect him from the danger of being surrounded and outnumbered by his foes; and the young hero's wrath was kindled when he observed that the Fena were falling back dismayed wherever that standard was borne.

Rushing through the opposing ranks like a lion

maddened by dogs, he approached the king; and the king laughed a grim laugh of joy when he saw him, and ordered his guards back; for he was glad in his heart, expecting to revenge his son's death by slaying with his own hand Finn's grandson, who was most loved of all the youthful champions of the Fena. Then these two great heroes fought a deadly battle; and many a warrior stayed his hand to witness this combat. It seemed as if both should fall; for each inflicted on the other many wounds. The king's rage knew no bounds at being so long withstood, for at first sight he despised Oscar for his youth and beauty; and he made an onset that caused Oscar's friends, as they looked on, to tremble; for during this attack the young hero defended himself, and no more. But now, having yielded for a time, he called to mind the actions and the fame of his forefathers, and attacked the king in turn, and, with a blow that no shield or buckler could withstand, he swept the head from the king's body.

Then a great shout went up from the Fena, and the foreigners instantly gave way; and they were pursued and slaughtered on every side. A few threw away their arms and escaped to the shore, where, hastily unmooring their ships, they sailed swiftly away to their own country, with tidings of the death of their king and the slaughter of their army.

THE

PURSUIT OF THE GILLA DACKER
AND HIS HORSE.

———◆◇◆———

CHAPTER I.

ARRIVAL OF THE GILLA DACKER AND HIS HORSE.

ONE day in the beginning of summer, Finn, the son
of Cumal, the son of Trenmore O'Baskin,[23] feasted the
chief people of Erin at Allen [23] of the broad hill-slopes.
And when the feast was over, the Fena reminded
him that it was time to begin the chase through the
plains and the glens and the wildernesses of Erin.

For this was the manner in which the Fena were
wont to spend their time. They divided the year
into two parts. During the first half, namely, from
Beltane to Samin,* they hunted each day with their
dogs; and during the second half, namely, from Samin
to Beltane, they lived in the mansions and the betas†
of Erin; so that there was not a chief or a great lord
or a keeper of a house of hospitality in the whole
country that had not nine of the Fena quartered on
him during the winter half of the year.

---

* Beltane, the first of May ; Samin, the first of November.
† Beta, a public house of hospitality.

Finn and his chiefs now held council as to which of the provinces of Erin they should begin with ; and they chose Munster for the first chase.

Next day they set out, both dogs and men; and they travelled through Offaly,* and by one side of Fera-call, and to Brosna of Slieve Bloma, and by the Twelve Mountains of Evlinn, till they came to Collkilla, which is now called Knockainy.

The chase was then set in order, and they scattered themselves over the broad plains of Munster. They began at Ardpatrick,† and they hunted over Kenn-

---

* Offaly, now the name of two baronies in the county Kildare.

Fera-call, or Fircal, an ancient territory in the present King's County.

Brosna, a small river rising in the Slieve Bloma, or Slieve Bloom mountains, which flows by Birr, and falls into the Shannon near Banagher ; usually called the Little Brosna, to distinguish it from the Great Brosna, which flows through King's County into the Shannon.

The Twelve Mountains of Evlinn. (See note, page 97.)

Knockainy, a small hill much celebrated in fairy lore, in the county Limerick, giving name to the village of Knockainy at its base. It appears from the text that it was more anciently called Collkilla, or hazel-wood.

† Ardpatrick, a beautiful green hill, with a remarkable church ruin and graveyard on its summit, two miles from Kilfinane, county Limerick.

Kenn-Avrat was the ancient name of Seefin mountain, rising over the village of Glenosheen, two miles from Ardpatrick. Slieve-Keen, the old name of the hill of Carrigeennamroanty, near Seefin.

Fermoy, a well-known town and barony in the county Cork. It appears from the text that the district was anciently known by the name of Coill-na-drua, or the wood of the druids.

Lehan, the ancient name of the district round Castlelyons, in the county Cork.

Fermorc, now the baronies of Connello, in Limerick. (See note, page 184.)

Curoi Mac Dara, a celebrated chief who flourished in the time of

Avrat of Slieve-Keen, and over Coill-na-drua, which
is now called the district of Fermoy; over the fruit-
ful lands of Lehan, and over the confines of Fermorc,
which is now called Hy Conall Gavra. Then south
to the patrimony of Curoi Mac Dara, and by the
shores of Loch Lein; afterwards along the blue-
streamy Suir, by Caher-Dun-Isca, over the great
plain of Femin, and across the speckled summit of
Slieve-na-man-finn; all over East Munster and West
Munster, as far as Balla-Gavran on the one side,
and on the other across the Shannon to Cratloe,
near Limerick of the blue waters.

In short, there was not a plain or a valley, a wood
or a brake, a mountain or a wilderness, in the two
provinces of Munster, that they did not hunt over
on that occasion.

Now it chanced at one time during the chase,
while they were hunting over the plain of Cliach,*
that Finn went to rest on the hill of Collkilla, which

the Red Branch Knights of Ulster, viz., in the first century of the
Christian era. Curoi had his residence on a mountain near Tralee,
still called Caherconree (the fortress of Curoi), and his "patrimony"
was South Munster. The remains of Curoi's great stone fortress
are still to be seen on Caherconree.

Loch Lein, the Lakes of Killarney.

Caher-Dun-Isca, now the town of Caher, on the Suir, in Tipperary.

Femin was the name of the great plain lying to the south and west
of the mountain of Slievenaman, or Slieve-na-man-finn, near Clonmel,
in Tipperary.

Balla-Gavran, or the pass of Gavran, an ancient road, which ran
by Gavran (now Gowran), in the county Kilkenny.

Cratloe, a well-known district on the Clare side of the Shannon,
near Limerick.

* Cliach, the old name of the plain lying round Knockainy.

is now called Knockainy; and he had his hunting-tents pitched on a level spot near the summit. Some of his chief heroes tarried with him; namely, his son Oisin; the valiant Oscar, the son of Oisin; Gaul Mac Morna of the Mighty Deeds; Finn's shield-bearer, Skeabrac; Kylta Mac Ronan; Dermat O'Dyna of the Bright Face; Ligan Lumina the Swift-footed; Conan Mail of the Foul Tongue; and Finn Ban Mac Bresal.

When the king and his companions had taken their places on the hill, the Fena unleashed their gracefully shaped, sweet-voiced hounds through the woods and sloping glens. And it was sweet music to Finn's ear, the cry of the long-snouted dogs, as they routed the deer from their covers, and the badgers from their dens; the pleasant, emulating shouts of the youths; the whistling and signalling of the huntsmen; and the encouraging cheers of the mighty heroes, as they spread themselves through the glens and woods, and over the broad, green plain of Cliach.

Then did Finn ask who of all his companions would go to the highest point of the hill directly over them, to keep watch and ward, and to report how the chase went on. For, he said, the Dedannans[1] were ever on the watch to work the Fena mischief by their druidical spells, and more so during the chase than at other times.

Finn Ban Mac Bresal stood forward and offered to go; and, grasping his broad spears, he went to the

top, and sat viewing the plain to the four points of
the sky.   And the king and his companions brought
forth the chess-board and chess-men,[26] and sat them
down to a game.

Finn Ban Mac Bresal had been watching only
a little time, when he saw on the plain to the east,
a Fomor* of vast size coming towards the hill,
leading a horse.   As he came nearer, Finn Ban
observed that he was the ugliest-looking giant his
eyes ever lighted on.   He had a large, thick body,
bloated and swollen out to a great size; clumsy,
crooked legs; and broad, flat feet, turned inwards.
His hands and arms and shoulders were bony and
thick and very strong-looking; his neck was long
and thin; and while his head was poked forward, his
face was turned up, as he stared straight at Finn
Mac Bresal.   He had thick lips, and long, crooked
teeth; and his face was covered all over with bushy
hair.

He was fully armed; but all his weapons were
rusty and soiled and slovenly looking.   A broad
shield of a dirty, sooty colour, rough and battered,
hung over his back; he had a long, heavy, straight
sword at his left hip; and he held in his left hand
two thick-handled, broad-headed spears, old and rusty,
and seeming as if they had not been handled for
years.   In his right hand he held an iron club, which

* Fomor, a gigantic warrior, a giant; its primitive meaning is
"a sea-robber," commonly called a Fomorian.   (See note 5 at the
end.)

he dragged after him, with its end on the ground; and, as it trailed along, it tore up a track as deep as the furrow a farmer ploughs with a team of oxen.

The horse he led was even larger in proportion than the giant himself, and quite as ugly. His great carcase was covered all over with tangled, scraggy hair, of a sooty black; you could count his ribs, and all the points of his big bones through his hide; his legs were crooked and knotty; his neck was twisted; and as for his jaws, they were so long and heavy that they made his head look twice too large for his body.

The giant held him by a thick halter, and seemed to be dragging him forward by main force, the animal was so lazy and so hard to move. Every now and then, when the beast tried to stand still, the giant would give him a blow on the ribs with his big iron club, which sounded as loud as the thundering of a great billow against the rough-headed rocks of the coast. When he gave him a pull forward by the halter, the wonder was that he did not drag the animal's head away from his body; and, on the other hand, the horse often gave the halter such a tremendous tug backwards that it was equally wonderful how the arm of the giant was not torn away from his shoulder.

Now it was not an easy matter to frighten Finn Ban Mac Bresal; but when he saw the giant and his horse coming straight towards him in that wise, he was seized with such fear and horror that he sprang

from his seat, and, snatching up his arms, he ran down
the hill-slope with his utmost speed towards the king
and his companions, whom he found sitting round the
chess-board, deep in their game.

They started up when they saw Finn Ban looking
so scared; and, turning their eyes towards where he
pointed, they saw the big man and his horse coming
up the hill. They stood gazing at him in silent
wonder, waiting till he should arrive; but although
he was no great way off when they first caught sight
of him, it was a long time before he reached the
spot where they stood, so slow was the movement of
himself and his horse.

When at last he had come up, he bowed his head,
and bended his knee, and saluted the king with great
respect.

Finn addressed him; and after having given him
leave to speak, he asked him who he was, and what
was his name; from which of the three chief divisions
of the world he had come, and whether he belonged
to one of the noble or ignoble races; also what was
his profession or craft, and why he had no servant
to attend to his horse—if, indeed, such an ugly old
spectre of an animal could be called a horse at all.

The big man made answer and said, " King of the
Fena, I will answer everything you ask me, as far as
lies in my power. Whether I come of a noble or of an
ignoble race, that, indeed, I cannot tell, for I know not
who my father and mother were. As to where I came
from, I am a Fomor of Lochlann [6] in the north; but I

have no particular dwelling-place, for I am continually travelling about from one country to another, serving the great lords and nobles of the world, and receiving wages for my service.

"In the course of my wanderings I have often heard of you, O king, and of your greatness and splendour and royal bounty; and I have come now to visit you, and to ask you to take me into your service for one year; and at the end of that time I shall fix my own wages, according to my custom.

"You ask me also why I have no servant for this great horse of mine. The reason of that is this: at every meal I eat, my master must give me as much food and drink as would be enough for a hundred men; and whosoever the lord or chief may be that takes me into his service, it is quite enough for him to have to provide for me, without having also to feed my servant.

"Moreover, I am so very heavy and lazy that I should never be able to keep up with a company on march if I had to walk; and this is my reason for keeping a horse at all.

"My name is the Gilla Dacker,* and it is not without good reason that I am so called. For there never was a lazier or worse servant than I am, or one that grumbles more at doing a day's work for his master. And I am the hardest person in the whole world to deal with; for, no matter how good or noble I may

---

* Gilla Dacker means "a slothful fellow"—a fellow hard to move, hard to manage, hard to have anything to do with.

think my master, or how kindly he may treat me, it is hard words and foul reproaches I am likely to give him for thanks in the end.

"This, O Finn, is the account I have to give of myself, and these are my answers to your questions."

"Well," answered Finn, "according to your own account, you are not a very pleasant fellow to have anything to do with; and of a truth there is not much to praise in your appearance. But things may not be so bad as you say; and, anyhow, as I have never yet refused any man service and wages, I will not now refuse you."

Whereupon Finn and the Gilla Dacker made covenants, and the Gilla Dacker was taken into service for a year.

Then the big man turned to Conan Mail, and asked him whether the foot-service or the horse-service had the better pay among the Fena; and Conan answered that the horsemen had twice as much pay as the footmen.

"If that be so," replied the Gilla Dacker, "I will join the horse-service, as I have a fine steed of my own; and indeed, if I had known this before, I would certainly have come hither on horseback, instead of walking.

"And now, as to this same horse of mine, I find I must attend to him myself, as I see no one here worthy of putting a hand near him. So I will lead him to the nearest stud, as I am wont to do, and let him graze among your horses. I value him greatly, however,

and it would grieve me very much if any harm were to
befall him; so," continued he, turning to the king, "I
put him under your protection, O king, and under the
protection of all the Fena that are here present."

At this speech the Fena all burst out laughing, to
see the Gilla Dacker showing such concern for his
miserable, worthless old skeleton of a horse.

Howbeit, the big man, giving not the least heed to
their merriment, took the halter off the horse's head,
and turned him loose among the horses of the Fena.

But now, this same wretched-looking old animal,
instead of beginning to graze, as every one thought he
would, ran in among the horses of the Fena, and began
straightway to work all sorts of mischief. He cocked
his long, hard, switchy tail straight out like a rod, and,
throwing up his hind legs, he kicked about on this side
and on that, maiming and disabling several of the
horses. Sometimes he went tearing through the
thickest of the herd, butting at them with his hard,
bony forehead; and he opened out his lips with a
vicious grin, and tore all he could lay hold on, with
his sharp, crooked teeth, so that none were safe that
came in his way either before or behind. And the end
of it was, that not an animal of the whole herd
escaped, without having a leg broken, or an eye
knocked out, or his ribs fractured, or his ear bitten off,
or the side of his face torn open, or without being in
some other way cut or maimed beyond cure.

At last he left them, and was making straight
across to a small field where Conan Mail's horses were

grazing by themselves, intending to play the same tricks among them. But Conan, seeing this, shouted in great alarm to the Gilla Dacker, to bring away his horse, and not let him work any more mischief; and threatening, if he did not do so at once, to go himself and knock the brains out of the vicious old brute on the spot.

But the Gilla Dacker took the matter quite cool; and he told Conan that he saw no way of preventing his horse from joining the others, except some one put the halter on him and held him, which would, of course, he said, prevent the poor animal from grazing, and would leave him with a hungry belly at the end of the day.

He said, moreover, that as he had no horse-boy, and must needs do everything for himself, he thought it quite time enough to look after his horse when he had to make ready for a journey. "But," said he to Conan, "there is the halter; and if you are in any fear for your own animals, you may go yourself and bring him away from the field."

Conan was in a mighty rage when he heard this; and as he saw the big horse just about to cross the fence, he snatched up the halter, and running forward, with long strides, he threw it over the animal's head and thought to lead him back. But in a moment the horse stood stock still, and his body and legs became as stiff as if they were made of wood; and though Conan pulled and tugged with might and main, he was not able to stir him an inch from his place.

He gave up pulling at last, when he found it was no use; but he still kept on holding the halter, while the big horse never made the least stir, but stood as if he had been turned into stone; the Gilla Dacker all the time looking on quite unconcernedly, and the others laughing at Conan's perplexity. But no one offered to relieve him.

At last Fergus Finnvel, the poet, spoke to Conan, and said, "I never would have believed, Conan Mail, that you could be brought to do horse-service for any knight or noble in the whole world; but now, indeed, I see that you have made yourself a horse-boy to an ugly foreign giant, so hateful-looking and low-born that not a man of the Fena would have anything to say to him. As you have, however, to mind this old horse in order to save your own, would it not be better for you to mount him, and revenge yourself for all the trouble he is giving you, by riding him across the country, over the hill-tops, and down into the deep glens and valleys, and through stones and bogs and all sorts of rough places, till you have broken the heart in his big, ugly body?"

Conan, stung by the cutting words of the poet, and by the jeers of his companions, jumped upon the horse's back, and began to beat him mightily with his heels, and with his two big, heavy fists, to make him go; but the horse seemed not to take the least notice and never stirred.

"I know the reason he does not go," said Fergus Finnvel; "he has been accustomed to carry a horseman

far heavier than you, that is to say, the Gilla Dacker;
and he will not move till he has the same weight on
his back."

At this Conan Mail called out to his companions,
and asked which of them would mount with him, and
help to avenge the damage done to their horses.

"I will go," said Coil Croda the Battle Victor, son
of Criffan; and up he went.   But the horse never
moved.

Dara Donn Mac Morna next offered to go, and
mounted behind the others; and after him Angus
Mac Art Mac Morna.   And the end of it was, that
fourteen men of the Clann Baskin and Clann Morna[23]
got up along with Conan; and all began to thrash the
horse together, with might and main.   But they were
none the better of it, for he remained standing stiff
and immovable as before.   They found, moreover, that
their seat was not at all an easy one—the animal's
back was so sharp and bony.

CHAPTER II.

CONAN AND FIFTEEN OF THE FENA ARE CARRIED OFF BY THE GILLA DACKER'S HORSE.

WHEN the Gilla Dacker saw the Fena beating his horse
at such a rate, he seemed very angry, and addressed
the king in these words—

"King of the Fena, I now see plainly that all the

fine accounts I heard about you and the Fena are false, and I will not stay in your servive—no, not another hour. You can see for yourself the ill usage these men are giving my horse without cause; and I leave you to judge whether any one could put up with it—any one who had the least regard for his horse. The time is, indeed, short since I entered your service, but I now think it a great deal too long; so pay me my wages, and let me go my ways."

But Finn said, "I do not wish you to go; stay on till the end of your year, and then I will pay you all I promised you."

"I swear," answered the Gilla Dacker, "that if this were the very last day of my year, I would not wait till morning for my wages, after this insult. So, wages or no wages, I will now seek another master; but from this time forth I shall know what to think of Finn Mac Cumal and his Fena!"

With that the Gilla Dacker stood up as straight as a pillar, and, turning his face towards the south-west, he walked slowly away.

When the horse saw his master leaving the hill, he stirred himself at once and walked quietly after him, bringing the fifteen men away on his back. And when the Fena saw this they raised a loud shout of laughter, mocking them.

The Gilla Dacker, after he had walked some little way, looked back, and seeing that his horse was following, he stood for a moment to tuck up his skirts. Then, all at once changing his pace, he set out with long, active strides; and if you know what the speed of a swallow is, flying across a mountain-side, or the dry, fairy wind of a March day sweeping over the plains, then you can understand the swiftness of the Gilla Dacker, as he ran down the hill-side towards the south-west.

Neither was the horse behindhand in the race; for, though he carried a heavy load, he galloped like the wind after his master, plunging and bounding forward with as much freedom as if he had nothing at all on his back.

The men now tried to throw themselves off; but this, indeed, they were not able to do, for the good reason that they found themselves fastened firmly, hands and feet and all, to the horse's back.

And now Conan, looking round, raised his big voice, and shouted to Finn and the Fena, asking them were they content to let their friends be carried off in that manner by such a horrible, foul-looking old spectre of a horse.

Finn and the others, hearing this, seized their arms and started off in pursuit. Now the way the Gilla Dacker and his horse took was first through Fermorc,* which is at the present day called Hy Conall Gavra; next over the wide, heathy summit of Slieve Lougher;

* Fermorc, now the baronies of Connello, in Limerick. Slieve Lougher, a celebrated mountain near Castle Island, in Kerry. Corca Divna, now the barony of Corkaguiny, the long peninsula lying west of Tralee, and containing the town of Dingle, and the mountain range of Slieve Mish. Cloghan Kincat, now called Cloghan, a small village on the northern coast of the peninsula.

from that to Corca Divna; and they ran along by Slieve Mish, till they reached Cloghan Kincat, near the deep green sea.

During all this time Finn and his people kept them in view, but were not able to overtake them; and Ligan Lumina, one of the swiftest of the Fena, kept ahead of the others.

The horse now passed by Cloghan Kincat without in the least abating his speed; and when he had arrived on the beach, even at the very water's edge, Ligan overtook him, and caught him by the tail with his two hands, intending to hold him till the rest of the Fena came up. He gave a mighty pull back; but the horse, not in the least checked by this, made no more ado but plunged forward through the waves, dragging Ligan after him hanging at his tail. And Ligan now found that he could neither help his friends nor free himself, for his two hands clung fast to the tail of the horse.

And so the great horse continued his course without stop or stay, bringing the sixteen Fena with him through the sea. Now this is how they fared in the sea, while the horse was rushing swiftly farther and farther to the west: they had always a dry, firm strand under them, for the waters retired before the horse while behind them was a wild, raging sea, which followed close after, and seemed ready every moment to topple over their heads. But, though the billows were tumbling and roaring all round, neither horse nor riders were wetted by as much as a drop of brine or a dash of spray.

CHAPTER III.

PURSUIT.

Now as to Finn and the others. They stood on the bank over the beach, watching the horse and men till they lost sight of them in the sea afar off; and then they sat them down, weary after their long chase, and full of sadness for the loss of their companions.

After a long silence, Finn spoke and asked the chiefs what they thought best to be done. But they replied that he was far beyond them all in knowledge and wisdom; and they told him they would follow whatsoever counsel he and Fergus Finnvel, the poet, gave them. Then Finn told Fergus to speak his mind; and Fergus said—

"My counsel is that we go straightway to Ben Edar,* where we shall find a ship ready to sail. For our forefathers, when they wrested the land from the gifted, bright-complexioned Dedannans, bound them by covenant to maintain this ship for ever, fitted with all things needful for a voyage, even to the smallest article, as one of the privileges of Ben Edar; so that if at any time one of the noble sons of Gael Glas † wished to sail to distant lands from Erin, he should have a ship lying at hand in the harbour ready to begin his voyage."

* Ben Edar, now Howth Hill, near Dublin.
† Gael Glas, the traditional ancestor of the Gaels.

They agreed to this counsel, and turned their steps without delay northwards towards Ben Edar. They had not gone far when they met two noble-looking youths, fully armed, and wearing over their armour beautiful mantles of scarlet silk, fastened by brooches of gold. The strangers saluted the king with much respect; and the king saluted them in return. Then, having given them leave to converse, he asked them who they were, whither they had come, and who the prince or chief was that they served. And the elder answered—

"My name is Feradach, and my brother's name is Foltlebar; and we are the two sons of the king of Innia. Each of us professes an art; and it has long been a point of dispute between us, which art is the better, my brother's or mine. Hearing that there is not in the world a wiser or more far-seeing man than thou art, O king, we have come to ask thee to take us into thy service among thy household troops for a year, and at the end of that time to give judgment between us in this matter."

Finn asked them what were the two arts they professed.

"My art," answered Feradach, "is this: If at any time a company of warriors need a ship, give me only my joiner's axe and my crann-tavall,* and I am able to provide a ship for them without delay. The only thing I ask them to do is this—to cover their

---

* Crann-tav'all, a sort of sling for projecting stones, made of an elastic piece of wood, and strung somewhat like a cross-bow.

heads close, and keep them covered, while I give the crann-tavall three blows of my axe. Then I tell them to uncover their heads; and lo, there lies the ship in harbour, ready to sail!"

Then Foltlebar spoke and said, "This, O king, is the art I profess: On land I can track the wild duck over nine ridges and nine glens, and follow her without being once thrown out, till I drop upon her in her nest. And I can follow up a track on sea quite as well as on land, if I have a good ship and crew."

Finn replied, "You are the very men I want; and I now take you both into my service. At this moment I need a good ship and a skilful pilot more than any two things in the whole world. And though our own track-men, namely, the Clann Navin, are good, yet we now need some one still more skilful, to follow the Gilla Dacker through unknown seas."

Then the two brothers asked Finn what strait he was in at that moment, and why he wanted a ship and pilot so much. Whereupon Finn told them the whole story of the Gilla Dacker's doings from beginning to end. "And we are now," said he, "on our way to Ben Edar, to seek a ship, that we may follow this giant and his horse, and rescue our companions."

Then Feradach said, "I will get you a ship— a ship that will sail as swiftly as a swallow can fly!"

And Foltlebar said, "I will guide your ship in the track of the Gilla Dacker till ye lay hands on him, in whatsoever quarter of the world he may have hidden himself!"

And so they turned back to Cloghan Kincat. And when they had come to the beach, Feradach told them to cover their heads; and they did so. Then he struck three blows of his axe on the crann-tavall; after which he bade them look. And lo, they saw a ship, fully fitted out with oars and sails, and with all things needed for a long voyage, riding before them in the harbour!

Then Kylta Mac Ronan went to the top of a high hill; and, turning his face inland, he uttered three mighty shouts, which were taken up by the people of the next valley, and after them by those of the next valley beyond. And so the signal spread, till a shout of alarm was heard in every plain and hill-side, glen and valley, wood and wilderness, in the two provinces of Munster. And when the Fena heard these shouts, they ceased anon from their sports and pastimes; for they knew their king was in danger or strait of some kind. And they formed themselves into ranks and troops and battalions, and began their march; and it is not told how they fared till they reached Cloghan Kincat.

Finn told them the whole story of the Gilla Dacker and his horse, and how he had carried away Conan and fifteen others to some far-off island in the Western Ocean. He also showed them the ship, and told them that he himself and a chosen band of the Fena were about to sail westward in quest of their friends.

And Oisin asked him how many of the chief men of the Fena he wished to take with him.

Finn replied, "I foresee that this will be a perilous quest; and I think all the chiefs here present few enough to bring with me."

"Say not so, O king," said Oisin; "too many have gone already, and some must be left behind to guard the country, and to keep order. If fifteen good men go with you, and that you find the others, the whole party will be a match for any foe you are like to meet in these western lands."

And Oscar and Gaul Mac Morna spoke in like manner.

To this Finn agreed. Then he picked out fifteen men, the bravest and best, the most dexterous at the sword, and the swiftest of foot among the Fena.

The question then arose, who should lead the Fena in the king's absence; and what they agreed on was that Oisin should remain behind and take command, as he was the eldest and bravest and wisest of the king's sons.

Of those who were chosen to go with Finn, the chief men were Dermat O'Dyna; Gaul Mac Morna; Oscar, the son of Oisin; Aed Beg, the son of Finn; Fergus Finnvel, the poet; the three sons of Encarda; and Feradach and Foltlebar, the two sons of the king of Innia.

So the king and his party took leave of Oisin and the rest. And sad, indeed, were they on both sides; for no one knew how far the king might have to sail among unknown seas and islands, or how long he should be away from Erin, or the spells and dangers he and his men might encounter in this pursuit.

Then they went on board, and launched their ship on the cold, bright sea; and Foltlebar was their pilot and steersman. And they set their sail and plied their slender oars, and the ship moved swiftly westward till they lost sight of the shores of Erin; and they saw nothing all round them but a wide girdle of sea. After some days' sailing, a great storm came from the west, and the black waves rose up against them, so that they had much ado to keep their vessel from sinking. But through all the roaring of the tempest, through the rain and blinding spray, Foltlebar never stirred from the helm or changed his course, but still kept close on the track of the Gilla Dacker.

At length the storm abated, and the sea grew calm. And when the darkness had cleared away, they saw to the west, a little way off, a vast rocky cliff towering over their heads to such a height, that its head seemed hidden among the clouds. It rose up sheer from the very water, and looked at that distance as smooth as glass, so that at first sight there seemed no way to reach the top.

Foltlebar, after examining to the four points of the sky, found the track of the Gilla Dacker as far as the cliff, but no farther. And he accordingly told the heroes that he thought it was on the top of that rock the giant lived; and that, anyhow, the horse must have made his way up the face of the cliff with their companions.

When the heroes heard this they were greatly cast down and puzzled what to do; for they saw no way of reaching the top of the rock; and they feared they should have to give up the quest and return without their companions. And they sat down and looked up at the cliff, with sorrow and vexation in their hearts.

CHAPTER IV.

DERMAT O'DYNA, IN QUEST OF THE GILLA DACKER, ENCOUNTERS THE WIZARD-CHAMPION AT THE WELL.

WHEN now they had been silent for a time, Fergus Finnvel, the poet, arose and said—

"My friends, we have here amongst us one who has been fostered and taught from the child to the man, by Mannanan Mac Lir[8] in Fairyland, and by Angus,[1] the wisest of the Dedannans, at Bruga of the Boyne. He has been carefully trained by both in everything a warrior should learn, and in much druidical lore besides; so that he is skilled beyond us all in manly arts and champion-feats. But now it seems that all his arts and accomplishments go for nought, seeing that he is unable to make use of them just at the time that we stand most in need of them. On the top of that rock, doubtless, the Gilla Dacker lives, and there he holds Conan and the others in bondage; and surely this hero, who now sits idly with us here in our ship, should be able to climb up the face of that cliff, and bring us back tidings of our dear friends and companions."

When Dermat O'Dyna heard this speech, his cheek grew red with shame, and he made this reply—

"It is of me you have spoken these words, Fergus. Your reproaches are just; and though the task is hard, I will attempt to follow the track of the Gilla Dacker, and find out some tidings of our friends."

So saying, Dermat arose, and girded on his armour, and put on his glittering helmet. He hung his sword at his left hip; and he took his two long, deadly spears, one in each hand, namely, the Crann-boi and the Ga-derg;* and the battle-fury of a warrior descended on him, so that he looked a dreadful foe to meet in single combat.

Then, leaning on the handles of his spears, after the manner of skilful champions, he leaped with a light, airy bound on the nearest shelf of rock. And using his spears and his hands, he climbed from ledge to ledge, while his companions watched him anxiously from below; till, after much toil, he measured the soles of his two feet on the green sod at the top of the rock. And when, recovering breath, he turned round and looked at his companions in the ship far below, he started back with amazement and dread at the dizzy height.

He now looked inland, and saw a beautiful country

* See note, page 302.

spread out before him :—a lovely, flowery plain straight in front, bordered with pleasant hills, and shaded with groves of many kinds of trees. It was enough to banish all care and sadness from one's heart to view this country, and to listen to the warbling of the birds, the humming of the bees among the flowers, the rustling of the wind through the trees, and the pleasant voices of the streams and waterfalls.

Making no delay, Dermat set out to walk across the plain. He had not been long walking when he saw, right before him, a great tree laden with fruit, overtopping all the other trees of the plain. It was surrounded at a little distance by a circle of pillar-stones; and one stone, taller than the others, stood in the centre near the tree. Beside this pillar-stone was a spring well, with a large, round pool as clear as crystal; and the water bubbled up in the centre, and flowed away towards the middle of the plain in a slender stream.

Dermat was glad when he saw the well; for he was hot and thirsty after climbing up the cliff. He stooped down to take a drink; but before his lips touched the water, he heard the heavy tread of a body of warriors, and the loud clank of arms, as if a whole host were coming straight down on him. He sprang to his feet and looked round; but the noise ceased in an instant, and he could see nothing.

After a little while he stooped again to drink; and again, before he had wet his lips, he heard the very same sounds, nearer and louder than before. A second time he leaped to his feet; and still he saw no one. He knew not what to think of this; and as he stood wondering and perplexed, he happened to cast his eyes on the tall pillar-stone that stood on the brink of the well; and he saw on its top a large, beautiful drinking-horn, chased with gold and enamelled with precious stones.

"Now surely," said Dermat, "I have been doing wrong; it is, no doubt, one of the virtues of this well that it will not let any one drink of its waters except from the drinking-horn."

So he took down the horn, dipped it into the well, and drank without hindrance, till he had slaked his thirst.

Scarcely had he taken the horn from his lips, when he saw a tall wizard-champion* coming towards him from the east, clad in a complete suit of mail, and fully armed with shield and helmet, sword and spear. A beautiful scarlet mantle hung over his armour, fastened at his throat by a golden brooch; and a broad circlet of sparkling gold was bended in front across his forehead, to confine his yellow hair, and keep it from being blown about by the wind.

As he came nearer, he increased his pace, moving

---

* The original word, which I have translated "wizard-champion," is *gruagach*. This word literally means "hairy," "a hairy fellow;" and it is often used in the sense of "giant." But in these romantic tales it is commonly used to signify a champion who has always something of the supernatural about him, yet not to such a degree as to shield him completely from the valour of a great mortal hero like Dermat O'Dyna.

with great strides; and Dermat now observed that he looked very wrathful.   He offered no greeting, and showed not the least courtesy; but addressed Dermat in a rough, angry voice—

"Surely, Dermat O'Dyna, Erin of the green plains should be wide enough for you; and it contains abundance of clear, sweet water in its crystal springs and green bordered streams, from which you might have drunk your fill.   But you have come into my island without my leave, and you have taken my drinking-horn, and have drunk from my well; and this spot you shall never leave till you have given me satisfaction for the insult."

So spoke the wizard-champion, and instantly advanced on Dermat with fury in his eyes.   But Dermat was not the man to be terrified by any hero or wizard-champion alive.   He met the foe half-way; and now, foot to foot, and knee to knee, and face to face, they began a fight, watchful and wary at first, but soon hot and vengeful, till their shields and helmets could scarce withstand their strong thrusts and blows.   Like two enraged lions fighting to the death, or two strong serpents intertwined in deadly strife, or two great opposing billows thundering against each other on the ocean border; such was the strength and fury and determination of the combat of these two heroes.

And so they fought through the long day, till evening came, and it began to be dusk; when suddenly the wizard-champion sprang outside the range

of Dermat's sword, and leaping up with a great
bound, he alighted in the very centre of the well.
Down he went through it, and disappeared in a
moment before Dermat's eyes, as if the well had
swallowed him up. Dermat stood on the brink,
leaning on his spear, amazed and perplexed, looking
after him in the water; but whether the hero had
meant to drown himself, or that he had played some
wizard trick, Dermat knew not.

He sat down to rest, full of vexation that the
wizard-champion should have got off so easily. And
what chafed him still more was that the Fena knew
nought of what had happened, and that when he
returned, he could tell them nothing of the strange
hero; neither had he the least token or trophy to show
them after his long fight.

Then he began to think what was best to be done;
and he made up his mind to stay near the well all
night, with the hope of finding out something further
about the wizard-champion on the morrow.

He walked towards the nearest point of a great
forest that stretched from the mountain down to the
plain on his left; and as he came near, a herd of
speckled deer ran by among the trees. He put his
finger into the silken loop of his spear, and, throwing
it with an unerring cast, brought down the nearest of
the herd.

Then, having lighted a fire under a tree, he skinned
the deer and fixed it on long hazel spits to roast,
having first, however, gone to the well, and brought

away the drinking-horn full of water. And he sat beside the roasting deer to turn it and tend the fire, waiting impatiently for his meal; for he was hungry and tired after the toil of the day.

When the deer was cooked, he ate till he was satisfied, and drank the clear water of the well from the drinking-horn; after which he lay down under the shade of the tree, beside the fire, and slept a sound sleep till morning.

Night passed away and the sun rose, bringing morning with its abundant light. Dermat started up, refreshed after his long sleep, and, repairing to the forest, he slew another deer, and fixed it on hazel spits to roast at the fire as before. For Dermat had this custom, that he would never eat of any food left from a former meal.

And after he had eaten of the deer's flesh and drunk from the horn, he went towards the well. But though his visit was early, he found the wizard-champion there before him, standing beside the pillar-stone, fully armed as before, and looking now more wrathful than ever. Dermat was much surprised; but before he had time to speak the wizard-champion addressed him—

"Dermat O'Dyna, you have now put the cap on all your evil deeds. It was not enough that you took my drinking-horn and drank from my well: you have done much worse than this, for you have hunted on my grounds, and have killed some of my speckled deer. Surely there are many hunting-grounds in

Erin of the green plains, with plenty of deer in them; and you need not have come hither to commit these robberies on me. But now for a certainty you shall not go from this spot till I have taken revenge for all these misdeeds."

And again the two champions attacked each other, and fought during the long day, from morning till evening. And when the dusk began to fall, the wizard-champion leaped into the well, and disappeared down through it, even as he had done the day before.

The selfsame thing happened on the third day. And each day, morning and evening, Dermat killed a deer, and ate of its flesh, and drank of the water of the well from the drinking-horn.

On the fourth morning, Dermat found the wizard-champion standing as usual by the pillar-stone near the well. And as each morning he looked more angry than on the morning before, so now he scowled in a way that would have terrified any one but Dermat O'Dyna.

And they fought during the day till the dusk of evening. But now Dermat watched his foe narrowly; and when he saw him about to spring into the well, he closed on him and threw his arms round him. The wizard-champion struggled to free himself, moving all the time nearer and nearer to the brink; but Dermat held on, till at last both fell into the well. Down they went, clinging to each other, Dermat and the wizard-champion; down, down, deeper and deeper they went; and Dermat tried to look round, but nothing could he

see save darkness and dim shadows.   At length there
was a glimmer of light; then the bright day burst
suddenly upon them; and presently they came to the
solid ground, gently and without the least shock.

———◆———

CHAPTER V.

DERMAT O'DYNA IN TIR-FA-TONN.*

At the very moment they reached the ground, the
wizard-champion, with a sudden effort, tore himself
away from Dermat's grasp and ran forward with great
speed.   Dermat leaped to his feet; and he was so
amazed at what he saw around him that he stood
stock still and let the wizard-champion escape: a
lovely country, with many green-sided hills and fair
valleys between, woods of red yew trees, and plains
laughing all over with flowers of every hue.

Right before him, not far off, lay a city of great
tall houses with glittering roofs; and on the side
nearest to him was a royal palace, larger and grander
than the rest.   On the level green in front of the
palace were a number of knights, all armed, and
amusing themselves with various warlike exercises
of sword and shield and spear.

Straight towards this assembly the wizard-cham-

* Tir-fa-tonn, literally "the country beneath the wave." (See
note 13 at the end.)

pion ran; which, when Dermat saw, he set off in pursuit, hoping to overtake him. But the wizard-champion had too long a start, and when he reached the exercise green, the knights opened to the right and left, leaving a broad way through which he rushed. He never halted or looked behind till he had got inside the palace gate; and the moment he had passed in, the knights closed their ranks, and stood facing Dermat with threatening looks and gestures.

Nothing daunted, Dermat held on his pace towards them; and now those of the front rank started forward with spears and swords, intending to crush him at once, and hew his body to mincemeat. But it was not terror nor weakness nor a desire of flight that this produced in Dermat, for his battle-fury was on him; and he rushed through them and under them and over them, as a hawk rushes among a flight of sparrows, or like a whale through a shoal of little fishes, or like a raging wolf among a flock of sheep, or like a vast billow among a fleet of small vessels, or like a great brown torrent rushing down the steep side of a mountain, that sweeps everything headlong before it. So did Dermat cleave a wide laneway through the hosts, till, from a solid band of warriors, he turned them into a scattered crowd, flying in all directions. And those that did not fall by his hand, ran hither and thither, some to hide themselves in the thick forests and remote, wooded glens of the surrounding country; while others rushed in through the outer gate of the palace, and shut themselves up in the strongest part of the fortress, neither did they deem themselves safe till they had shot home every bolt, and securely fastened every strong iron lock.

At last not a living soul remained on the green, and Dermat sat down, weary after his battle-toil, and smarting all over with wounds. He was grieved and downcast also, for he knew not where he was, and he saw no chance that he should be able either to find any tidings of the friends he was in search of, or to return to his companions in the ship.

At length, being quite overcome with weariness, he fell into a deep sleep. After sleeping for some time, he was awakened by a smart blow. He started up, and saw a young man standing over him, tall, and of a commanding appearance, with long, golden hair, and a manly, open countenance. Now this young man had come to Dermat, and finding him asleep in such a dangerous place, he struck him with the flat of his sword to awaken him. In an instant Dermat sprang to his feet and seized his arms; but the youth addressed him in a friendly voice, and said—

"Dermat O'Dyna, put up your arms; I am no enemy, and I have come, not to harm, but to serve you. This, indeed, is a strange place for you to fall asleep, before the very door of the castle, and within sight of your enemies. Come now with me, and I will give you a better place to sleep in, where you will also get a welcome and kindly entertainment."

This speech pleased Dermat very much; and he thanked the young man and went with him. After

walking for some time, they came to a large splendid
house, and passing through the outer gate they entered
the banqueting hall. There they found a noble company of twelve score and ten knights, and almost as
many beautiful ladies, with their long hair falling on
their shoulders, shining like the golden flower of the
marsh-flag, and gentle and modest in their looks and
conversation. They wore mantles of scarlet satin,
and each mantle was fastened in front by a brooch
of burnished gold.

The company sat at tables round the walls of the
banquet hall, some feasting, some playing chess, and
some listening to the music of harps. When the two
heroes entered, all the knights and ladies rose and
received them with much respect, and they welcomed
Dermat and invited him to join their entertainment.
But the young prince—for he was in truth a prince
—pointing to Dermat's clothes and arms, all soiled
and stained, told them that he had endured much
toil that day, and that he wanted rest and refresh-
ment.

He then brought Dermat away, and ordered the
attendants to prepare a bath in a great caldron. He
put soothing balsams and healing herbs into it with
his own hands, and when Dermat had bathed he was
immediately healed of his wounds, and he came forth
refreshed and cheerful. The prince then directed that
his clothes should be put aside, and had him clad in
rich garments like the others.

Dermat now joined the company, and ate and

drank, for he had taken neither food nor drink since he had made his meal on the deer early that morning near the well; after which he talked and was cheerful with the others. . Then rose up the harpers, and the professors of divers arts and sciences, and one after another they played their sweet music, and recited their poems and their tales of the heroes of the olden time. And when they had ended, the knights gave them gifts of gold and silver and jewels. At last the company broke up, and Dermat was shown to a bed richly ornamented, and soft with the red feathers of wild fowl, and soon he fell into a sound sleep after his long day's adventures.

Now Dermat marvelled much at all he saw and heard; and he knew not what place he was in, or who the people were, that had treated him with such kindness. So next morning, when the company had again assembled, he stood up, and addressed the prince with gentle words and modest demeanour; and this is what he said—

"I am much surprised, O prince, at what I have seen, and at all that has befallen me in this land. Though I am here a stranger, thou hast shown me much kindness, and these noble knights and ladies have permitted me to join their sports, and have treated me with much gentleness and consideration. I wish to know, then, who thou art, O prince, and what country this is, of which I have never before heard, and who is the king thereof. Tell me also, I pray thee, the name of the champion who fought with me for four days at the well, till at last he escaped from me at the palace."

The prince replied, " I will tell you all, Dermat, as you have asked, concealing nothing. This country is Tir-fa-tonn; the champion who fought with you is called the Knight of the Fountain, and that very champion is king of this land. I am the brother of the king, and my name is the Knight of Valour. Good reason indeed have I to be kind to you, Dermat O'Dyna, for though you do not remember me, I spent a year and a day in the household of Finn the son of Cumal.

"A part of this kingdom belongs by right to me. But the king and his son have seized on my patrimony, and have banished me from the palace, forcing me to live here in exile with a few of my faithful followers.

"It is my intention, however, to make war on the king for my part of the kingdom; and right glad I am that you have come hither, for I would rather have you on my side than all the other Fena put together, for your nobleness of mind and your valour in battle.

"I have here in my household seven score and ten heroes, all champions of great deeds; and if you consent to aid me, these shall be placed under your command. By day you shall fight against the king of Tir-fa-tonn and his son, and by night you shall feast and rest and sleep with me in this palace. If you enter into friendship with me and fight on my side, well I know that I shall win back my right without delay."

Dermat agreed to this. So he and the Knight of Valour made a covenant; and, placing hand in hand, they pledged themselves to observe faithfully the conditions of the league of friendship.

———◆———

CHAPTER VI.

FINN, IN QUEST OF DERMAT, FIGHTS MANY BATTLES.

As to Finn Mac Cumal and those that remained behind with him in the ship, I will now relate what befell them.

It was now many days since Dermat had left them, and they marvelled much that he did not return with tidings of the Gilla Dacker. At length, when they began to be alarmed, the two sons of the king of Innia offered to go in search of him; but Finn said no, for that they should all go together.

So Feradach and Foltlebar took all the cables and ropes they could find in the ship, and tied them end to end in hard, sure knots, till they had a rope long enough to reach from the top of the rock to the bottom. Then they clambered up the steep face of the cliff, bringing with them the end of the rope; and one by one they drew up Finn and the rest. And when they looked round, they were as much surprised and delighted as Dermat was at the look of the country.

Foltlebar now made a search, and soon found the track of Dermat; and the whole party set out to walk across the plain, Foltlebar leading the way. Having travelled some distance, they saw the great fruit tree afar off; and, turning to the left, they found a place where a fire had been lighted, and near it the remains of several meals of deer's flesh. By this they knew that it was here Dermat had slept, for all were well aware of his custom not to eat of what was left from a meal.

They then went towards the tree, and there they found the traces of deadly combat—the ground all trampled and ploughed up, and a broken spear handle lying at the brink of the well. While they stood pondering on these things, with anxious hearts, they saw a horseman at a distance, speeding towards them across the plain. In a little while he came up and reined in.

He was a young man of majestic mien, fair and noble of countenance; and he rode a beautiful chestnut steed, with a bridle of twisted gold, and a saddle of surpassing splendour, ornamented all over with gold and jewels.

He alighted and saluted Finn and the Fena, and told them they were welcome to his country, for that he was king; and he put his hand on Finn's neck and kissed his cheek three times. Then he invited them to go with him, saying that the Plain of the Fountain was a comfortless resting-place after a long journey.

Finn's heart was glad at this, for he and his com-

panions were weary; and they set out to walk across
the plain with the young king. Having walked a
good distance, they came in sight of a noble palace,
with tall towers and carved front. As they came near,
they were met by a company of knights on the level
green in front, who welcomed them with gentle words.
And so they passed into the palace. A bath was prepared, and they bathed and were refreshed after their
toils. Then they sat down to supper; and while they
ate and drank, the harpers played for them, and the
poets told their tales and sang their songs.

They slept that night in the palace; and next
day they mingled with the knights on the green,
and took part in their games and pastimes. In the
evening they sat down to a feast. The people of the
palace were ranged at tables according to rank and
inheritance, every man in his proper place.

Then the feast went on; and abundance of the
newest food and of the oldest drink was served out;
and they ate of the savoury food, and drank of the
sparkling wines and of the strong ales, till they
became merry and gently intoxicated. And Finn
could not call to mind that he ever saw an entertainment in the house of either king or chief better
ordered. In this manner they were feasted and
entertained for three days and three nights.

At the end of that time a meeting was held by
the king on the palace green. And Finn stood up
and said—

"Tell me, I pray thee, thy name and the name of

this country, which I have never seen before, or even heard of."

"This country," replied the king, "is called Sorca, of which I am king; and although you know us not, we know you well, for the fame of your deeds has reached even to this land. But now I wish to know why you have come hither; also the reason why you have brought so few companions, and where the rest have tarried."

Then Finn told him the whole story from beginning to end; how the Gilla Dacker and his great horse had carried off sixteen of their chief men; "And," added Finn, "I and these fifteen companions of mine are now in quest of them."

The king replied, "This is a dangerous undertaking; and you and your fifteen men, valiant even as you are, are too few to venture into unknown lands, where you may meet with many enemies. Now my knights are brave and generous, and they love battle and adventure. Wherefore I will place a band of them under your command, who will follow you whithersoever you go, and who will not be behindhand even with the Fena in facing hardship and danger."

Finn stood up to thank the king; but before he had time to speak, they saw a messenger speeding towards them across the plain from the north-west, breathless, and begrimed all over with mud and dust. When he had come in presence of the company, he bowed low to the king, and, standing up, waited impatient for leave to speak.

The king asked him what news he had brought and he replied—

"Bad and direful news I have for thee, O king. A foreign fleet has come to our shores, which seems to cover all the sea, even as far as the eye can reach; and until the stars of heaven are counted, and the sands of the sea, and the leaves of the woods, the hosts that are landing from their black ships shall not be numbered. Even already they have let loose their plunderers over the country, who are burning and spoiling the farmsteads and the great mansions; and many noble heroes and keepers of houses of hospitality, and many people of the common sort, have been slain by them. Some say that it is the King of the World and his host, who, after conquering every country he has yet visited, has come now to ravage this land with fire and sword and spear, and bring it under his power; but I know not if this be true. And this, O king, is the news I bring thee."

When the messenger had ended, the king spoke nought, though his countenance, indeed, showed trouble; but he looked earnestly at Finn. Finn understood this to mean that the king sought his help; and, with clear voice, he spoke—

"Thou hast been generous to me and my people in our day of need, O king of Sorca; and now thou shalt not find the Fena lacking in grateful memory of thy kindness. We will, for a time, give up the pursuit of the Gilla Dacker, and we will place ourselves under thy command, and help thee against

these marauders. Neither do I fear the outcome of
this war; for many a time have we met these
foreigners on the shores of Erin and elsewhere, and
they have always yielded to us in the battle-field."

The king of Sorca was glad of heart when he
heard these words; and he sent his swift scouts all
over the country to gather his fighting men. And
when all had come together, he arranged them in
fighting order, and marched towards the shore where
the foreigners were spoiling the land. And they met
the plundering parties, and drove them with great
slaughter back to their ships, retaking all the spoils.

Then they formed an encampment on the shore,
with ramparts and deep ditches and long rows of
pointed stakes all round. And each day a party of
the foreigners landed, led by one of their captains,
who were met by an equal number of the men of
Sorca, led by one of the Fena; and each time they
were driven back to their ships, after losing their best
men.

When, now, this had continued for many days,
the King of the World called a meeting of the chiefs
of his army, and asked their counsel as to what should
be done. And they spoke as one man, that their best
chiefs had fallen, and that they were in worse case
now for overcoming the men of Sorca than they were
at first; that their sages and prophets had declared
against them; and that they had met with ill luck
from the day of their arrival. And the advice they
gave the king was to depart from the shores of Sorca,

for there seemed no chance of conquering the country as long as the Fena were there to help the king.

So the king ordered the sails to be set, and he left the harbour in the night with his whole fleet, without bringing the king of Sorca under subjection, and without imposing tribute on the people.

CHAPTER VII.

FINN AND DERMAT MEET.

WHEN the people of Sorca and the Fena arose next morning, not a ship was in sight; and they began to rejoice greatly, finding themselves freed from this invasion. And while the king and Finn, with the chiefs and people, stood eagerly conversing on all these matters, they saw a troop at a distance coming towards them, with banners and standards and arms glittering in the morning sun. Now they wondered much who these might be; and Finn desired that some one might go and bring back tidings.

So Fergus Finnvel went with a few followers, and when he was yet a good way off, he knew Dermat O'Dyna at the head of the troop, and ran forward· with joy to meet him. And they embraced, even as brothers embrace who meet after being long parted. Then they came towards the assembly; and when the Fena saw Dermat they shouted with joy and welcome

And Dermat, on his part, could scarce restrain the excess of his joyfulness; for, indeed, he did not expect to meet his friends so soon; and he embraced them one by one, with glad heart, beginning with Finn.

Then Finn inquired from Dermat all particulars, what places he had visited since the day he had climbed up the rock, and whether he had heard any news of their lost companions; and he asked him also who were they—those valiant-looking fighting men— he had brought with him.

Dermat told him of all his adventures from first to last—of his long combat at the well with the Knight of the Fountain, of his descent to Tir-fa-tonn, and how the Knight of Valour had entertained him hospitably in his palace. He related also how he headed the men of the Knight of Valour, and made war on the king of Tir-fa-tonn (who was also called the Knight of the Fountain, the wizard-champion who fought with Dermat at the well), whom he slew, and defeated his army.

"And now," continued he, bringing forth the Knight of Valour from among the strange host, "this is he who was formerly called the Knight of Valour, but who is now the king of Tir-fa-tonn. Moreover, this king has told me, having himself found it out by his druidical art, that it was Avarta the Dedannan (the son of Illahan of the Many-coloured Raiment) who took the form of the Gilla Dacker, and who brought the sixteen Fena away to the Land of Promise,[8] where he now holds them in bondage."

Finn and the young king then put hand in hand and made covenants of lasting friendship with each other. And the Fena were much rejoiced that they had at last got some tidings of their lost companions.

CHAPTER VIII.

CONAN AND HIS COMPANIONS FOUND AND RESCUED.

Now after they had rested some days in the palace of the king of Sorca, Fergus Finnvel told Finn that it was time to begin once more their quest after Conan and the others. They held council, therefore; and the resolution they came to was to return to the rock at the spot where they had turned aside from the track of the Gilla Dacker, and to begin their search anew from that. And when both the king of Sorca and the king of Tir-fa-tonn would have sent men with them, Finn thanked them, but said that the small party of Fena he had with him were quite enough for that adventure.

So they took leave of the two kings, and went back to the rock, and Foltlebar at once found the track. He traced it from the very edge of the rock across the plain to the sea at the other side; and they brought round their ship and began their voyage. But this time Foltlebar found it very hard to keep on the track; for the Gilla Dacker, knowing that there were not in the world men more skilled in following up a quest than the Fena, took great pains to hide all traces of the flight of himself and his horse; so that Foltlebar was often thrown out; but he always recovered the track after a little time.

And so they sailed from island to island, and from bay to bay, over many seas and by many shores, ever following the track, till at length they arrived at the Land of Promise. And when they had made the land, and knew for a certainty that this was indeed the Land of Promise, they rejoiced greatly; for in this land Dermat O'Dyna had been nurtured by Mannanan Mac Lir of the Yellow Hair.

Then they held council as to what was best to be done; and Finn's advice was that they should burn and spoil the country, in revenge of the outrage that had been done to his people. Dermat, however, would not hear of this. And he said—

" Not so, O king. The people of this land are of all men the most skilled in druidic art; and it is not well that they should be at feud with us. Let us rather send to Avarta a trusty herald, to demand that he should set our companions at liberty. If he does so, then we shall be at peace; if he refuse, then shall we proclaim war against him and his people, and waste this land with fire and sword, till he be forced, even by his own people, to give us back our friends."

This advice was approved by all. And then Finn said—

" But how shall heralds reach the dwelling of this

enchanter; for the ways are not open and straight, as
in other lands, but crooked and made for concealment,
and the valleys and plains are dim and shadowy, and
hard to be traversed ? "

But Foltlebar, nothing daunted by the dangers
and the obscurity of the way, offered to go with a
single trusty companion; and they took up the track
and followed it without being once thrown out, till
they reached the mansion of Avarta.   There they
found their friends amusing themselves on the green
outside the palace walls; for, though kept captive in
the island, yet were they in no wise restrained, but
were treated by Avarta with much kindness.   When
they saw the heralds coming towards them, their joy
knew no bounds; they crowded round to embrace
them, and asked them many questions regarding their
home and their friends.

At last Avarta himself came forth, and asked who
these strangers were; and Foltlebar replied—

"We are of the people of Finn Mac Cumal, who
has sent us as heralds to thee.   He and his heroes
have landed on this island, guided hither by me; and
he bade us tell thee that he has come to wage war
and to waste this land with fire and sword, as a
punishment for that thou hast brought away his
people by foul spells, and even now keepest them in
bondage."

When Avarta heard this, he made no reply, but
called a council of his chief men, to consider whether
they should send back to Finn an answer of war or

of peace. And they, having much fear of the Fena, were minded to restore Finn's people, and to give him his own award in satisfaction for the injury done to him; and to invite Finn himself and those who had come with him to a feast of joy and friendship in the house of Avarta.

Avarta himself went with Foltlebar to give this message. And after he and Finn had exchanged friendly greetings, he told them what the council had resolved; and Finn and Dermat and the others were glad at heart. And Finn and Avarta put hand in hand, and made a league of friendship.

So they went with Avarta to his house, where they found their lost friends; and, being full of gladness, they saluted and embraced each other. Then a feast was prepared; and they were feasted for three days, and they ate and drank and made merry.

On the fourth day, a meeting was called on the green to hear the award. Now it was resolved to make amends on the one hand to Finn, as king of the Fena, and on the other, to those who had been brought away by the Gilla Dacker. And when all were gathered together, Finn was first asked to name his award; and this is what he said—

"I shall not name an award, O Avarta; neither shall I accept an eric from thee. But the wages I promised thee when we made our covenant at Knock-ainy, that I will give thee. For I am thankful for the welcome thou hast given us here; and I wish that there should be peace and friendship between us for ever."

But Conan, on his part, was not so easily satisfied; and he said to Finn—

"Little hast thou endured, O Finn, in all this matter; and thou mayst well waive thy award. But hadst thou, like us, suffered from the sharp bones and the rough carcase of the Gilla Dacker's monstrous horse, in a long journey from Erin to the Land of Promise, across wide seas, through tangled woods, and over rough-headed rocks, thou wouldst then, methinks, name an award."

At this, Avarta, and the others who had seen Conan and his companions carried off on the back of the big horse, could scarce keep from laughing; and Avarta said to Conan—

"Name thy award, and I will fulfil it every jot: for I have heard of thee, Conan, and I dread to bring the gibes and taunts of thy foul tongue on myself and my people."

"Well then," said Conan, "my award is this: that you choose fifteen of the best and noblest men in the Land of Promise, among whom are to be your own best beloved friends; and that you cause them to mount on the back of the big horse, and that you yourself take hold of his tail. In this manner you shall fare to Erin, back again by the selfsame track the horse took when he brought us hither—through the same surging seas, through the same thick thorny woods, and over the same islands and rough rocks and dark glens. And this, O Avarta, is my award," said Conan.

Now Finn and his people were rejoiced exceedingly when they heard Conan's award—that he asked from Avarta nothing more than like for like. For they feared much that he might claim treasure of gold and silver, and thus bring reproach on the Fena.

Avarta promised that everything required by Conan should be done, binding himself in solemn pledges. Then the heroes took their leave; and having launched their ship on the broad, green sea, they sailed back by the same course to Erin. And they marched to their camping-place at Knockainy, where they rested in their tents.

Avarta then chose his men. And he placed them on the horse's back, and he himself caught hold of the tail; and it is not told how they fared till they made harbour and landing-place at Cloghan Kincat. They delayed not, but straightway journeyed over the selfsame track as before, till they reached Knockainy.

Finn and his people saw them afar off coming towards the hill with great speed; the Gilla Dacker, quite as large and as ugly as ever, running before the horse; for he had let go the tail at Cloghan Kincat. And the Fena could not help laughing heartily when they saw the plight of the fifteen chiefs on the great horse's back; and they said with one voice that Conan had made a good award that time.

When the horse reached the spot from which he had at first set out, the men began to dismount. Then the Gilla Dacker, suddenly stepping forward, held up his arm and pointed earnestly over the heads of the

Fena towards the field where the horses were standing; so that the heroes were startled, and turned round every man to look.   But nothing was to be seen except the horses grazing quietly inside the fence.

Finn and the others now turned round again, with intent to speak to the Gilla Dacker and bring him and his people into the tents; but much did they marvel to find them all gone.   The Gilla Dacker and his great horse and the fifteen nobles of the Land of Promise had disappeared in an instant; and neither Finn himself nor any of his chiefs ever saw them afterwards.

So far we have related the story of the pursuit of the Gilla Dacker and his horse.

THE PURSUIT OF DERMAT AND GRANIA.

CHAPTER I.

FINN, THE SON OF CUMAL, SEEKS THE PRINCESS GRANIA TO WIFE.

On a certain day, Finn, the son of Cumal, rose at early morn in Allen of the broad hill-slopes, and, going forth, sat him down on the green lawn before the palace, without companion or attendant. And two of his people followed him, namely, Oisin his son, and Dering the son of Dobar O'Baskin.

Oisin spoke to him and asked, "Why, O king, hast thou come forth so early?"

"Cause enough have I indeed," replied Finn; "for I am without a wife since Manissa, the daughter of Garad of the Black Knee, died; and who can enjoy sweet sleep when his life is lonely like mine, with no wife to comfort and cheer him? This, my friends, is the cause of my early rising."

And Oisin said, "Why should you be without a wife if you desire one? For there is not, within the sea-circle of green Erin, a maiden that we will not bring you, either by consent or by force, if you only turn the light of your eyes on her."

Then Dering spoke and said, " I know where there is a maiden, who in all respects is worthy to be thy wife."

And when Finn asked who she was, Dering replied—

" The maiden is Grania, daughter of king Cormac,[22] the son of Art, the son of Conn the Hundred-fighter; the most beautiful, the best instructed, and the most discreet in speech and manner of all the maidens of Erin."

" There has been strife between me and Cormac for a long time," said Finn, "and it may happen that he will not give me his daughter in marriage. But go ye to Tara in my name, you and Oisin, and ask the maiden for me : if the king should refuse, so let it be ; but I can better bear a refusal to you than to myself."

" We will go," said Oisin; " but it is better that no man know of our journey till we return."

So the two heroes took leave of Finn and went their way ; and nothing is told of what befell them till they reached Tara. It chanced that the king was at this time holding a meeting ; and the chiefs and great nobles of Tara were assembled round him. And when the two warriors arrived, they were welcomed, and the meeting was put off for that day ; for the king felt sure that it was on some business of weight they had come.

After they had eaten and drunk, the king, sending

away all others from his presence, bade the two chiefs tell their errand. So Oisin told him they had come to seek his daughter Grania in marriage for Finn the son of Cumal.

Then the king said, " In all Erin there is scarce a young prince or noble who has not sought my daughter in marriage; and she has refused them all. And it is on me that the ill feeling and reproach caused by her refusals have fallen; for she has ever made me the bearer of her answers. Wherefore now you shall come to my daughter's presence, and I will not mention the matter to her till she give you an answer from her own lips: so shall I be blameless if she refuse.'

So they went to the apartments of the women, at the sunny side of the palace. And when they had entered the princess's chamber, the king sat with her on the couch and said—

" Here, my daughter, are two of the people of Finn the son of Cumal, who have come to ask thee as a wife for him."

And Grania, giving, indeed, not much thought to the matter, answered, " I know not whether he is worthy to be thy son-in-law; but if he be, why should he not be a fitting husband for me ? "

The two messengers were satisfied with this answer, and retired. And Cormac made a feast for them; and they ate and drank and made merry with the chiefs and nobles of the palace; after which the king bade them tell Finn to come at the end of a fortnight to claim his bride.

So the two heroes returned to Allen, and told how they had fared in their quest.   And as all things come at last to an end, so this fortnight wore slowly away; and at the end of the time, Finn, having collected round him the chief men of the seven standing battalions of the Fena to be his guard, marched to Tara.   The king received him with great honour, and welcomed the Fena, and they were feasted with the nobles of Erin in the great banquet hall of Micorta.*   And the king sat on his throne to enjoy the feast with his guests, having Finn on his right hand, and on his left the queen, Etta, the daughter of Atan of Corca; and Grania sat next the queen, her mother, on the left.   And all the others sat according to their rank and patrimony.

CHAPTER II.

DERMAT O'DYNA SECRETLY ESPOUSES THE PRINCESS GRANIA.

Now while the feast went on, it chanced that Dara of the Poems, one of Finn's druids, sat near Grania.   And he recited for her many lays about the deeds of her forefathers; after which a pleasant conversation arose between them.   And when they had talked for some time, she asked him—

* See foot-note, page 55.

"What means all this feasting? And why has Finn come with his people on this visit to my father the king?"

Dara was surprised at this question, and answered, "If thou dost not know, it is hard for me to know."

And Grania answered, "I wish, indeed, to learn from you what has brought Finn to Tara."

"It is strange to hear thee ask this question," said the druid. "Knowest thou not that he has come to claim thee for his wife?"

Grania was silent for a long time after hearing this. And again she spoke—

"If, indeed, Finn had sought me for his son Oisin, or for the youthful Oscar, there would be nothing to wonder at; but I marvel much that he seeks me for himself, seeing that he is older than my father."

Then Grania meditated in silence; and after a time she said to the druid—

"This is a goodly company, but I know not one among them, except only Oisin, the son of Finn. Tell me now who is that warrior on the right of Oisin."

"That knightly warrior," answered the druid, "is Gaul Mac Morna the Terrible in Battle."

"Who is the youthful champion to the right of Gaul?" asked Grania.

"That is Oscar, the son of Oisin," said the druid.

"Who is the graceful and active-looking chief sitting next Oscar?" asked the princess.

"That is Kylta Mac Ronan the Swift-footed," said the druid.

"Next to Kylta Mac Ronan sits a champion with fair, freckled skin, raven-black curls, a gentle, handsome, manly countenance, and soft voice: pray who is he?"

"That is Dermat O'Dyna of the Bright Face, the favourite of maidens, and beloved of all the Fena for his high-mindedness, his bravery, and his generous disposition."

"Who is he sitting at Dermat's shoulder?" asked Grania.

"That is Dering, the son of Dobar O'Baskin," replied the druid; "a valiant champion, and also a druid and a man of science."

Then Grania called her handmaid, and said to her, "Bring me the large jewelled, gold-chased drinking-horn that lies in my chamber."

The handmaid brought the drinking-horn; and Grania, having filled it to the brim, said—

"Take it now to Finn from me, and tell him that I desire him to drink from it."

The handmaiden did so, and Finn took a full draught. He passed the drinking-horn to the king, and the king drank; and after him the queen. Then again Grania bade the handmaid bring it to Carbri of the Liffey, the king's son; and she ceased not till all she wished to drink had drunk from the gold-chased horn. And after a little time, those who had drunk fell into a deep sleep, like the sleep of death.

Then the princess rose from her seat, and, walking softly across the hall, sat down near Dermat O'Dyna; and with downcast eyes and low voice, she said—

"Wilt thou, Dermat, return my love if I give it to thee?"

Dermat heard her at first with amazement and alarm. Then for a moment, even before he was aware, his heart leaped with joy; but when he bethought him of his duty to his chief, he hardened his mind, and answered with cold looks and words—

"The maiden who is betrothed to Finn, I will not love; and even if I were so minded, I dare not."

And with eyes still cast down, Grania said, "I know well it is thy duty, and not thy heart, that prompts thee to speak so. Thou seest how it is with me; and I am forced to speak more boldly than a maiden should. Finn has come to ask me for his wife; but he is an old man, even older than my father, and I love him not. But I love thee, Dermat, and I beseech thee to save me from this hateful marriage. And, lest thou think that my love for thee is only a passing fancy, hear now what befell.

"Of a day when a hurling match was played on the green of Tara, between Mac Luga and the Fena on the one side, and Carbri of the Liffey and the men of Tara on the other, I sat high up at the window of my sunny chamber to see the game. Thou didst remain sitting with some others that day, not meaning to take part in the play. But at last, when the game began to go against thy friends, I saw thee start up; and, snatching the hurlet from the man nearest to thee, thou didst rush into the thick of the crowd; and before sitting down thou didst win the goal three times on the men

of Tara. At that hour my eyes and my heart were
turned to thee; and well I knew thee to-day in this
banquet hall, though I knew not thy name till the
druid told me. At that same hour, too, I gave thee
my love—what I never gave, and never will give, to
any other."

Then was Dermat sore troubled. He strove with
himself, but strove in vain; for he could not help
loving the princess with his whole heart. Yet none
the less did he hide his thoughts; for his duty to his
chief prevailed. And with looks and words cold and
stern, he replied—

"I marvel greatly that thou hast not given thy love
to Finn, who deserves it much better than any other
man alive. And still more do I marvel that thou hast
lighted on me beyond all the princes and nobles of
Tara; for truly there is not one among them less worthy
of thy love than I. But that thou shouldst be my
wife, by no means can this be; for even were I to
consent, there is not in Erin a fastness or a wilderness,
however strong or remote, that could shelter us from
Finn's vengeance."

Then Grania said, "I read thy thoughts; and
I know thou art striving against what thy heart
prompts. And now, O Dermat, I place thee under
gesa,[12] and under the bonds of heavy druidical spells
—bonds that true heroes never break through, that
thou take me for thy wife before Finn and the others
awaken from their sleep; and save me from this
hateful marriage."

And Dermat, still unyielding, replied, "Evil are those gesa thou hast put on me; and evil, I fear, will come of them.   But dost thou not know, princess, that whenever Finn sleeps at Tara, it is one of his privileges to have in his own keeping the keys of the great gates; so that even if we so willed it, we should not be able to leave the fortress ?"

"There is a wicket gate leading out from my apartments," said Grania, "and through that we shall pass forth."

"That I cannot do," answered Dermat; "for it is one of my gesa[12] never to enter a king's mansion, or leave it, by a wicket gate."

And Grania answered, "I have heard it said that every true champion, who has been instructed in all the feats that a warrior should learn, can bound over the highest rampart of a fort by means of the handles of his spears; and well I know that thou art the most accomplished champion among the Fena.   I will now pass out through the wicket gate; and even if thou dost not follow, I will fly alone from Tara."

And so she went forth from the banquet hall.

Then Dermat, much doubting how to act, spoke to his friends and asked counsel of them.   And first he addressed Oisin, the son of Finn, and asked him how he should deal with the heavy gesa-bonds that had been laid on him by the princess; and what he should do in the case.

"You are blameless in regard to these bonds," answered Oisin; "and I counsel you to follow Grania; but guard yourself well against the wiles of Finn."

"O dear friend Oscar," spoke Dermat again, "what think you is best for me to do, seeing that these heavy gesa-bonds have been put on me?"

"I say you should follow Grania," answered Oscar; "for he, indeed, is but a pitiful champion who fears to keep his bonds."

"What counsel do you give me, Kylta?" said Dermat to Kylta Mac Ronan.

"I say," answered Kylta, "that I would gladly give the world's wealth that the princess had given me her love; and I counsel you to follow her."

Last of all, Dermat spoke to Dering, the son of Dobar O'Baskin, and said, "Give me your judgment in this hard matter, friend Dering."

And Dering answered, "If you espouse Grania, I foresee that your death will come of it, which grieves me even to think of; but even so, I counsel you to follow the princess rather than break through your gesa."

And Dermat, doubting even still, asked for the last time, "Is this, my friends, the counsel you all give?"

And they all answered, "Yes," as with the voice of one man.

Then Dermat arose and put on his armour and his helmet; and he took his shield, and his two heavy spears, and his sword. And with tears he bade farewell to his dear companions; for well he knew that it would be long before they should meet again; and he foresaw trouble and danger.

Then he went forth to where the steep side of the

inner mound overlooked the outer rampart; and, placing his two spears point downwards, and leaning on them after the manner of skilful champions, with two light, airy bounds he cleared rampart and ditch, and measured the length of his two feet on the level green outside. And there the princess met him; and he said to her, with voice and manner still distant and stern—

"Evil will certainly come of this espousal, O princess, both to thee and to me. Far better would it be for thee to choose Finn and to pass me by; for now we shall wander without home or rest, fleeing from his wrath. Return, then, princess, return even now through the wicket gate, for the sleepers have not yet awakened; and Finn shall never learn what has happened."

But Grania, gentle and sad indeed, but quite unmoved, replied, "I will never return; and until death takes me I will not part from thee."

Then at last Dermat yielded and strove no longer; and putting off his sternness of manner and voice, he spoke gently to the princess and said—

"I will hide my thoughts from thee no more, Grania. I will be thy husband, all unworthy of thee as I am; and I will guard thee and defend thee to the death from Finn and his hirelings."

And they plighted their faith, and vowed solemn vows to be faithful to each other as man and wife for ever.

CHAPTER III.

FLIGHT AND PURSUIT.

THEN Grania showed Dermat the fenced meadow
where her father's horses grazed, and bade him yoke
two horses to a chariot.   And when he had done so,
he and Grania sat in the chariot and travelled with
all speed westward, till they reached Ath-Luan.*

And when they had come to the ford, Dermat said,
" Finn will doubtless pursue us, and it will be all the
easier for him to follow our track, that we have the
horses."

And Grania answered, " As we are now so far from
Tara, we may leave the chariot and horses here, and
I will fare on foot henceforward."

So they alighted from the chariot; and Dermat,
leading one of the horses across, left them both some
distance above the ford, one at each side of the river.
And he took up Grania in his strong arms, and
brought her tenderly across the ford, so that not even
the sole of her foot, or the skirt of her mantle was
wetted.   Then they walked against the stream for
a mile, and turned south-west, till they reached the
Wood of the two Tents.†

---

* Ath-Luan, now Athlone, on the Shannon.   In ancient times the
river had to be crossed by a ford, where the bridge is now built.

† The Wood of the two Tents was situated in the territory of
Clanrickard, in the county Galway.

In the midst of the wood, where it was thickest, Dermat lopped off branches and wove a hut, where they rested. And he brought Grania the wild animals of the wood to eat, and gave her the water of a clear spring to drink.

As to Finn, the son of Cumal, I will now tell what befell him. When the king and his guests arose from their sleep at early dawn next morning, they found Dermat and Grania gone; and a burning jealousy seized on Finn, and his rage was so great that for a time all his strength left him. Then he sent for his track-ing-men, namely, the Clann Navin; and he commanded them forthwith to follow the track of Dermat and Grania. This they did with much ease as far as Ath-Luan, while Finn and the others followed after; but when they had come to the ford, they lost the track. Whereupon Finn, being now indeed easily kindled to wrath, told them that unless they took up the track again speedily, he would hang every man of the Clann Navin on the edge of the ford.

So the trackers, being sore afraid, searched upwards against the stream, and found the two horses where they had been left, one on each side of the river. And going on a mile further, they came to the spot where Dermat and Grania had turned from the river; and there they lighted on the south-west track, Finn and the Fena still following. And when the Clann Navin had pointed out to Finn the direction of the track, he said—

" Well do I know now where we shall find Dermat

and Grania; for of a certainty they have hidden themselves in the Wood of the two Tents."

Now it chanced that Oisin, and Oscar, and Kylta, and Dering were present when Finn spoke these words; and they were troubled, for they loved Dermat. And going aside, they held council among themselves, and Oisin spoke—

"There is much likelihood, friends, that Finn speaks truth; for he is far-seeing, and judges not hastily. It is needful, therefore, that we send Dermat warning, lest he be taken unawares. My counsel is that you, Oscar, find out Finn's hound, Bran, and tell him to go to the Wood of the two Tents with a warning to Dermat; for Bran does not love his own master Finn better than he loves Dermat."

So Oscar called Bran secretly, and told him what he should do. Bran listened with sagacious eye and ears erect, and understood Oscar's words quite well. Then, running back to the rear of the host, so that Finn might not see him, he followed the track without once losing it, till he arrived at the Wood of the two Tents. There he found Dermat and Grania asleep in their hut, and he put his head into Dermat's bosom.

Dermat started up from his sleep, and seeing Bran, he awakened Grania, and said—

"Here is Bran, Finn's hound; he has come to warn me that Finn himself is near."

And Grania trembled and said, "Let us take the warning, then, and fly!"

But Dermat answered, "I will not leave this hut; for however long we fly, we cannot escape from Finn; and it is not worse to fall into his hands now than at any other time. Howbeit, they shall not come into this fastness unless I permit them."

Then great fear fell on Grania; but, seeing Dermat gloomy and downcast, she urged the point no further.

Again Oisin spoke to his three companions and said, "I fear me that Bran may not have been able to baffle Finn, or that some other mischance may have hindered him from finding Dermat; so we must needs send him another warning. Bring hither, therefore, Fergor, Kylta's errand-man."

And Kylta brought forward Fergor.

Now this Fergor had a voice so loud that his shout was heard over the three nearest cantreds.

So they caused him to give three shouts that Dermat might hear. And Dermat heard Fergor's shouts, and, awakening Grania from her sleep, said to her—

"I hear the shout of Fergor, Kylta's errand-man. And he is with Kylta, and Kylta is with Finn; and I know that my friends have sent me this warning, as a sign that Finn himself is coming."

And again Grania trembled and said, "Let us take this warning and fly!"

But Dermat answered, "I will not fly; and we shall not leave this wood till Finn and the Fena overtake us. Howbeit, none shall come into this fastness unless I permit them."

And Grania was in great fear; but this time
Dermat looked gloomy and stern, and she pressed the
matter no further.

CHAPTER IV.

THE FASTNESS OF THE SEVEN NARROW DOORS.

Now as to Finn. He and the others went forward
till they reached the Wood of the two Tents. And he
sent forward the Clann Navin to make search; who
went, and having made their way to the thickest
part of the wood, they came to a fence which they
could not cross.

For Dermat had cleared a space round his hut, and
surrounded it with a fence that no man could pierce,
with seven narrow doors of strong poles woven with
saplings, to face seven different parts of the wood.

Then the Clann Navin climbed up to a high tree
branch, and looked over the fence; and they saw
Dermat with a lady. And when they had returned,
Finn asked them if Dermat and Grania were in the
wood. And they answered—

"Dermat, indeed, is there, and we saw a lady with
him; but whether she be Grania or not we cannot
tell, for we know not the princess."

"May ill luck attend Dermat, and all his friends for
his sake!" said Finn. "I know he is in this wood;
and he shall never leave it till he give me quittance
for the injury he has done me."

And Oisin said, "Certain it is, that you, Finn, are blinded by jealousy; else you would never think that Dermat would await you on this plain, with no stronger fastness to shelter him from your wrath than the Wood of the two Tents."

To which Finn, being angry, replied, "Your words will profit you nothing, Oisin; neither will your friendship for Dermat avail him aught. Well I knew, indeed, when I heard Fergor's three shouts, that it was ye who caused him to shout, as a warning signal to Dermat; and I know also that ye sent my dog Bran to him with another warning. But these warnings will not avail you; for he shall never leave this wood till he pay me such eric [10] as I seek for the injury he has done me."

Then Oscar spoke and said, "Surely, Finn, it is mere folly to believe that Dermat would wait here for you, knowing, as he does, that you seek his head."

As Oscar spoke these words, they arrived at the fence; and Finn answered, "Who then, think you, has cleared the wood in this manner, and fenced the space with this strong, sheltering enclosure, and fitted it with these narrow doors? But indeed," added he, "I will find out the truth of the matter in another way." So, raising his voice a little, he called out, "Tell us now, Dermat, which of us is telling truth, Oscar or I."

And Dermat, who would not hide when called on, answered from within, "You never erred in your judgment, O king: Grania and I are here; but none shall come in unless I permit them."

Then Finn placed his men around the enclosure, a company at each narrow door; and he said to each company, "If Dermat tries to escape by this door, seize him and keep him securely for me."

Now when Grania saw these preparations, and overheard Finn's words, she was overcome with fear, and wept and trembled very much.   And Dermat had pity on his wife, and comforted her; and he kissed her three times, bidding her be of good cheer, for that all would be well with them yet.

And when Finn saw this—for he stood with some others viewing the hut from a mound at a little way off—a flame of burning jealousy went through his heart; and he said—

"Now of a certainty Dermat shall not escape from me; and I shall have his head for all these injuries!"

Now Angus of Bruga,[1] the wisest and most skilled in magic arts of all the Dedannan race, was Dermat's foster father.   For he had reared him from childhood, and had taught him all the arts and accomplishments of a champion; and he loved him even as a father loves his only son.

And it was revealed to Angus that Dermat was in deadly strait.   So he arose and travelled on the wings of the cool, east wind, neither did he halt till he reached the Wood of the two Tents; and he passed into the hut without being perceived by Finn and his men.   And when Dermat saw the old man his heart leaped with joy.

Angus greeted Dermat and Grania, and said, "What is this thing thou hast done, my son?"

And Dermat answered, "The princess Grania, daughter of the king of Tara, asked me to take her for my wife, putting heavy gesa-bonds on me; and I did so, and we fled from her father's house. And Finn, the son of Cumal, has pursued us with intent to kill me, for he sought the princess to wife for himself."

And Angus said, "Come now, children, under my mantle, one under each border, and I will bring you both away from this place without the knowledge of Finn."

But Dermat answered, "Take Grania; but for me, I will not go with you. However, I will leave this place; and if I am alive I will follow you. But if they slay me, send the princess to her father, and tell him to treat her neither better nor worse on account of taking me for her husband."

Then Dermat kissed Grania, and bade her be of good cheer, for that he feared not his foes. And Angus placed her under his mantle, and, telling Dermat whither to follow, went forth from the enclosure without the knowledge of Finn and the Fena. They turned south then, and nothing is told of what befell them till they came to the Wood of the two Sallows, which is now called Limerick.

Now as to Dermat. After Angus and Grania had left him, he girded on his armour, and took his sharp weapons in his hands; and he stood up tall and straight like a pillar, meditating in silence for a space.

Then he went to one of the seven narrow doors, and asked who was outside.

"No enemy of thine is here, but Oisin and Oscar, with the men of the Clann Baskin. Come out to us, and no one will dare to harm thee."

"I must needs find the door where Finn himself keeps guard," answered Dermat; "so I will not go out to you."

He went to the second narrow door, and asked who was there.

"Kylta Mac Ronan with the Clann Ronan around him. Come out at this door, and we will fight to the death for thy sake."

"I will not go out to you," answered Dermat; "for I do not wish to bring Finn's anger on you for treating me with kindness."

He went to another narrow door, and asked who was there.

"Conan of the Grey Rushes and the Clann Morna. We are no friends to Finn; but thee we all love. Come out to us, then, and no one will dare to harm thee."

"Of a certainty I will not go out at this door," answered Dermat; "for well I know that Finn would rather see you all dead than that I should escape!"

He went to another narrow door, and asked who was there.

"A friend and a dear comrade of thine is here; Cuan, the chief of the Munster Fena, and his Munster men with him. Thou and we come from the same territory; and if need be we will give our lives in fight for thy sake."

"I will not go out to you," said Dermat; "for it would bring Finn's sure displeasure on you to act kindly towards me."

He went to another narrow door, and asked who was there.

"Finn, the son of Glore of the Loud Voice, chief of the Fena of Ulster, and the Ulster men around him. Thou and we come not from the same territory; but we all love thee, Dermat; and now come forth to us, and who will dare to wound or harm thee?"

"I will not go out to you," replied Dermat; "you are a faithful friend of mine, and your father in like manner; and I do not wish you to earn the enmity of Finn on my account."

He went to another narrow door, and asked who was there.

"No friend of thine! Here stand the Clann Navin watching for thee; namely, Aed the Lesser, and Aed the Tall, and Gonna the Wounder, and Gothan the Loud-voiced, and Cuan the Tracker, with all their men. We bear thee no love; and if thou come out at this door, we shall make thee a mark for our swords and spears!"

And Dermat answered, "Lying and mean-faced dogs! It is not fear of you that keeps me from going forth at this door; but I do not wish to defile my spear with the blood of your shoeless, tracking vagabonds!"

And he went to another narrow door, and asked who was there.

"Finn, the son of Cumal, the son of Art, the son of Trenmore O'Baskin, and with him the Leinster Fena. No love awaits thee here; and if thou come forth we will cleave thee, flesh and bones!"

"The door I have sought I have found at last!" cried Dermat; "for the door where thou, Finn, standest, that, of a certainty, is the very door by which I shall pass out!"

Then Finn charged his men, under pain of death, not to let Dermat pass. But Dermat, watching an unguarded place, rose by means of his two spears with a light, airy bound over the fence, and alighted on the clear space outside; and running swiftly forward, was in a moment beyond the reach of sword and spear. And so dismayed were they by his threatening look, that not a man attempted to follow him.

Then, turning southward, he never halted till he came to the Wood of the two Sallows, where he found Angus and Grania in a warm hut, with a boar fixed on hazel spits roasting before a great flaming fire. Dermat greeted them; and the spark of life all but leaped from Grania's heart with joy when she saw him.* So he told them all that had befallen him; and they ate their meal and slept in peace that night, till the morning of next day filled the world with light.

Then Angus arose with the dawn, and said to

---

* Original: "It was little but that the salmon of her life fled through her mouth with joy before Dermat."

Dermat, "I will now depart, my son; but Finn will still pursue you, and I leave you this counsel to guide you when I am gone. Go not into a tree having only one trunk; never enter a cave that has only one opening; never land on an island of the sea that has only one channel of approach; where you cook your food, there eat it not; where you eat, sleep not there; and where you sleep to-night, sleep not there to-morrow night!"

So Angus bade them farewell; and they were sad after him.

CHAPTER V.

THE THREE SEA-CHAMPIONS AND THEIR THREE VENOM-OUS HOUNDS ON THE TRACK OF DERMAT AND GRANIA.

AFTER Angus was gone, Dermat and Grania journeyed westward, keeping the Shannon on their right, till they reached the Rough Stream of the Champions, which is now called the Laune.* They rested there; and Dermat killed a salmon with his spear, and fixed it on a hazel spit to broil on the near bank; and he crossed the river with Grania, to eat it on the further bank, as Angus had told him. And after they had eaten, they sought a sleeping-place further west.

They rose early next morning, and journeyed still

---

* The river Laune, flowing from the Lakes of Killarney into Dingle Bay.

west, till they reached the Grey Moor of Finnlia.*
There they met a man of great size, noble in gait and
feature, but with arms and armour not befitting his
appearance. Dermat greeted him, and asked who he
was; and he replied—

"My name is Modan, and I am seeking a lord
whom I may serve for pay."

"If I take you into my service," asked Dermat,
"what can you do for us?"

"I will serve you by day and watch for you by
night," answered Modan.

Whereupon they entered into bonds of agreement
with one another, Modan to serve by day and watch
by night, and Dermat to pay him wages.

Then the three went westward till they reached
the river of Carra,† and Modan lifted Dermat and
Grania with the greatest ease, and bore them dry
across the stream. From that further west to Beha,‡
and Modan bore them over this stream in like manner.
Here they found a cave, on the side of the hill over
that part of the sea called Tonn Toma,§ namely, the

* The Grey Moor of Finnlia (*Bogach-Fhinnléithe* in the original)
was somewhere between the river Laune and the river Caragh, but the
name is now forgotten.

† The river of Carra, the Caragh river, flowing into Dingle Bay
from the beautiful lake Caragh, twenty miles west of Killarney.

‡ Beha, the river Behy, about a mile and a half west from the
Caragh, flowing through Glanbehy into Rossbehy creek.

§ Tonn Toma, the wave of Toma (a woman). The word Tonn (a
wave or billow) was often applied to the sea-waves that break over
certain sandbanks and rocks with an exceptionally loud roaring.
Tonn Toma is the name of a sandbank at the head of Dingle Bay,
just outside the extreme point of Rossbehy peninsula; and in the

hill of Curra-Kenn-Ammid; and Modan prepared a couch of soft rushes and birch tops in the innermost part of the cave, for Dermat and Grania. After this he went to the nearest wood and cut him a long, straight quicken tree rod; and, having put a hair and a hook on the rod, and a holly berry on the hook, he stood on the brink of the stream, and with three casts he hooked three salmon. Then he put the rod by for next day; and, putting the hook and the hair under his girdle, he returned to Dermat and Grania. And he broiled the fish, and they ate their meal, Modan giving the largest salmon to Dermat, the second in size to Grania, and keeping the smallest for himself. After which Dermat and Grania went to sleep in the cave, and Modan kept watch and ward at the mouth, till morning arose with its abundant light.

Dermat rose early and set out for the nearest high hill, to look round the country, telling Grania to keep watch at the mouth of the cave while Modan slept. Having come to the top of the hill, he viewed the country all round to the four points of the sky; and after a

winter storms, the sea thunders on this sandbank, and indeed on the whole length of the beach of the peninsula, so as often to be heard twenty miles inland. This roaring is popularly believed to predict rain.

There is a chain of three hills, Stookaniller, Knockatinna, and Knockboy, lying between Behy bridge on the east and Drung mountain on the west, and isolated from the hills to the south-east by the valley of Glanbehy. These hills rise directly over Tonn Toma; and the old Gaelic name, Currach-Cinn-Adhmuid (the moor of the head [or hill] of timber) must have been anciently applied to one or all of them.

(See, for an account of the great historical *tonns* of Ireland, the author's "Origin and History of Irish Names of Places," series ii. page 251.)

little while, he saw a fleet of black ships approaching
from the west.   When they had come near enough to
the shore, a company of nine nines landed at the very
foot of the hill where Dermat stood.   He went to
them, and, after greeting them, asked who they were,
and from what country they had come.

"We are three sea-champions from the Iccian Sea,*
who are at the head of this troop," replied they, "and
our names are Ducoss, Fincoss, and Trencoss;† and we
have come hither at the suit of Finn the son of Cumal.
For a certain chief named Dermat O'Dyna has rebelled
against him, and is now an outlaw, flying through the
country from one fastness to another.   And Finn has
asked us to come with our fleet to watch the coast,
while he himself watches inland, so that this marauder
may no longer escape punishment.   We hear, moreover,
that this Dermat is valiant and dangerous to attack,
and we have brought hither three venomous hounds to
loose them on his track, and scent him to his hiding-
place : fire cannot burn them, water cannot drown
them, and weapons cannot wound them.   And now
tell us who thou art, and whether thou hast heard any
tidings of this Dermat O'Dyna."

"I saw him, indeed, yesterday," answered Dermat.
"I know him well too, and I counsel you to follow
your quest warily; for if you meet with Dermat O'Dyna
you will have no common man to deal with."

---

* Iccian Sea (Irish, *Muir nIcht*), the Irish name for the sea
between England and France.

† Ducoss, Fincoss, and Trencoss, *i.e.* Blackfoot, Whitefoot, and
Strongfoot.

Then he asked if they had got any wine in their ships. They replied that they had; so he asked that a tun might be brought, as he wished to drink; and he told them he would show them a champion-feat after he had drunk. Two men were accordingly sent on board for a tun of wine. When they had brought it, Dermat raised it in his arms and drank; and the others drank in like manner till the tun was empty.

Then he said, "I will now show you a champion-feat that Dermat O'Dyna taught me; and I challenge any man among you to do it after me. And from this you may learn what manner of man you will have to deal with, should you have the ill luck to meet with Dermat himself."

So saying, he brought the tun to the crest of the hill, and set it down at the edge of a steep cliff. Then, leaping up on it, he turned it cunningly aside from the cliff, and let it roll down the smooth slope of the hill till it reached the very bottom, while he himself remained standing on it the whole time. And three times did he do this while the strangers looked on.

But they laughed, mocking him, and said, "Do you call that a champion-feat indeed? Truly, you have never in your life seen a good champion-feat!"

Thereupon one among them started up and brought the tun to the top of the hill, intending to do the same feat; and, placing it on the edge of the cliff, he leaped up on it. And while he stood on it, Dermat pushed it with his foot to set it going. But the moment it moved, the man lost his balance, and while the tun went rolling down the face of the hill, he himself fell over the cliff, and was dashed to pieces on the sharp edges and points of the rocks.

Another man tried the same thing, and he in like manner fell down and was killed among the rocks. And the end of the matter was, that before they would acknowledge themselves beaten, fifty of their men attempted the feat, and every man of the fifty fell over the cliff and was killed. So the others went on board their ships, gloomy and heart-sore.

Dermat returned to the cave, and Grania's heart was glad when she saw him. Modan went then, and putting the hair and the hook on the rod as before, he hooked three salmon; and he went back to the cave and broiled them on hazel spits. And they ate their meal; and Modan kept watch and ward, while Dermat and Grania slept in the cave, till the pleasant morning filled the world with light.

Dermat rose up with the dawn, and telling Grania to keep watch while Modan slept, he went to the same hill, and found the three sea-champions with their men on the shore before him. He greeted them, and asked whether they wished for any more champion-feats. But they answered that they would much rather he would give them some tidings of Dermat O'Dyna. Whereupon he said—

"I have seen a man who saw him this very morning. And now I will show you a champion-feat he taught me, in order that you may know what is before you, should you meet with Dermat O'Dyna himself."

When he had said this, he threw off helmet and tunic and armour, till only his shirt remained over his brawny shoulders; and, taking the Ga-boi,* the spear of Mannanan Mac Lir, he fixed it firmly in the earth, standing point upwards. Then, walking back some little way, he ran towards the spear, and, rising from the earth with a bird-like bound, he alighted softly on the very point; and, again leaping off it, he came to the ground on his feet without wound or hurt of any kind.

Then arose one of the strange warriors and said, "If you call that a champion-feat, it is plain that you have never seen a good champion-feat in your life!"

And so saying, he ran swiftly towards the spear and made a great bound; but he fell heavily on the sharp point, so that it pierced him through the heart, and he was taken down dead. Another man attempted the feat, and was killed in like manner; and before they ceased, fifty of their men were slain by Dermat's spear. Then they bade him draw his spear from the earth, saying that no more should try that feat; and they went on board their ships.

So Dermat returned to the cave; and Modan hooked three salmon; and Dermat and Grania ate their meal and slept till morning, Modan keeping watch.

---

* Dermat had two spears, the great one called the Ga-derg or Crann-derg (red javelin), and the small one called Ga-boi or Crann-boi (yellow javelin): he had also two swords: the Morallta (great fury), and the Begallta (little fury). These spears and swords he got from Mannanan Mac Lir and from Angus of the Bruga. He carried the great spear and sword in affairs of life and death; and the smaller in adventures of less danger.

Next morning, Dermat went to the hill, bringing
two strong forked poles cut from the wood. He found
the three sea-champions with their men on the shore ;
and he greeted them, and said—

"I have come to-day to show you a champion-feat I
learned from Dermat O'Dyna, that you may know what
to expect if you should meet with Dermat himself."

He then fixed the poles standing firmly in the
earth ; and he placed the Morallta, that is, the long
sword of Angus of the Bruga, in the forks, edge upwards, the hilt on one, and the point on the other,
binding it firmly with withes. Then, rising up with a
bound, he alighted gently on the edge ; and he walked
cunningly three times from hilt to point, and from
point to hilt, and then leaped lightly to the earth
without wound or hurt. And he challenged the
strangers to do that feat.

Then one arose and said, " There never yet was
done a champion-feat by a man of Erin, that one
among us will not do likewise."

And he leaped up, intending to alight on his feet ;
but he came down heavily on the sharp edge, so that
the sword cut him clean in two. Another tried the
same, and was killed also ; and, they ceased not till as
many were killed that day by Dermat's sword as were
killed on each of the two days before.

When they were about to return to their ships,
they asked him had he got any tidings of Dermat
O'Dyna ; and he answered—

"I have seen him this day : I will now go to seek

him, and methinks I shall bring him to you in the morning."

Then he returned to the cave; and he and Grania ate their meal, and slept that night, while Modan kept watch.

Next morning, Dermat arose with the dawn, and this time he arrayed himself for battle. He put on his heavy armour—no man who wore it could be wounded through it, or above it, or beneath it. He hung the Morallta at his left hip, the sword of Angus of the Bruga, which never left anything for a second blow; and he took his two thick-handled spears, the Ga-derg and the Ga-boi, whose wounds no one ever recovered.

Then he awakened Grania, telling her to keep watch till he returned, that Modan might sleep. And when she saw him so arrayed, she trembled with fear, for she well knew that this was his manner of preparing for battle. And she asked him what he meant to do to-day, and whether Finn's pursuers had found them. But he, to quiet her fears, put off the matter lightly, and said, "It is better to be prepared, lest the enemy come in my way;" and this soothed her.

So he went to the hill, and met the strangers on the shore as before. And they asked him had he any tidings to give them of Dermat O'Dyna.

He answered, "He is not very far off, for I have seen him just now."

"Then," said they, "lead us to his hiding-place, that we may bring his head to Finn the son of Cumal."

"That would, indeed, be an ill way of repaying friendship," answered he. "Dermat O'Dyna is my friend; and he is now under the protection of my valour: so of this be sure, I will do him no treachery."

And they replied wrathfully, "If thou art a friend to Dermat O'Dyna, thou art a foe to Finn; and now we will take thy head and bring it to him along with the head of Dermat."

"You might indeed do that with much ease," answered Dermat, "if I were bound hand and foot; but being as I am, free, I shall defend myself after my usual custom."

Then he drew the Morallta from its sheath, and, springing forward to meet them as they closed on him, he clove the body of the foremost in two with one blow. Then he rushed through them and under them and over them, like a wolf among sheep, or a hawk among sparrows, cleaving and slaughtering them, till only a few were left, who hardly escaped to their ships.

CHAPTER VI.

WHAT BEFELL THE THREE SEA-CHAMPIONS AND THEIR THREE VENOMOUS HOUNDS.

AFTER this Dermat returned to the cave without wound or hurt; and he and Grania ate and slept, and Modan watched till morning. Then he repaired to the

hill, fully armed as before, and standing right over the
ships, he struck his hollow-sounding shield* with his
spear for a challenge, till the whole shore and the surrounding hills re-echoed. And Ducoss straightway
armed himself and came ashore to fight Dermat single
hand.

Now Dermat by no means wished to slay his foe
immediately, being, indeed, intent on worse punishment.
So he closed with Ducoss; and the two champions,
throwing aside their weapons, seized each other round
the waists with their sinewy arms. Then they twisted
and tugged and wrestled in deadly silence; and their
swollen sinews strained and crackled; and the earth
trembled beneath their feet; like two great writhing
serpents, or like two raging lions, or like two savage
bulls that strive and struggle to heave each other with
horns interlocked. Thus did the heroes contend; till
at last Dermat, heaving Ducoss on his shoulder, dashed
him helpless and groaning to the ground; and instantly
seizing him, he bound him in hard iron bonds.

Fincoss came next against Dermat, and after him
Trencoss; but he overcame them both, and bound them
with like bonds; and then, leaving the three writhing
with pain, he said to them—

"I would strike off your heads, but that I wish to

---

* A usual form of challenge among the ancient Irish warriors. It
is very curious that this custom is remembered to the present day in
the *patois* of the peasantry, even where the Irish language is no
longer spoken. In the south, and in parts of the west, they call a
distinguished fighting man a *buailim sciach*, an expression which
means literally, "I strike the shield."

prolong your torment; for none can release you from these bonds till you die!"

Dermat then returned to the cave; and he and Grania ate their meal and slept that night, Modan watching. In the morning, Dermat told Grania all that had happened from beginning to end; how fifty of the foreigners had been killed each day for the first three days; how he had slain a much greater number on the fourth day; and how he had overcome and bound the three sea-champions in hard iron bonds.

"I have left them bound on the hill," continued he, "instead of killing them; because I would rather their torment to be long than short. For there are only four men in Erin that can loosen the bonds I tie; that is to say, Oisin, and Oscar, and Mac Luga, and Conan Mail; and I think no one of these will free them. Finn will doubtless hear of their state, and the news will sting him to the heart. But he will know that we are here; so we must now leave this cave, to escape him, and also to escape the three venomous dogs."

So they came forth from the cave, and travelled eastward till they came to the Grey Moor of Finnlia; and whenever Grania was tired, or when they had to walk over rugged places, Modan lifted her tenderly and carried her, without ever being in the least tired himself. And so they journeyed, till they reached the broad, heathery slopes of Slieve Lougher;* and they

* Slieve Lougher, a mountain near Castle Island. (See note, page 237.)

sat down to rest on the green bank of a stream that wound through the heart of the mountain.

Now as to the sea-strangers. Those of them that were left alive landed from their ships, and coming to the hill, found their three chiefs bound tightly, hand and foot and neck. And they tried to loose them, but only made their bonds the tighter. While they were so engaged, they saw Finn's errand-woman coming towards them, with the speed of a swallow, or of a weasel, or of the swift, cold wind blowing over a mountain-side. When she had come near, she greeted them, and, seeing the bodies of the slain, she asked who it was that had made that fearful slaughter.

"Tell us first," said they, "who art thou that makest this inquiry?"

"I am Derdri of the Black Mountain, the errand-woman of Finn the son of Cumal," she replied; "and he has sent me hither to look for you."

And they said, "We know not who made this slaughter; but we can tell thee his appearance, for that we know well. He was a tall warrior, with a fair, handsome, open countenance, and jet-black, curly hair. He has been three days fighting against us; and what grieves us even more than the slaughter of our men is that our three chiefs lie here bound by him so firmly that we are not able to loose them from their bonds."

"Alas, friends!" said Derdri; "you have sped but badly at the very beginning of your quest; for this man was Dermat O'Dyna himself. And now loose

your three venomous dogs on his track without delay;
and I will return and send Finn to meet you."

Then they brought forth the three hounds, and
loosed them on the track of Dermat; and leaving one
of their druids to attend to the three fettered chiefs,
they followed the hounds till they came to the cave,
where they found the soft, rushy bed of Dermat and
Grania. From that they fared east, and crossing the
Carra, and the Grey Moor of Finnlia, and the Laune,
they reached at length the broad, heathy Slieve
Lougher.

As Dermat sat by the mountain stream with
Grania and Modan, looking westward, he saw the
silken banners of the foreigners at a distance as they
approached the hill. In front of all marched three
warriors with mantles of green, who held the three
fierce hounds by three chains. And Dermat, when he
saw the hounds, was filled with loathing and hatred
of them. Then Modan lifted Grania, and walked a
mile with Dermat up the stream into the heart of
the mountain.

When the green-clad warriors saw them, they
loosed one of the three hounds; and when Grania
heard his hoarse yelps down the valley, she was in
great dread. But Modan bade her not fear, for that
he would deal with this hound; and then, turning
round, he drew forth from beneath his girdle a small
hound-whelp, and placed it on the palm of his hand.
There it stood till the great hound came up raging,
with jaws wide open; when the little whelp leaped

from Modan's hand down the dog's throat, and broke his heart, so that he fell dead. And after that the whelp leaped back again on Modan's hand; and Modan put him under his girdle.

Then they walked another mile up the stream through the mountain, Modan bringing Grania. But the second hound was loosed, and soon overtook them; and Dermat said—

"I will try the Ga-derg on this hound. For no spell can guard against the magic spear of Angus of the Bruga; and I have heard it said also that there is no charm that can shield the throat of an animal from being wounded."

Then, while Modan and Grania stood to look, Dermat, putting his finger into the silken loop of the spear, threw a cast, and drove the spear-head down the hound's throat, so that the entrails of the brute were scattered about; and Dermat, leaping forward, drew the spear, and followed Modan and Grania.

After they had walked yet another mile, the third hound was loosed; and Grania, seeing him coming on, said, trembling—

"This is the fiercest of the three, and I greatly fear him; guard yourself, Dermat, guard yourself well against this hound!"

Even while she spoke, the hound overtook them at the place called Duban's Pillar-stone; and as they stood looking back at him, Dermat stepped in front of Grania to shield her. The hound rose with a great spring over Dermat's head to seize Grania; but

Dermat grasped him by the two hind legs as he passed, and, swinging him round, he struck his carcase against a rock and dashed out his brains.

Then, putting his tapering finger into the silken string of the Ga-derg, he threw the spear at the foremost of the green-clad knights, and slew him. He made another cast of the Ga-boi and brought down the second warrior; and, drawing the Morallta, he sprang on the third, and swept off his head.

When the foreigners saw their leaders slain, they fled hither and thither in utter rout. And Dermat fell upon them with sword and spear, scattering and slaughtering them, so that there seemed no escape for them, unless, indeed, they could fly over the tops of the trees, or hide themselves under the earth, or dive beneath the water. And when Derdri of the Black Mountain saw this havoc, she ran, panic-stricken and crazed with fright, off the field towards the hill where the three kings lay bound.

Now as to Finn. Tidings were brought to him of what happened to the three sea-kings, and how they were lying bound in hard bonds on the hill over Tonn-Toma. So he set out straightway from Allen, and travelled by the shortest ways till he reached the hill. And when he saw the three champions, he was grieved to the heart; for he knew of old that the iron fetters bound by Dermat slew by slow torment, and that none could loose them except Oisin, or Oscar, or Mac Luga, or Conan Mail.

And Finn asked Oisin to loose the bonds and relieve the kings.

"I cannot do so," answered Oisin, "for Dermat bound me under gesa [12] never to loose any warrior that he should bind."

He next asked Oscar; but the young warrior answered, "None shall be released by me who seeks to harm Dermat O'Dyna. Fain would I indeed put heavier bonds on them."

And when he asked Mac Luga and Conan, they refused in like manner.

Now while they were speaking in this wise, they saw the errand-woman, Derdri of the Black Mountain, running towards them, breathless and with failing steps, and her eyes starting from the sockets with terror. And Finn asked her what tidings she had brought.

"Tidings indeed, O king, tidings of grievous mishap and woe!" Whereupon she told him all that she had seen—how Dermat O'Dyna had killed the three fierce hounds, and had made a slaughter of the foreigners. "And hardly, indeed," she cried, "hardly have I myself got off scathless with the news!"

The three kings, hearing this, and being worn out with the straitness and torment of their bonds, died at the same moment. And Finn caused them to be buried in three wide graves; and flagstones were placed over them with their names graved in Ogam; * and their funeral rites were performed. Then, with heart full of grief and gall, Finn marched northwards with his men to Allen of the green hill-slopes.

* See note, page 36.

CHAPTER VII.

SHARVAN, THE SURLY GIANT, AND THE FAIRY QUICKEN TREE OF DOOROS.

Now touching Dermat and Grania. They travelled eastward from Slieve Lougher, through Hy Conall Gavra, keeping the Shannon on their left, till they reached the Wood of the two Sallow Trees, which is now called Limerick. Here they rested; and Dermat killed a wild deer, and they ate of its flesh, and drank pure spring water, and slept that night. Next morning Modan bade them farewell, and left them. And Dermat and Grania were sad after him, for he was very gentle, and had served them faithfully.

On that same day they departed from the Wood of the two Sallows; and nothing is related of what befell them till they arrived at the Forest of Dooros, in the district of Hy Ficra* of the Moy, which was at that time guarded by Sharvan the Surly, of Lochlann.

Now this is the history of Sharvan the Surly, of Lochlann. On a certain occasion, a game of hurley was played by the Dedannans against the Fena, on the plain beside the Lake of Lein of the Crooked Teeth.† They played for three days and three nights, neither side being able to win a single goal from the other during the whole time. And when the Dedannans

---

* Hy Ficra, now the barony of Tireragh, in Sligo.
† The Lake of Lein of the Crooked Teeth, *i.e.* Loch Lein, or the Lakes of Killarney

found that they could not overcome the Fena, they suddenly withdrew from the contest, and departed from the lake, journeying in a body northwards.

The Dedannans had for food during the game, and for their journey afterwards, crimson nuts and arbutus apples and scarlet quicken berries, which they had brought from the Land of Promise. * These fruits were gifted with many secret virtues; and the Dedannans were careful that neither apple nor nut nor berry should touch the soil of Erin. But as they passed through the Wood of Dooros, in Hy Ficra of the Moy, one of the scarlet quicken berries dropped on the earth; and the Dedannans passed on, not heeding.

From this berry a great quicken tree † sprang up, which had the virtues of the quicken trees that grow in Fairyland. For its berries had the taste of honey, and those who ate of them felt a cheerful flow of spirits, as if they had drunk of wine or old mead; and if a man were even a hundred years old, he returned to the age of thirty, as soon as he had eaten three of them.

Now when the Dedannans heard of this tree, and knew of its many virtues, they would not that any one should eat of the berries but themselves; and they sent a Fomor‡ of their own people to guard it, namely, Sharvan the Surly, of Lochlann; so that no man dared even to approach it. For this Sharvan was a giant of

---

* The Land of Promise, or Fairyland.   (See note 8 at the end.)
† Quicken tree. (See note, page 177.)
‡ Fomor, a giant. (See note, page 227.)

the race of the wicked Cain, burly and strong; with heavy bones, large, thick nose, crooked teeth, and one broad, red, fiery eye in the middle of his black forehead. And he had a great club tied by a chain to an iron girdle which was round his body. He was, moreover, so skilled in magic that fire could not burn him, water could not drown him, and weapons could not wound him; and there was no way to kill him but by giving him three blows of his own club. By day he sat at the foot of the tree, watching; and at night he slept in a hut he had made for himself, high up among the branches.

Into this land Dermat came, knowing well that he should be safe there from the pursuit of Finn. For Sharvan did not let any of the Fena hunt in Hy Ficra. And neither they nor any others dared to come near the great Wood of Dooros, for dread of the giant; so that the land around the quicken tree for many miles was a wilderness.

Dermat, leaving Grania behind in safe shelter, went boldly to the giant, where he sat at the foot of the tree, and told him he wished to live amidst the woods of Hy Ficra, and chase its wild animals for food. Whereupon the giant, bending his red eye on him, told him, in words few and surly, that he might live and hunt where he pleased, as long as he did not take and eat the berries of the quicken tree.

So Dermat built him a hunting-booth near a spring, in the thick of the Forest of Dooros; and, clearing a space all round, fenced it with strong stakes interwoven with tough withes, leaving one narrow door well barred and secured. And they lived in peace for a time, eating the flesh of the wild animals of Dooros, which Dermat brought down each day in the chase, and drinking the water of the well.

Now let us speak of Finn, the son of Cumal. One day, soon after his return to Allen, as he and his household troops were on the exercise green before the palace, a company of fifty horsemen were seen approaching from the east, led by two taller and nobler looking than the others. Having come near, they bowed low and greeted the king; and when he asked them who they were, and from whence they had come, they answered—

"We are enemies of thine, who now desire to make peace; and our names are Angus, the son of Art Mac Morna, and Aed, the son of Andala Mac Morna. Our fathers were present at the battle of Knocka,[27] aiding those who fought against thy father, Cumal, when he was slain; for which thou didst afterwards slay them both, and didst outlaw us, their sons, though indeed we were blameless in the matter, seeing that we were not born till after the death of Cumal. However, we have come now to ask this boon of thee: that thou make peace with us, and give us the places our fathers held in the ranks of the Fena."

"I will grant your request," answered Finn, "provided you pay me eric for the death of my father."

"We would indeed pay thee eric willingly if we could," answered they; "but we have neither gold, nor silver, nor cattle, nor wealth of any kind to give."

And then Oisin spoke and said, "Ask them not for eric, O king; surely the death of their fathers should be eric enough."

But Finn replied, "Of a truth, I think, Oisin, that if any one should slay me, it would not be hard to satisfy you in the matter of an eric. But, indeed, none of those who fought at Knocka against my father, and none of their sons, shall ever get peace from me, or join the Fena, without such eric as I demand."

Then Angus, one of the two, asked, "What eric dost thou require, O king?"

"I ask only one or the other of two things," answered Finn; "namely, the head of a warrior, or the full of my hand of the berries of a quicken tree."

"I will give you counsel, ye sons of Morna, that will stand you in good stead, if you follow it," said Oisin, addressing the two strange chiefs; "and my counsel is, that you return to the place from whence you came, and seek this peace no longer. Know that the head the king seeks from you is the head of Dermat O'Dyna, the most dangerous of all the Fena to meddle with, who is well able to defend himself, even if you were twenty times as many as you are; and who will certainly take your heads if you attempt to take his. Know also that the berries Finn seeks from you are the berries of the quicken tree of Dooros. And it is hard to say if this be not a more perilous quest than the other; for the quicken tree belongs to the Dedannans, who have sent Sharvan, the surly giant of Lochlann, to guard it day and night."

But the two chiefs, unmoved by what they had heard from Oisin, said that they would rather perish in seeking out the eric than return to their mother's country. So, leaving their people in the care of Oisin, they set out on their quest. They travelled through the Wood of the two Sallows, and from that to Dooros of the Moy, where they found the track of Dermat and Grania, and followed it till they came to the hunting-booth. Dermat heard their voices and footsteps outside, and, snatching up his weapons, went to the door and asked who was there.

"We are Aed, the son of Andala Mac Morna, and Angus, the son of Art Mac Morna," they replied. "We have come hither from Allen of Leinster, to get either the head of Dermat O'Dyna, or a handful of the berries of the quicken tree of Dooros; for Finn, the son of Cumal, has demanded of us that we bring him either the one or the other, as an eric for the killing of his father."

Dermat laughed when he heard this, and said, "Truly this is not pleasant news for me to hear, for I am Dermat O'Dyna. But however, friends, I am not willing to give you my head, and you will find it no easy matter to take it. And as for the berries, these are quite as hard to get; for you will have to fight the surly giant Sharvan, who cannot be burned with fire, or drowned with water, or wounded with weapons. But woe to the man who falls under the

power of Finn, the son of Cumal. And you have come,
methinks, on a bootless quest; for even if you should
be able to bring him either of the two things he asks
for, he will not grant you the place or the rank ye
seek after all. And now," asked Dermat, "which of
the two do ye wish to strive for first, my head or the
quicken berries?"

And they answered, "We will do battle with thee
first."

So Dermat opened the door, and they made ready
for the combat. Now this is the manner in which
they agreed to fight: to throw aside their weapons,
and to use the strength of their hands alone. And if
the sons of Morna were able to overcome Dermat, they
should take his head to Finn; but if, on the other
hand, they were overpowered and bound by Dermat,
their heads should be in like manner forfeit to him.
But the fight was, indeed, a short one; for these two
chiefs were even as children in Dermat's hands, and
he bound them in close and bitter bonds.

Now when Grania heard of the berries of the
quicken tree, she was seized with a longing desire to
taste them. At first she strove against it and was
silent, knowing the danger; but now she was not able
to hide it any longer, and she told Dermat that she
should certainly die if she did not get some of the
berries to eat. This troubled Dermat, for he did not
wish to quarrel with the giant Sharvan; but, seeing
that harm might come to Grania if she did not get the
berries, he told her he would go and get some for her,
either by good will or by force.

When the sons of Morna heard this, they said, "Loose these bonds, and we will go with thee and help thee to fight the giant."

But Dermat answered, "Not much help, indeed, could ye give me, as I think, for the mere sight of this giant would be enough to unman you. But even were it otherwise, I would not seek your help, for if I fight at all I shall fight unaided."

And they said, "Even so, let us go. Our lives are now forfeit to thee, but grant us this request before we die, to let us see thee fight this giant."

And he consented to this.

So Dermat went straightway to the quicken tree, followed by the two sons of Morna; and he found the giant lying asleep at the foot of the tree. He dealt him a heavy blow to awaken him, and the giant, raising his head, glared at him with his great red eye, and said—

"There has been peace between us hitherto; do you now wish for strife?"

"I seek not strife," answered Dermat; "but the Princess Grania, my wife, the daughter of king Cormac Mac Art, longs to taste of these quicken berries; and if she does not get them she will die. This is why I have come; and now I pray you give me a few of the berries for the princess."

But the giant answered, "I swear that if the princess and her child were now dying, and that one of my berries would save them, I would not give it!"

Then Dermat said, "I do not wish to deal unfairly

with you; and I have accordingly awakened you from
your sleep, and made my request openly, wishing for
peace.   But now understand that before I leave this
spot, I will have some of these quicken berries, whether
you will or no."

When the giant heard this, he rose up, and, seizing
his club, dealt Dermat three great blows, which the
hero had much ado to ward off; nor did he escape
without some hurt, even though his shield was tough
and his arm strong.   But now, watching narrowly,
and seeing that the giant expected to be attacked with
sword and spear, he suddenly threw down his weapons
and sprang upon him, taking him unguarded.   He
threw his arms round his body, and, heaving him
with his shoulder, hurled him with mighty shock to
the earth; and then, seizing the heavy club, he dealt
him three blows, dashing out his brains with the
last.

Dermat sat down to rest, weary and breathless.
And the sons of Morna, having witnessed the fight
from beginning to end, came forth rejoiced when they
saw the giant slain.   Dermat told them to drag the
body into the wood and bury it out of sight, lest
Grania might see it and be affrighted; and when they
had done so, he sent them for the princess.   When she
had come, Dermat said to her—

"Behold the quicken berries, Grania: take now
and eat."

But she answered, "I will eat no berries except
those that are plucked by the hands of my husband."

So Dermat stood up and plucked the berries; and Grania ate till she was satisfied. And he also plucked some for the sons of Morna, and said—

"Take these berries now, friends, as much as you please, and pay your eric to Finn; and you may, if you are so minded, tell him that it was you who slew Sharvan the Surly, of Lochlann."

They answered, "We will bring to Finn as much as he demanded, one handful and no more; and we grudge even so much."

Then they thanked Dermat very much; for he had given them the berries, what they should never have been able to get for themselves; and though their lives were forfeit to him, he had not so much as mentioned the matter, but had allowed them to return freely. And after bidding Dermat and Grania farewell, they went their ways.

After that Dermat left his hunting-booth, and he and Grania lived thenceforth in Sharvan's hut among the branches. And they found the berries on the top of the tree the most delicious of all; those on the lower branches being as it were bitter in comparison.

When the sons of Morna reached Allen, Finn asked them how they had fared, and whether they had brought him the eric: and they answered—

"Sharvan, the surly giant of Lochlann, is slain; and here we have brought thee the berries of the quicken tree of Dooros as eric for the death of thy father, Cumal, that we may have peace from thee, and be placed in our due rank among the Fena."

Finn took the berries and knew them; and he smelled them three times, and said—

"These, indeed, are the berries of the quicken tree of Dooros; but they have passed through the hands of Dermat O'Dyna, for I smell his touch. And sure I am that it was Dermat, and not you, who slew Sharvan, the surly giant. It shall profit you nothing, indeed, to have brought me these berries; neither will you get from me the peace you seek, nor your place among the Fena, till you pay me fair eric for my father's death. For you have gotten the berries not by your own strength; and you have, besides, made peace with my enemy. And now I shall go to the Wood of Dooros, to learn if Dermat abides near the quicken tree."

After this he gathered together the choice men of the seven battalions of the Fena, and marched with them to Dooros of Hy Ficra. They followed Dermat's track to the foot of the quicken tree, and found the berries without any one to guard them; and they ate of them as much as they pleased.

Now it was noon when they had come to the tree; and the sun shone hot, and Finn said—

"We shall rest under this tree till evening come, and the heat pass away; for well I know that Dermat O'Dyna is on the tree among the branches."

And Oisin said, "Truly your mind must be blinded by jealousy, if you think that Dermat O'Dyna has waited for you on that tree, since he knows well that you seek his head."

Finn answered nothing to this speech, but called for a chess-board and men.[26]   And he and Oisin sat down to a game; while Oscar and Mac Luga and Dering, the son of Dobar O'Baskin, sat near Oisin to advise him; for Finn played against them all. They played on for a time warily and skilfully, till at last Oisin had only one move to make; and Finn said—

"One move more would win you the game, Oisin, but I challenge all your helpers to show you that move."   And Oisin was puzzled.

Dermat had been viewing the game from the beginning, where he sat among the branches; and he said, speaking to himself—

"Pity that you should be in a strait, Oisin, and I not near to advise your move."

Grania, sitting near, overheard him, and said, "It is a small matter whether Oisin win or lose a game; far worse is it for you to be in this hut, while the men of the seven battalions of the Fena are round about you, waiting to kill you."

Then Dermat, not giving heed to Grania's words, plucked a berry, and, flinging it down with true aim, struck Oisin's chess-man—the man that should be moved.   And Oisin moved the man, and won the game against Finn.

The game was begun again, and it went on till it came to the same pass as before, Oisin having to make only one move to win, but that move hard to make out.   And again Dermat threw a berry and struck

the right man; and Oisin made the move, and won
the game.

A third time the game went on, and Dermat struck
the chess-man as before ; and Oisin won the game the
third time. Whereupon the Fena raised a mighty shout.

"I marvel not that you should win the game,
Oisin," said Finn, "seeing that you have the best
help of Oscar, and the zeal of Dering, and the skill
of Mac Luga; and that, along with all, you have been
prompted by Dermat O'Dyna."

"It shows a mind clouded by great jealousy," said
Oscar, "that you should think that Dermat O'Dyna
is in that tree waiting for you to kill him."

"Which of us tells truth, Dermat," said Finn,
looking up, "Oscar or I ? "

"You, Finn, have never yet erred in your judg-
ment," answered Dermat from the tree; "for indeed
I am here with the princess Grania, in the hut of
Sharvan, the surly giant of Lochlann."

And, looking up, Finn and the others saw them
plainly through an opening in the branches.

But now Grania, seeing the danger, began to
tremble with great fear, and to weep; and Dermat,
taking pity on her, comforted her and kissed her
three times.

And Finn, seeing this, said, "Much more than this
did it grieve me the night you espoused Grania, and
brought her away from Tara before all the men of
Erin; but even for these kisses you shall certainly
pay quittance with your head ! "

Whereupon Finn, being now bent on killing Dermat, arose, and ordered his hirelings to surround the tree, catching hand in hand, so as to leave no gap; and he warned them, on pain of death, not to let Dermat pass out. Having done this, he offered a suit of armour and arms, and a high place of honour among the Fena, to any man who would go up into the tree, and either bring him the head of Dermat O'Dyna, or force him to come down.

Garva of Slieve Cua* started up and said, "Lo, I am the man! For it was Dermat's father, Donn, that slew my father; and I will now avenge the deed."

And he went up the tree.

Now it was revealed to Angus of the Bruga that Dermat was in deadly strait; and he came to the tree to his aid, without the knowledge of the Fena; and Dermat and Grania were filled with joy when they saw the old man.

And when Garva, climbing from branch to branch, had come near the hut, Dermat dealt him a blow with his foot, which dashed him to the ground among the Fena. And Finn's hirelings cut off his head on the spot, for Angus had caused him to take the shape of Dermat; but after he was slain he took his own shape, so that all knew that it was Garva of Slieve Cua that had been killed.

Then Garva of Slieve Crot† said, "It was Der-

---

* Slieve Cua, the ancient name of the highest of the Knockmeal-down mountains, in Waterford.

† Slieve Crot, the ancient name of the Galty mountains.

mat's father, Donn, that slew my father; and I will now avenge the deed on Dermat."

So saying, he went up the tree. But Angus gave him a blow which hurled him to the ground under the shape of Dermat, so that the hirelings fell on him and slew him. And then Finn told them that it was not Dermat they had killed, but Garva of Slieve Cua.

Garva of Slieve Gora* next started up, and said that his father had been slain by Dermat's father; and he began to climb up the tree to take Dermat's head in revenge. But Dermat flung him down like the others, while Angus gave him for the time the shape of Dermat, so that the hirelings slew him.

And so matters went on till the nine Garvas had fallen; namely, Garva of Slieve Cua, Garva of Slieve Crot, Garva of Slieve Gora, Garva of Slieve Mucka,† Garva of Slieve-more, Garva of Slieve Luga, Garva of Ath-free, Garva of Slieve Mish, and Garva of Drom-more. And full of grief and bitterness was the heart of Finn, witnessing this.

Then Angus said he would take Grania away from that place of danger. And Dermat was glad, and said—

"Take her with thee; and if I live till evening I

---

* Slieve Gora, a mountainous district in the barony of Clankee, County Cavan.

† Slieve Mucka, now Slievenamuck (the mountain of the pig), a long mountain ridge in Tipperary, separated from the Galties by the Glen of Aherlow. Slieve Luga, a mountainous district, formerly belonging to the O'Garas, in the barony of Costello, county Mayo. Slieve Mish, a mountain range west of Tralee.

will follow you. But if Finn slays me, send her to Tara to her father, and tell him to use her well."

Then Dermat kissed his dear wife; and Angus, having thrown his mantle round her, passed out from the tree without the knowledge of the Fena, and went straightway to Bruga of the Boyne.

After Angus and Grania had gone, Dermat, addressing Finn from the tree, said—

"I will now go down from this tree; and I will slaughter many of thy hirelings before they slay me. For I see that thou art resolved to compass my death; and why should I fear to die now more than at a future time? There is, indeed, no escape for me, even should I pass from this place unharmed; since I can find no shelter in Erin from thy wrath. Neither have I a friend in the far-off countries of this great world to give me protection, seeing that I have from time to time dealt defeat and slaughter among them, every one, for thy sake. For never have the Fena been caught in any strait or danger, that I did not venture my life for them and for thee. When we went to battle, moreover, I was always in front of you; and I was always behind you when leaving the field. And now I care no longer to seek to prolong my life; but of a certainty thou shalt purchase my death dearly, for I shall avenge myself by dealing destruction among thy hirelings."

"Dermat speaks truly," said Oscar; "and now let him have mercy and forgiveness; for he has suffered enough already."

"I swear that I will never grant him peace or forgiveness to the end of my life," answered Finn, "till he has given me the eric I seek from him for the injury he has done me; that is to say, his head."

"Shame it is to hear thee say so, and a sure mark of jealousy," answered Oscar. "And now I take the body and life of Dermat under the protection of my knighthood and valour; and I pledge the word of a true champion, that sooner shall the firmament fall on me, or the earth open up and swallow me, than that I shall let any man harm Dermat O'Dyna!"

Then, looking upwards, he said, "Come down now, Dermat, and thou shalt certainly go in safety from this place; for as long as I am alive, no man will dare to offer thee hurt!"

Then Dermat, choosing that side of the tree where the men stood nearest to the trunk, walked along a thick branch unseen, and, leaning on the shafts of his spears, he sprang forward and downward with a light, airy bound, and alighted outside the circle of those who stood round with joined hands; and in a moment he was beyond the reach of sword and spear. And Oscar joined him, looking back threateningly, so that no man of Finn's hirelings durst follow.

So the two heroes fared on together, crossing the Shannon; and nothing is told of what befell them till they reached Bruga of the Boyne, where they met Angus and Grania. And Grania was almost beside herself with joy when she saw Dermat without wound or hurt of any kind. And the two champions were welcomed by Angus; and Dermat related to him and Grania the whole story, how he had escaped from Finn and his hirelings, Oscar helping. And as Grania listened, her spirit almost left her, at the deadly peril Dermat had passed through.

CHAPTER VIII.

THE ATTACK OF THE WITCH-HAG.

Now as regards Finn. After the departure of Dermat and Oscar, his heart was filled with anger and bitterness, and he vowed he would never rest till he had revenged himself on Dermat. And, leaving the Wood of Dooros, he marched eastward till he reached Allen. Making no delay, he ordered his trusted servants to make ready his best ship, and to put therein food and drink for a voyage. Then going on board, he put out to sea; and nothing is told of him till he reached the Land of Promise,[8] where his old nurse lived.

When he appeared before her, she gave him a joyful welcome. And after he had eaten and drunk, she asked him the cause of his journey, knowing that some weighty matter had brought him thither. So he told her the whole story of what Dermat O'Dyna had done against him; and said that he had come to seek counsel from her how he should act. "For," he said, "no strength or cunning of men can compass his death; magic alone can overmatch him."

Then the old woman told him that she would go
with him next day and work magic against Dermat.
Whereupon Finn was much rejoiced, and they rested
that night.

Next day, they set out, Finn and his people and
his nurse; and it is not told how they fared till they
reached Bruga of the Boyne. And the men of Erin
knew not that they had come thither, for the witch-
hag threw a druidical mist round them, so that no
man might see them.

It chanced that Dermat hunted that day in the
forest, alone; for Oscar had gone from Bruga the day
before. When this was known to the witch-hag, she
caused herself to fly into the air by magic, on a water-
lily, having by her spells turned the pale flat leaf
into a broad millstone with a hole in the middle.
And, rising over the tops of the trees, she floated on
the clear, cold wind, till she had come straight over
the hero. Then, standing on the flat millstone, she
began to aim deadly poisoned darts at him through
the hole. And no distress Dermat ever suffered could
compare with this; for the darts stung him even
through his shield and armour, the witch having
breathed venomous spells on them.

Seeing at last that there was no escape from
death unless he could slay the witch-hag, he seized
the Ga-derg, and, leaning backwards, flung it with
sure aim at the millstone, so that it went right
through the hole, and pierced the hag; and she fell
dead at Dermat's feet. Then he beheaded her, and

brought the head to Angus of the Bruga; and he related to him and to Grania how he had escaped that great danger.

CHAPTER IX.

PEACE AND REST AT LAST.

ANGUS arose next morning, and, going to Finn, asked him whether he would make peace with Dermat. Finn, seeing that he was worsted in every attempt against the hero, and that moreover he had lost his nurse and many of his men, told Angus that he was weary of the quarrel, and that he was fain to make peace on whatever terms Dermat should choose.

He next went to Tara to the king, Cormac, the grandson of Conn. Him he asked in like manner whether he was willing to grant Dermat peace and forgiveness; and Cormac answered that he was quite willing.

Then he came to Dermat and said, "Peace is better for thee: art thou willing now to be at peace with Finn and Cormac?"

And Dermat answered, "Gladly will I make peace, if they grant me such conditions as befit a champion and the husband of the princess Grania."

And when Angus asked what these conditions were, he answered—

"The cantred which my father had, that is to say, the cantred of O'Dyna,* without rent or tribute to the king of Erin; also the cantred of Ben-Damis,† namely, Ducarn of Leinster. These two to be granted to me by Finn; and he shall not hunt over them, nor any of his Fena, without my leave. And the king of Erin shall grant me the cantred of Kesh-Corran, ‡ as a dowry with his daughter. On these conditions will I make peace."

Angus went to Finn, and afterwards to the king, with these conditions. And they granted them, and forgave Dermat all he had done against them during the time he was outlawed. So they made peace. And Cormac gave his other daughter to Finn to wife.

Dermat and Grania went to live in the cantred of Kesh-Corran, far away from Finn and Cormac; and they built a house for themselves, namely, Rath-Grania, in which they abode many years in peace. And Grania bore Dermat four sons and one daughter. And his possessions increased year by year, insomuch that people said that no man of his time was richer than Dermat, in gold and silver and jewels, in sheep, and in cattle-herds.

---

* The cantred of O'Dyna, now the barony of Corkaguiny, in Kerry. (See note, page 237.)

† The cantred of Ben-Damis, or Ducarn of Leinster, probably the district round Douce mountain, in the county Wicklow.

‡ The district round the mountain of Kesh-Corran, in Sligo.

CHAPTER X.

THE DEATH OF DERMAT.

Now when many years had passed, Grania said one day to Dermat—

"It is surely a thing unworthy of us, seeing the greatness of our household and our wealth, and the number of our folk, that we should live in a manner so much removed from the world. And in a special manner it is unbecoming that the two most illustrious men in Erin have never been in our house, namely, my father the king, and Finn the son of Cumal."

For indeed she had not seen her father since the night she had left Tara with Dermat, and her heart yearned for him.

"Wherefore say you this, Grania?" answered Dermat; "for though there is indeed peace between us, they are both none the less enemies of mine; and for this reason have I removed my dwelling far apart from them."

And Grania said, "Their enmity has surely softened with length of time: and now I would that you give them a feast: so shall we win back their friendship and love."

And in an evil hour Dermat consented.

For a full year were they preparing for that great feast, and when it was ready, messengers were sent to invite the king, with his house-folk, and Finn, with

the chief men of the seven batallions of the Fena. So
they came, with their attendants and followers, their
horses and dogs; and they lived for a whole year in
Rath-Grania, hunting and feasting.

It chanced one night, at the end of the year, long
after all had gone to rest, that Dermat heard, through
the silence of the night, the distant yelping of a
hound; and he started up from his sleep. But Grania,
being scared, started up also, and, throwing her arms
round him, asked him what he had seen.

"I have heard the voice of a hound," answered
Dermat; "and I marvel much to hear it at midnight."

"May all things guard thee from harm!" said
Grania. "This is surely a trap laid for thee by the
Dedannans, unknown to Angus of the Bruga: and now
lie down on thy bed again."

Dermat lay down, but did not sleep, and again he
heard the hound's voice. He started up, and this time
was fain to go and look to the matter; but Grania
caught him and kept him back a second time, saying
that it was not meet for him to seek a hound whose
voice he heard in the night.

A gentle slumber now fell on Dermat, and he slept
through a good part of the night. But the yelping of
the hound came a third time, and awakened him, so
that he started up; and it being now broad day, he
told Grania that he would go to seek the hound, and
find out why he was abroad in the night.

And though Grania consented, she felt, she knew
not why, ill at ease; and she said—

"Bring with you the Morallta, the sword of Mannanan Mac Lir, and the Ga-derg,* Angus's spear; for there may be danger."

But Dermat, regarding the matter lightly, and forced by fate to the worse choice, answered—

"How can danger arise from such a small affair? I will bring the Begallta and the Ga-boi;* and I will also bring my good hound Mac-an-coill, leading him by his chain."

So Dermat went forth, and he delayed not till he reached the summit of Ben-Gulban,† where he found Finn; and Dermat, offering him no salute, asked him who it was that held the chase. Finn answered—

"Some of our men came out from Rath-Grania at midnight with their hounds; and one of the hounds coming across the track of a wild boar, both men and dogs have followed it up. I indeed would have held them back, but the men were eager, and left me here alone. For this is the track of the wild boar of Ben-Gulban, and they who follow him are bent on a vain and dangerous pursuit. Often has he been chased; and he has always escaped, after killing many men and dogs. Even now thou canst see in the distance that the Fena are flying before him; and he has slain several this morning. He is coming towards this hillock where we stand; and the sooner we get out of his way the better."

But Dermat said he would not leave the hillock through fear of any wild boar.

---

* See note, page 302.

† Now Benbulbin, a mountain five miles north of the town of Sligo.

"It is not meet that thou shouldst tarry here," answered Finn. "Dost thou not know that thou art under gesa [12] never to hunt a boar?"

Dermat answered, "I know nothing of these gesa; wherefore were they placed on me?"

And Finn said, "I will tell thee of this matter, for well do I remember it. When thou wert taken to Bruga of the Boyne, to be fostered by Angus, the son of Angus's steward was fostered with thee, that he might be a companion and playmate to thee. Now the steward, being a man of the common sort, agreed to send each day to Bruga, food and drink for nine men, as a price for having his son fostered with thee—thy father, Donn, being one of the nobles of the Fena. And thy father was accordingly permitted to visit the house of Angus when it pleased him, with eight companions, and claim the food sent by the steward; and when he did not come, it was to be given to Angus's house-folk.

"It chanced on a certain day that I was at Allen of the broad hill-slopes, with the chief men of the seven battalions of the Fena. And Bran Beg O'Bucan brought to my mind, what indeed I had forgotten, that it was forbidden to me to sleep at Allen more than nine nights one after another, and that the next would be the tenth.

"Now this restriction had not been placed on any of the Fena save myself, and they all went into the hall except thy father and a few others. Then I asked where we should get entertainment for that night. And thy father, Donn, answered that he would give me entertainment at Bruga of the Boyne; where food and drink awaited himself and his companions whenever he visited Angus. Donn said, moreover, that he had not been to see his son for a year, and that we were sure to get a welcome.

"So Donn and I and the few that were with us went to the house of Angus, bringing our hounds; and Angus welcomed us. And thou and the steward's son were there, two children. After a while we could see that Angus loved thee, Dermat, very much, but that the house-folk loved the son of the steward; and thy father was filled with jealousy, that the people should show fondness for him and not for thee.

"After night had fallen, it chanced that our hounds quarrelled over some broken meat we had thrown to them, and began to fight in the court; and the women and lesser people fled from them hither and thither. The son of the steward happened to run between thy father's knees, who, calling now to mind how the people favoured him more than thee, gave him a sudden strong squeeze with his knees, and killed him on the spot. And, without being seen by any one, he threw him under the feet of the hounds.

"When at last the dogs were put asunder, the child was found dead; and the steward uttered a long, mournful cry. Then he came to me and said—

"'Of all the men in Angus's house to-night, I have come worst out of this uproar; for this boy was my only child. And now, O Finn, I demand eric from thee for his death; for thy hounds have slain him.'

"I told him to examine the body of his son, and that if he found the mark of a hound's tooth or nail, I would give him eric. So the child was examined, but no hurt—either bite or scratch—was found on him.

"Then the steward laid me under fearful bonds of druidical gesa,[12] to find out for him who slew his son. So I called for a chess-board and some water, and, having washed my hands, I put my thumb under my tooth of knowledge;[25] and then it was revealed to me that the boy had been slain by thy father. Not wishing to make this known, I now offered to pay eric for the boy; but the steward refused, saying that he should know who killed his son. So I was forced to tell him : whereupon he said—

" 'It is easier for Donn to pay me eric than for any other man in this house. And the eric I demand is that his son be placed between my knees : if the lad gets off safe, then I shall follow up the matter no further.'

"Angus was very wroth at this; and thy father would have struck off the steward's head if I had not come between and saved him.

"The steward said no more, but went aside and brought forth a druidical magic wand, and, striking his son with it, he turned him into a great bristly wild boar, having neither ears nor tail. And, holding the wand aloft, he chanted this incantation over the boar—

" By this magical wand,
  By the wizard's command.
I appoint and decree,
For Dermat and thee,
The same bitter strife,
The same span of life :
In the pride of his strength,
Thou shalt slay him at length:
Lo, Dermat O'Dyna
  Lies stretched in his gore ;
Behold my avengers,
  The tusks of the boar !
And thus is decreed,
For Donn's cruel deed,
Sure vengeance to come—
His son's bloody doom ;
By this wand in my hand,
By the wizard's command !

"The moment he had ended the incantation, the boar rushed out through the open door, and we knew not whither he betook himself.

"When Angus heard the steward's words, he laid a command on thee never to hunt a wild boar, that so thou mightest avoid the doom foretold for thee.

"That same boar is the wild boar of Binbulbin ; and he is now rushing furiously towards us. Come, then, let us leave this hill at once, that we may avoid him in time !"

"I know nothing of these incantations and prohibitions," replied Dermat ; " or if, as thou sayest, they were put on me in my boyhood, I forget them all now. And neither for fear of this wild boar of Ben-Gulban nor of any other wild beast will I leave this hillock. But thou, before thou goest, leave me thy hound, Bran, to help and encourage my dog, Mac-an-coill."

"I will not leave him," answered Finn; "for often has Bran chased this boar, and has always barely escaped with his life. And now I leave; for lo, here he comes over yonder hill-shoulder."

So Finn went his ways, and left Dermat standing alone on the hill. And after he had left Dermat said—

"I fear me, indeed, that thou hast begun this chase hoping that it would lead to my death. But here will I await the event; for if I am fated to die in this spot, I cannot avoid the doom in store for me."

Immediately the boar came rushing up the face of the hill, with the Fena following far behind. Dermat loosed Mac-an-coill against him, but to no profit; for the hound shied and fled before him at the first glance. Then Dermat said, communing with himself—

"Woe to him who does not follow the advice of a good wife! For this morning Grania bade me bring the Morallta and the Ga-derg; but I brought instead the Begallta and the Ga-boi, disregarding her counsel."

Then, putting his white taper finger into the silken loop of the Ga-boi, he threw it with careful aim, and struck the boar in the middle of the forehead; but to no purpose, for the spear fell harmless to the ground, having neither wounded nor scratched the boar, nor disturbed even a single bristle.

Seeing this, Dermat, though indeed he knew not fear, felt his courage a little damped. And thereupon drawing the Begallta from its sheath, he dealt a blow on the boar's neck, with the full strength of his brawny arm. But neither did he fare better this time; for the sword flew in pieces, leaving the hilt in his hand, while not a bristle of the boar was harmed.

And now the boar rushed on him as he stood defenceless, and with furious onset hurled him headlong to the earth; and, turning round, he gashed the hero's side with his tusk, inflicting a deep and ghastly wound. Turning again, he was about to renew the attack, when Dermat flung the hilt of the sword at him, and drove it through the skull to his brain, so that the brute fell dead on the spot.

Finn and the Fena now came up, and found Dermat lying pale and bleeding, in the pangs of death. And Finn said—

"It likes me well, Dermat, to see thee in this plight; only I am grieved that all the women of Erin cannot see thee also. For now, indeed, the surpassing beauty of thy form, that they loved so well, is gone from thee, and thou art pale and deformed!"

And Dermat answered, "Alas, O Finn! these words surely come from thy lips only, and not from thy heart. And indeed it is in thy power to heal me even now if thou wilt."

"How should I heal thee?" asked Finn.

"It is not hard for thee to do so," answered Dermat. "For when, at the Boyne, the noble gift of foreknowledge was given to thee,[25] this gift also thou didst receive—that to whomsover thou shouldst give a drink of water from the closed palms of thy two hands, he

should be healed from sickness or wounds, even though
he stood at the point of death."

"Why should I heal thee by giving thee drink
from my hands?" replied Finn. "For of a certainty
thou of all men dost least deserve it from me."

"Thou surely speakest hastily, not remembering
past services," answered Dermat. "Well, indeed, do I
deserve that thou shouldst heal me. Dost thou forget
the day thou didst go with the chiefs and nobles of
the Fena, to the house of Derca, the son of Donnara, to
a banquet? And even as we sat down, and before the
feast began, Carbri of the Liffey, son of Cormac,
with the men of Tara, and of Bregia, and of Meath,
and of Carmna, surrounded the palace, intent on slaying thee and all thy people. And they uttered three
great shouts, and threw firebrands to burn the palace
over our heads. Then thou didst arise and prepare to
issue forth, but I put thee back and bade thee enjoy
thy feast; and, leaving the banquet untasted, I rushed
forth with a chosen few of my own men, and quenched
the flames. Thrice we made a circuit of the palace,
dealing slaughter amongst thy foes, so that we left
fifty of them dead after each circuit. And having put
Carbri and his men to flight, we returned to join the
feast. Had I asked thee for a drink that night, gladly
wouldst thou have given it to me. And yet, not more
justly was it due to me then than it is now."

"Ill dost thou deserve a healing drink from me, or
any other favour," said Finn; "for it was thy part to
guard Grania the night we came to Tara; but thou

didst espouse her secretly, and didst fly with her from
Tara, knowing that she was betrothed to me."

"Lay not the blame of that on me," said Dermat;
"for Grania put me under heavy gesa, which for all the
wealth of the world I would not break through—no,
not even for life itself. Neither did I rest on my own
judgment in the matter; for well thou knowest that
Oisin, and Oscar, and Dering, and Mac Luga counselled
me to the course I took.

"And now, O Finn, I pray thee let me drink from
thy hands, for I feel the weakness of death coming on
me. And thou wilt not gainsay that I deserve it, if
thou wilt only remember the feast that Midac, the son
of Colga, made for thee in the Fairy Palace of the
Quicken Trees.* To this feast Midac invited thee and
thy companions; while to the Palace of the Island he
brought secretly the King of the World with a great
host, and the three kings of the Island of the Torrent,
with intent to slay thee and all thy Fena.

"Now Midac caused some of the clay of the Island
of the Torrent to be placed under you, with foul spells,
in the Palace of the Quicken Trees, so that your feet
and your hands clove to the ground. And it was
revealed to thee that the King of the World was about
to send a chief with a troop of warriors, to slay you,
helpless as you were, and to bring him your heads to
the Palace of the Island.

"But at that same time, I came to thee outside the
Palace of the Quicken Trees; and thou didst make

---

* See this story told at length, page 177.

known to me your deadly strait. Then did I take thee, Finn, and those who were with thee, under the protection of my knighthood and valour; and I went to the ford to defend it against the foreigners.

"And after a little time the three dragon-like kings of the Island of the Torrent came towards the palace : but I defended the ford, and, venturing my life for thee, I bore their attack and slew them all three. And I swept off their heads, and brought them, all gory as they were, in the hollow of my shield, to the palace where you lay miserably bound ; and, sprinkling the clay with the blood, I broke the spell and set you free. And had I asked thee for a drink on that night, O Finn, of a surety thou wouldst not have refused me.

"And many another deadly strait did I free you from, since the day I was admitted among the Fena, always putting myself forward to the post of danger, and perilling my life for your safety; and now why dost thou requite me with this foul treachery ?

"Moreover, many a king's son and many a brave warrior hast thou slain; and thou hast earned the enmity of powerful foes : neither is there yet an end of it. For the day will come—I see it even now—a day of direful overthrow and slaughter,* when few, alas! of the Fena will be left to tell the tale. Then thou shalt sorely need my help, O Finn, and sorely shalt thou rue this day. I grieve not, indeed, for thee, but for my

* A prophetic allusion to the battle of Gavra. (See note 28 at the end.)

dear, faithful companions—for Oscar and Mac Luga and Dering, and more than all for Oisin, who shall long outlive the others in sad old age.* Alas! how deadly shall be their strait when I am not near to aid them!"

Then Oscar, moved with pity even to tears, addressing Finn, said, "Although I am nearer akin to thee, O king, than to Dermat, yet I cannot suffer that he die, when a drink from thy hands would heal him. Bring him, then, a drink without delay."

And Finn answered, "I know of no well on this mountain from which to bring drink."

"Therein thou speakest not truth," said Dermat; "for thou knowest that not more than nine paces from thee, hidden under yonder bush, is a well of crystal water."

Thereupon Finn went to the well, and, holding his two hands tightly together, he brought up some of the water, and came towards Dermat; but after he had walked a little way, he let it spill through his fingers, saying that he was not able to bring water in his hands so far.

"Not so, Finn," said Dermat. "I saw thee that of thy own will thou didst let it spill. And now, O king, hasten, for death is on me."

Again he went to the well, and was bringing the water slowly, while Dermat followed the dripping hands with his eyes; but when Finn thought of

---

* A prophetic allusion to the events related in the story of "Oisin. in Tirnanoge," page 385.

Grania he let the water spill a second time. And Dermat, seeing this, uttered a piteous sigh of anguish.

And now was Oscar no longer able to contain his grief and rage; and he said, "I swear, O king, if thou dost not bring the water, that only one of us two— thou or I—shall leave this hill alive!"

Hearing Oscar's words, and seeing the frowning looks of the others, Finn dipped up the water a third time, and was hastening forward; but before he had got half-way, Dermat's head dropped backwards, and his life departed.

And all the Fena present raised three long loud cries of sorrow for Dermat O'Dyna.

Then Oscar, looking fiercely on Finn, spoke and said, "Would that thou thyself lay dead here instead of Dermat! For now indeed the noblest heart of the Fena is still; and our mainstay in battle and danger is gone. Ah! why did I not foresee this? Why was I not told that Dermat's life was linked with the life of the wild boar of Ben-Gulban? Then would I have stayed this chase, and put off the evil day!"

And Oscar wept; and Oisin, and Dering, and Mac Luga wept also, for Dermat was much loved by all.

After a time, Finn said, "Let us now leave this hill, lest Angus of the Bruga overtake us. For although we had no hand in Dermat's death, nevertheless he may not believe us."

So Finn and the Fena departed from the hill, Finn leading Dermat's dog, Mac-an-coill. But Oisin, and Oscar, and Dering, and Mac Luga turned back, and

with tears, threw their mantles over Dermat; after
which they followed the others.

Grania sat that day on the highest rampart of
Rath-Grania, watching for Dermat's return; for a dark
fear haunted her mind on account of this chase. And
when at last the Fena came in view, she saw Dermat's
dog led by Finn; but not seeing Dermat himself, she
said—

"Ah me! what is this I see? Surely if Dermat
were alive, it is not by Finn that Mac-an-coill would
be led to his home!"

And as she spoke she fell forward off the rampart,
and lay long in a swoon as if her spirit had fled,
while her handmaid stood over her, weeping and dis-
tracted. And when at last she opened her eyes, then
indeed they told her that Dermat was dead; and she
uttered a long and piteous cry, so that her women and
all the people of the court came round her to ask the
cause of her sorrow. And when they were told that
Dermat had perished by the wild boar of Ben-Gulban,
they raised three loud, bitter cries of lamentation,
which were heard in the glens and wildernesses
around, and which pierced the clouds of heaven.

When at length Grania became calm, she ordered
that five hundred of her people should go to Ben-Gulban,
to bring home the body of Dermat. Then, turning to
Finn, who still held Mac-an-coill in his hand, she
asked him to leave her Dermat's hound; but Finn
refused, saying that a hound was a small matter, and
that he might be allowed to inherit at least so much

of Dermat's riches. When Oisin heard this, he came forward and took the hound from the hand of Finn and gave him to Grania.

At the time that the men left Rath-Grania to go for the body of Dermat, it was revealed to Angus that the hero was lying dead on Ben-Gulban. And he set out straightway, and travelling on the pure, cool wind, soon reached the mountain; so that when Grania's people came up, they found him standing over the body, sorrowing, with his people behind him. And they held forward the wrong sides of their shields in token of peace.

Then both companies, having viewed the dead hero, raised three mighty cries of sorrow, so loud and piercing that they were heard in the wastes of the firmament, and over the five provinces of Erin.

And when they had ceased, Angus spoke and said, "Alas! why did I abandon thee, even for once, O my son? For from the day I took thee to Bruga, a tender child, I have watched over thee and guarded thee from thy foes, until last night. Ah! why did I abandon thee to be decoyed to thy doom by the guileful craft of Finn? By my neglect hast thou suffered, O Dermat; and now, indeed, I shall for ever feel the bitter pangs of sorrow!"

Then Angus asked Grania's people what they had come for. And when they told him that Grania had sent them to bring the body of Dermat to Rath-Grania, he said—

"I will bring the body of Dermat with me to

Bruga of the Boyne; and I will keep him on his bier, where he shall be preserved by my power, as if he lived. And though I cannot, indeed, restore him to life, yet I will breathe a spirit into him, so that for a little while each day he shall talk with me."

Then he caused the body to be placed on a golden bier, with the hero's javelins fixed one on each side, points upwards. And his people raised the bier and carried it before him; and in this manner they marched slowly to Bruga of the Boyne.

Grania's people then returned; and when they had told her the whole matter, though she was grieved at first, yet in the end she was content, knowing how Angus loved Dermat.

THE CHASE OF SLIEVE CULLINN.

IN WHICH IT IS RELATED HOW FINN'S HAIR WAS CHANGED IN ONE DAY
FROM THE COLOUR OF GOLD TO SILVERY GREY.*

———◦✧◦———

CULAND, the smith of the Dedannans,[1] who lived at
Slieve Cullinn,† had two beautiful daughters, Milucra
and Aina. They both loved Finn,[23] and each sought
him for her husband.

As they walked together one evening near Allen,‡
they fell to talking of many things; and their conversation turning at last on their future husbands,
Aina said she would never marry a man with grey
hair.

When Milucra heard this, she resolved with herself
that if she could not get Finn, she would plan so that
he should not marry her sister Aina. So she departed
immediately, and, turning her steps northwards, she
summoned the Dedannans to meet her at Slieve

* It is necessary to remind the reader that this story and the two
following are related by Oisin, in his old age, to St. Patrick. (See
the prefatory note to the story of " Oisin in Tirnanoge," p. 385; and
see also note 23 at the end.)

† Now Slieve Gullion, a lofty, isolated mountain in the south of
the county Armagh, celebrated in legendary lore.

‡ The Hill of Allen, in Kildare, where Finn had his palace. (See
note 23 at the end.)

Cullinn. Having brought them all together, she caused them to make her a lake* near the top of the mountain; and she breathed a druidical virtue on its waters, that all who bathed in it should become grey.

On a morning not long after this, Finn happened to be walking alone on the lawn before the palace of Allen, when a doe sprang out from a thicket, and, passing quite close to him, bounded past like the wind. Without a moment's delay, he signalled for his companions and dogs; but none heard except his two hounds, Bran and Skolan. He instantly gave chase, with no other arms than his sword, Mac-an-Lona, and accompanied only by his two dogs; and before the Fena[23] knew of his absence, he had left Allen of the green slopes far behind.

The chase turned northwards; and though the hounds kept close to the doe, the chief kept quite as close to the hounds the whole way. And so they continued without rest or pause, till they reached Slieve Cullinn, far in the north.

Here the doe made a sudden turn and disappeared;

---

* The little lake for which this legendary origin is assigned lies near the top of Slieve Gullion. There were several wells in Ireland which, according to the belief of old times, had the property of turning the hair grey. Giraldus Cambrensis tells us of such a well in Munster; and he states that he once saw a man who had washed a part of his head in this well, and that the part washed was white, while the rest was black!

It is to be observed that the peasantry of the district retain to this day a lingering belief in the power of the lake of Slieve Gullion to turn the hair grey.

and what direction she took, whether east or west, Finn knew not, for he never caught sight of her after. And he marvelled much that any doe in the world should be able to lead Bran and Skolan so long a chase, and escape from them in the end. Meantime they kept searching, Finn taking one side of the hill and the dogs another, so that he was at last left quite alone.

While he was wandering about the hill and whistling for his hounds, he heard the plaintive cry of a woman at no great distance; and, turning his steps towards the place, he saw a lady sitting on the brink of a little lake, weeping as if her heart would break. Never before did the chieftain see a maiden so lovely. The rose colour on her cheeks was heightened by her grief; her lips were like ruddy quicken berries; the delicate blossom of the apple tree was not more white than her neck; her hair fell in heavy golden ringlets on her shoulders; and as she looked up at the chief, her eyes beamed like stars on a frosty night.

Finn accosted her; and, seeing that she ceased her weeping for a moment, he asked her had she seen his two hounds pass that way.

"I have not seen thy hounds," she replied, "nor have I been at all concerned in the chase; for, alas, there is something that troubles me more nearly, a misadventure that has caused me great sorrow!"

And as she spoke these words, she burst out weeping and sobbing more bitterly than before.

Finn was greatly moved at this, so much so, that he quite forgot all about his hounds and his own troubles; and he asked her—

"What is the cause of this great grief, gentle lady? Has death robbed you of your husband or your child, or what other evil has befallen you? I am much concerned to see a lady in such distress; and I wish you to tell me if anything can be done to lighten your sorrow, or to remove the cause of it?"

She replied, "I had a precious gold ring on my finger, which I prized beyond anything in the world; and it has fallen from me into the water. I saw it roll down the steep slope at the bottom, till it went quite out of my sight. This is the cause of my sorrow, and thou canst remedy the mishap if thou wilt. The Fena are sworn never to refuse help to a woman in distress; and I now put on thee those gesa[12] that true heroes dare not break through, to search for the ring, and cease not till thou find it and restore it to me."

Though the chief had indeed at the moment no inclination to swim, he could not refuse a prayer urged in this manner. So he plunged in without a moment's hesitation, and examined the lake on all sides, diving and searching into every nook and cranny at the bottom.

After swimming in this manner three times round and round the lake, he found the ring at last; and approaching the lady, he handed it to her from the water. The moment she had got it she sprang into the lake before his eyes, and, diving down, disappeared in an instant.

The chief, wondering greatly at this strange behaviour, stepped forth from the water; but as soon as his feet had touched the dry land, he lost all his strength, and fell on the brink, a withered, grey old man, shrunken up and trembling all over with weakness. He sat him down in woful plight; and soon his hounds came up. They looked at him wistfully and sniffed and whined around him; but they knew him not, and, passing on, they ran round the lake, searching in vain for their master.

On that day the Fena were assembled in the banquet hall of the palace of Allen; some feasting and drinking, some playing chess, and others listening to the sweet music of the harpers. While all were in this wise pleasantly engaged, Kylta Mac Ronan [28] stood up in the midst, and said in the hearing of all—

"I have observed, friends, that our master and king, Finn the son of Cumal, has not been amongst us to-day, as is his wont; and I wish to know whither he has gone."

This speech caused a sudden alarm amongst us; for no one knew aught of the chief, or was aware till that moment that he was absent at all; and we knew not wherefore he had disappeared or whither he had gone. In the midst of our anxious tumult, the envious and foul-mouthed Conan Mail [28] stood up, and said—

"I have never heard sweeter music than your words, Kylta! The Fena are now about to seek for their king; and my only wish is that their quest may

last for a whole year, and that it may prove a vain
search in the end! Be not cast down, however, O
Fena; if you should fail to find the son of Cumal, you
will not be so ill off as you think; for I will undertake to be your king from this time forth!"

Though we were at the time more inclined to be
sad than mirthful, being weighed down with much
anxiety, we could not help laughing when we heard
the loud, foolish talk of Conan Mail; but we took
no further notice of him.

Inquiring now from the lesser people about the
palace, we found that the chief and his two dogs had
followed a doe northwards. So, having mustered
a strong party of the Fena, we started in pursuit.
Kylta and I took the lead, the rest keeping close
behind; and in this order we followed the track,
never taking rest or slackening speed till we reached
Slieve Cullinn.

We began to search round the hill, hoping to find
either the chief himself or some person who might
give us tidings of him. After wandering among
brakes and rough, rocky places, we at last espied a
grey-headed old man sitting on the brink of a lake.
I went up to him to ask a question, followed by the
rest of the Fena. At first I thought he might be a
fisherman who had come up from the plains to fish;
but when we came near him, he seemed so wretched
an old creature, all shrivelled up, with the skin
hanging in wrinkles over the bare points of his bones,
that I felt quite sure he was not a fisherman, and that

he was reduced to that state more by sickness and want than by old age.

I asked the poor old man if he had seen a noble-looking hero pass that way, with two hounds, chasing a doe. He never answered a word, neither did he stir from where he sat, or even look up; but at the question, his head sank on his breast, and his limbs shook all over as with palsy. Then he fell into a sudden fit of grief, wringing his hands and uttering feeble cries of woe.

We soothed him and used him gently for a time, hoping he might speak at last; but to no purpose, for he still kept silent. Then at last growing impatient, and thinking that this might be a mere headstrong humour, we drew our swords, and threatened him with instant death if he did not at once tell us all he knew of the chief and his hounds—for we felt sure he had seen them. But he only lamented the more, and still answered nothing.

At last, after this had gone on for some time, and when we were about to leave him, he beckoned to Kylta Mac Ronan; and when Kylta had come near, the old man whispered into his ear the dreadful secret. And then we all came to know the truth. When we found that the withered old man was no other than our beloved king, Finn, himself, we uttered three shouts of lamentation and anger, so loud and prolonged that the foxes and badgers rushed affrighted from their dens in the hollows of the mountain.

Conan now stepped forward, looking very fierce;

and, unsheathing his sword with mighty bluster, he
began in a loud voice to revile Finn and the Fena
with the foulest language he could think of. And he
ended by saying that he meant to slay the king that
moment—

"Now, O Finn Mac Cumal, I will certainly strike
off your head; for you are the man that never gave me
credit for valour, or praised my noble deeds in battle.
Ever since your father, Cumal of the Hosts, was slain
on the field of Knocka* by the Clann Morna[28] of the
Golden Shields, you have been our bitter foe; and it is
against your will that any of us are now alive. I am
very glad to see you, Finn Mac Cumal, brought down
to what you now are; and I only wish that the rest of
the Clann Baskin[28] were like you. Then should I
very soon make short work of them all; and joyful to
me would be the task of raising a great carn to their
memory!"

To which Oscar replied with great scorn, "It is
not worth while drawing a sword to punish thee,
Conan Mail, vain and foolish boaster as thou art; and
besides, we have at present something else to think of.
But if it were not for the trouble that now lies heavy
on us on account of our king, I would of a certainty
chastise thee by breaking all the bones of thy mouth
with my fist!"

"Cease, Oscar," returned Conan, in a voice still
louder than before; "cease your foolish talk! It is
actions and not words that prove a man; and as to

* Knocka, now Castleknock, near Dublin. (See note 27 at the
end.)

the noble warlike deeds done in past times by the Fena, it was by the Clann Morna they were performed, and not by the chicken-hearted Clann Baskin!"

The fiery Oscar could bear this no longer. He rushed towards Conan Mail; but Conan, terrified at his vengeful look, ran in amongst the Fena with great outcry, beseeching them to save him from the rage of Oscar. We straightway confronted the young hero, and checked him in his headlong career; and after much ado, we soothed his anger and made peace be tween him and Conan.

When quietness was restored, Kylta asked Finn how this dread evil had befallen him, who was the enchanter, and whether there was any hope of restoring him to his own shape. Finn told him that it was the daughter of Culand the smith who had transformed him by her spells. And then he recounted how she had lured him to swim in the lake, and how, when he came forth, he was turned into a withered old man.

We now made a framework litter of slender poles, and, placing our king on it, we lifted him tenderly on our shoulders. And, turning from the lake, we marched slowly up-hill till we came to the fairy palace of Slieve Cullinn, where we knew the daughter of Culand had her dwelling deep under ground.[19] Here we set him down, and the whole troop began at once to dig, determined to find the enchantress in her cave-palace, and to take vengeance on her if she did not restore our chief.

For three days and three nights we dug, without a moment's rest or pause, till at length we reached her hollow dwelling; when she, affrighted at the tumult and at the vengeful look of the heroes, suddenly started forth from the cave and stood before us. She held in her hand a drinking-horn of red gold, which was meant for the king. Yet she appeared unwilling, and held it back, notwithstanding the threatening looks of the Fena. But, happening to cast her eyes on the graceful and manly youth, Oscar, she was moved with such admiration and love for him that she wavered no longer, but placed the fairy drinking-horn in the hands of the king. No sooner had he drunk from it, than his own shape and features returned, save only that his hair remained of a silvery grey.

When we gazed on our chief in his own graceful and manly form, we were all pleased with the soft, silvery hue of the grey hairs. And, though the enchantress appeared ready to restore this also, Finn himself told her that it pleased him as it pleased the others, and that he chose to remain grey for the rest of his life.

When the king had drunk from the horn, he passed it to Mac Reth, who drank from it in like manner and gave it to Dering. Dering, after drinking, was about to hand it to the next, when it gave a sudden twist out of his hand, and darted into the loose earth at our feet, where it sank out of sight. We ran at once to recover it; but, though we turned up the earth deeply all round, we were not able to find the drinking-horn. This was a disappointment that vexed us exceedingly, for if we had all drunk from it, we should have been gifted with a foreknowledge of future events.

A growth of slender twigs grew up afterwards over the spot where it sank into the ground; and this little thicket is still gifted with a part of the virtue of the golden drinking-horn. For any one who looks on it in the morning fasting, will know in a moment all things that are to happen that day.

So ended the Chase of Slieve Cullinn; and in this wise it came to pass that Finn's hair was turned in one day from golden yellow to silvery grey.

THE CHASE OF SLIEVE FUAD.

IN WHICH IT IS RELATED HOW AILNA, THE WIFE OF MERGAH OF THE
SHARP SPEARS, IN ORDER TO BE REVENGED ON THE FENA FOR
THE DEATH OF HER HUSBAND, TRANSFORMED HERSELF INTO A DEER,
AND DECOYED THEM TILL SHE GOT THEM INTO THE POWER OF HER
BROTHER, DRYANTORE, A GIANT AND AN ENCHANTER; HOW HE
THREW THEM INTO A DUNGEON, WITH INTENT TO KILL THEM;
AND HOW THEY WERE IN THE END SET FREE BY CONAN MAIL.*

FINN and the Fena[23] went one day to hunt at Slieve
Fuad.† When they had come very near to the top
of the mountain, a deer suddenly bounded from a
thicket right before them, very large and fierce, with
a great pair of sharp, dangerous antlers. At once they
loosed their dogs and gave chase; and those who were
scattered here and there about the hill gave up
the pursuit of smaller game to join the main body
for it was very seldom they fell in with a deer that
promised better sport.

She led them through rugged places, over rocks
and bogs, and into deep glens. The hounds several
times surrounded her; but she fought her way with

---

* This story is told by Oisin to St. Patrick. (See the prefatory
note to the next story, " Oisin in Tirnanoge," page 385.

† Slieve Fuad was the ancient name of the highest of the Fews
mountains, near Newtown Hamilton, in Armagh; but the name is
now lost.

so much strength and fury that she always escaped, after killing many of the dogs and disabling some of the men.

Soon she left Slieve Fuad behind, nor did she slacken speed till she reached the green hill of Lidas, while the hunters and dogs followed in full chase close behind. She then made her way across the open country to a rugged and bushy hill—the hill of Carrigan;* and here they suddenly lost her among the rocks and thickets. They searched round the hill without avail, north, south, east, and west, till all, both men and dogs, were quite scattered; and Finn and Dara the Melodious were left alone.

At length Finn's dog, Skolan, started the deer once more, and again the chase began. Back over the self-same course she ran, by the hill of Lidas, and straight on towards Slieve Fuad, Finn and Dara close on her track; while the main body of the Fena followed far behind, guided by the cries of the dogs.

When the deer reached Slieve Fuad, she again took cover and disappeared at the very spot where they had first started her; and the two chiefs, after beating the thickets on every side, were at length forced to give up the search.

A druidical mist now rose up, darkening the air, and enfolding them on every side; so that they lost their way. They tried many times to regain the path, but to no purpose; for they only lost themselves

---

* Now probably the village of Carrigans, on the river Foyle, five miles south-west of Londonderry.

more and more among the quagmires and thickets.
At last they sat down to rest, weary and baffled; and
Dara played a mournful strain on his timpan; after
which they sounded the Dord-Fian,* as a signal to
their friends.

When the Fena heard the Dord-Fian sounding afar
off, they felt sure that their leader was in trouble
or strait of some kind; and they started to his relief,
making northwards straight towards the point from
which they thought the signal came. But they had
not gone far when they heard it sounding from the
east, and altered their course accordingly. Again it
changed to the west; and no sooner had they set
forward in that direction than it seemed to come from
the south. In this manner were they led hither and
thither, till they became quite bewildered; and they
found themselves no nearer to those they were in
search of, for every time they heard the Dord-Fian,
it seemed as far off as ever.

Meantime Finn and Dara, after resting for a time,
again started off, intent on trying once more to reach
their friends; for they heard their shouts, and knew
they were seeking them. As they were making their
way through the thick fog, they heard a voice at a
little distance, as if from one in distress; and, turning
their steps that way, they met a young woman, very
beautiful, and very pleasing in manner, but looking
weary and sore perplexed, and all over in sad plight
from the bogs and brambles.

* Dord-Fian, a sort of musical war-cry. (See note, page 195.)

Finn accosted her in a gentle voice, asking how she came to be alone in a place so wild.

She replied, "I and my husband were journeying along over the plain, when we heard the melodious cry of hounds; and he left me to follow the chase, telling me to continue along the same path, and promising to rejoin me without delay. But this fairy fog has risen around me, and I have lost my way, so that I know not now in what direction to go."

Finn then asked her name and the name of her husband.

"My husband's name is Lavaran, and mine is Glanlua. But I perceive that you are one of the Fena; and indeed I think, from your arms and from your noble mien, that you must be the great chief Finn himself. If this be so, I place myself under your protection; and I know well that you will lead me safely out of this place to my husband; for the Fena never yet refused their help to a woman in distress."

Finn replied, "You are quite right, lady, for I am Finn; and this chase that has parted you and your husband belongs to me. We will certainly take you under our protection, and we will neither abandon you on this mountain, nor suffer any one to harm you. But as to leading you to your husband, it is not at present in our power to do that; for you must know, lady, that we also have been set astray by this magical fairy fog. Nevertheless, we will do the best we can; and now you had better come with us."

So the three set forward in the direction they thought most likely to lead to the open plain.

After walking for some time, they heard a low, sweet strain of fairy music; and they stopped to listen. It seemed to be near them and around them in the fog, so that Finn thought it came from the spot where the lady stood; and she thought it came from Finn or Dara: and the music was followed by shouts and noise, as if from a great company. When the noise ceased, the music began again more sweetly than before; so that they felt heavy, and as if inclined to sleep. Still more drowsy and powerless they became as they listened; and at last they all three sank on the ground, in a trance deep and deathlike.

After a time they awoke, and slowly regained their senses; though they were so weak that they could scarcely move. The fog had cleared away, leaving the air bright and warm; and when they were able to look around, they found themselves on the margin of a blue lake. The part of the lake that lay in front of them was narrow, and quite calm and smooth; but on each side, to the right and left, it opened out into two broad, green-bordered seas, with great waves tumbling wildly about, as if the waters were torn up by whirlwinds. But where they sat, not a breath was blowing. And looking across the narrow part, they saw a stately palace right before them on the opposite shore.

As they were gazing at all these strange things, silent and much astonished, they saw a warrior coming

forth from the palace, in size like a giant, rough and
fierce-looking, with a beautiful woman by his side.
The two walked quickly down to the shore, and,
plunging in, they swam straight across the middle
of the lake. And Dara and Glanlua, turning to Finn,
said—

"Of a surety, it is not for our good yonder
strangers are approaching; but to work us treachery
and mischief!"

This forecast turned out to be true. The large
warrior and the beautiful lady had no sooner gained
the land than they came up to Finn and his two
companions; and without speaking a word, the giant
seized them roughly, and led them down to the shore
of the lake. For the two heroes were still so weak
from the spell of the fairy music that they were not
able to raise a hand to defend either the lady or themselves.

The giant and his companion, making no delay,
plunged in, and swam back towards the palace,
bringing the three with them; and as soon as they
had reached the shore, the strange warrior, addressing
Finn in a fierce and surly manner, said—

"For a long time have I sought Finn Mac Cumal,
the evil-minded and crafty; and now, O Finn, now
that thou hast been by a well-laid plan cast under
my power, I will take good care that thou shalt not
escape till I take revenge, even to the full, for all
the injuries thou hast done to me and to my sister!"

Finn listened to this speech with much surprise,

for he could not call to mind that he had ever seen the
hero before; and he said—

"Tell me, I pray thee, who thou art; for I know
thee not; neither do I know of any injury thou hast
suffered at my hands. Thou art, indeed, large of body,
and fierce and boastful in speech; but know that
to take revenge on a foe who is unable to defend
himself, is a deed quite unbecoming a hero!"

The large man replied, "Do you not remember the
treachery you practised on Mergah of the Sharp
Spears, and on my sons, two fair youths, whom you
slew by unfair means, at the battle of Knockanare?*
Well indeed do I know thee, Finn, for I am Dryantore,
and this is Ailna my sister, the wife of Mergah. She
is left without her husband, and I without my sons,
by your cruel wiles; for it was by fraud and foul
play, and not by fair fighting, that you gained the
battle of Knockanare, and slew Mergah and his host!"

"I remember well," said Finn, "that they all fell
on the battle-field; but it was not by craft or
treachery. Mergah of the Sharp Spears came with
a mighty host to conquer Erin, and lay it under
tribute. But they were met at Knockanare, and every
man of them slain in fair, open fight, though not
without sore loss to the Fena."

---

* Knockanare (the hill of slaughter), where a great battle was
fought between the Fena under Finn, and the foreigners under
Mergah of the Sharp Spears, in which Mergah was defeated and
slain. This battle forms the subject of a poetical romance. It may
be as well to observe that this hill is *not* Knockanore in Kerry, near
the mouth of the Shannon, as some say.

"You may say what you please on the matter," said Dryantore; "but it is quite enough for me that you have slain Ailna's husband and my two sons. And now, indeed, I shall take revenge—of that be sure—both on you and on all the Fena that come within my reach."

And having so spoken, he began without more ado to bind Finn, Dara, and Glanlua in strong fetters ; and having done so, he threw them into a dungeon, where he left them without food or drink or comfort of any kind.

Meantime the Fena ceased not to search for their king. They knew, by the sad strain they had heard in the distance, and by the strange manner in which the music had shifted from place to place, that he was caught under some druidic spell; and they vowed they would never rest till they had found him and punished the enchanter, whoever he might be.

Next day, Ailna visited the dungeon; and Finn addressed her—

"Hast thou forgotten, Ailna, that when thou didst come to Erin after the death of thy husband, Mergah of the Sharp Spears, the Fena received thee hospitably, and, pitying thy distress, treated thee with much kindness ? But for this thou hast indeed given us an ungrateful and unbecoming return; for thou hast shut us up in this dungeon, without food or drink, having, by guileful druidical spells, taken away our strength."

"I remember very well," said Ailna, "that you treated me kindly. But you killed my husband; and

I am well pleased that it has now come to my turn to avenge his death. I do not feel the least pity for you; and I only wish that the whole of the Fena were with you in that dungeon, to be dealt with by my brother."

Then, casting her eyes on Glanlua, she began to upbraid her in bitter words for having been in the company of Finn and Dara. But Glanlua explained the matter, saying that she had never seen either of the chiefs before, and that it was only by chance she had fallen on them when she had lost her way in the fog."

"If that be so," said Ailna, "it is not just that you should be punished for the evil deeds of the others."

And she went and told Dryantore, who came forthwith to release the lady.

Glanlua took leave of Finn and Dara, and left the prison, grieving much for their evil plight; for she was grateful for their kindness on the mountain. Ailna led her to the palace; and, having placed food before her, bade her eat. But Glanlua, being overcome by weakness, suddenly fell into a swoon, and remained for a long time without sense or motion, like one dead. When at last she opened her eyes, she saw Ailna standing near, holding in her hand a golden drinking-horn. And Ailna gave her to drink, and immediately the spells lost their power; and she regained her strength; and the bloom and beauty of her countenance returned.

But now she bethought her of the two heroes;

and, remembering their dismal plight in the dungeon, she became sorrowful, and began to sigh and weep. And when Ailna and Dryantore came to know the cause of her tears, they told her with much severity that Finn and Dara deserved their punishment; and that both should stay in prison till the time had come to put them to death.

"I seek not to release them from prison or to save them from death," said Glanlua; "but that they are left without food and drink—this it is that moves me to pity."

And Dryantore said, "If only that has caused your tears, you may, if you so please, bring them food. Besides, I do not mean to put them to death immediately. I shall let them live yet awhile, that I may decoy by them the other Fena, who are now wandering hither and thither in quest of their chief. And it is my firm belief that in a little time I shall have them all in that dungeon."

So Glanlua went to the prison, bringing food and drink, and Ailna went with her. They found the heroes sitting on the floor, sorrowing, their strength and activity all gone; for the music-spell still held them, and they suffered also from want of food. And when they saw the two ladies, they shed bitter tears. Glanlua, on her part, wept with pity when she looked on the wasted face of the chief. But not so Ailna; she was pleased at their distress, for her heart was hardened with vengeance, and she longed for the time when they should suffer death. Howbeit, Glanlua placed food and drink before them, and they ate and drank and were strengthened for the time.

When the two ladies returned, Dryantore asked Glanlua if it were true what he had heard, that Dara was a favourite among the Fena; and why it was that they loved him so.

Glanlua replied, "I only know that he is a very skilful musician; for I never heard melody sweeter than the strains he played yesterday, when I met himself and Finn in the fog."

"I should like very much to hear this music," said Dryantore, "if it be so melodious as you say;" and as he spoke these words he went towards the dungeon.

And when he had come to the door, he said to Dara, in a loud, harsh, surly voice—

"I have heard that you are a skilful musician, and can play very sweet strains. I wish you to play for me now that I may know if this be true."

To which Dara replied, "If I had the Fena around me, I could delight them with the melody of my timpan; but as for you, guileful and cruel as you are, I do not believe that you can take any pleasure in music. Moreover, how can you expect that I should play sweet music for you, seeing that I am shut up here in this dismal dungeon, and that all manly strength and cheerfulness of mind have left me through your foul spells?"

"I will take off the spells if only you play for me," said Dryantore; "and if your strains be as delightful as I have heard reported, I will bring you forth from your prison, and I will keep you for ever in my castle, and you shall play for me whensoever I wish for music."

"I shall never consent to be released, neither will I play any music for you, so long as my chief lies in bondage and under enchantment," said Dara; "for I grieve not indeed for myself, but for him."

Dryantore replied, "I will lift the spells from both of you for a time; but as to releasing Finn, that is a matter I do not wish to talk of now."

Whereupon Dryantore removed the spells, and the heroes regained their strength and courage.

Dara then played a low, sweet tune; and Dryantore, who had never before heard such music, listened with delight and wonder. He was so charmed that he called Ailna and Glanlua, that they also might hear; and they were as much delighted as the giant. But what pleased Glanlua most was to see the heroes restored to their wonted cheerfulness.

Now all this time the Fena were seeking among the glens and hollows of the mountain for Finn and Dara. After walking for some time over a stony and rugged way, a faint strain of music struck on their ears. They stopped to listen, breathless; and every man knew the sound of Dara's timpan; and they raised a shout of gladness, which reached Finn and Dara in their dungeon. At the same moment they came in view of the palace, and they drew their swords and put their shields and spears in readiness, as men do going to battle. And they went forward

warily, for they feared foul play, and their hearts had
a forecast that a foe was near. But, indeed, they little
deemed what manner of foe they should meet.

When Dryantore heard the shouts, he hid himself
from the view of the Fena, and forthwith betook him
to his magic arts. And again the spell fell on the two
heroes, and their strength departed; and Dara's hand,
losing its cunning, trembled on the strings, so that his
music became dull and broken.

And when Dara's music ceased, the Fena heard
a low, hoarse murmur, which, growing each moment
louder, sounded at last like the hollow roar of waves.
And anon their strength and their swiftness left
them, and they fell to the ground every man, in a
deep trance as if they slept the sleep of death.

Then Dryantore and Ailna came forth, and having
bound them one by one in strong, hard fetters, they
roused them up and led them helpless and faltering to
the dungeon, where they shut them in with Finn and
Dara.

The Fena looked sadly on their king; and he, on
his part, shed bitters tears to think that he had
decoyed them — though, indeed, he had done so
unwittingly—into the hands of their foe.

In the midst of their sighs and tears they heard
the loud voice of the giant, who, looking in on them
from the open door, addressed them—

"Now at last, ye Fena, you are in my safe keeping.
Truly you have done great deeds in your time, but
yet, methinks, you will not be able to escape from this

prison till I have taken just vengeance on you for
slaying Mergah of the Sharp Spears, and my two
sons, at the battle of Knockanare!"

And having so spoken, he shut the door and went
his way.

When he came to the palace, he found that Glanlua's husband, Lavaran, had been there.   Upon which
he fell into a mighty rage; for he feared to let any
man know the secrets of the palace; and he feared also
that Lavaran might try to aid Finn and the others.
He inquired of the two ladies whither he had gone;
but they replied they did not know.   He then began
to search through the rooms, and, raising his voice, he
called aloud for Lavaran; and the Fena, even in their
dungeon, heard the roar quite plainly.

Lavaran, hearing him, was sore afraid, and answered from a remote part of the palace.   And as he
came forward, the giant placed him under his spells,
and, having bound him, flung him into the dungeon
with the others.

Dryantore's fury had not in the least abated; and,
entering the dungeon, he struck off the heads of
several of the Fena with his great sword, saying he
would visit them each day, and do in like manner till
he had killed them all.

During this time the Fena were unable to defend
themselves; for, besides that their strength had gone
out from their limbs on account of the spells, they
found that from the time the enchanter entered the
prison, they were all fixed firmly in their places, every

man cleaving to the ground, in whatsoever position he chanced to be, sitting, lying, or standing. And Finn shed tears—even tears of blood in sight of all—seeing his men fall one by one, while he had to look on without power to help them.

After Dryantore had in this manner slain several, he approached Conan Mail,[23] with intent to end that day's work by cutting off his head; and as it chanced, Conan was lying full length on the floor. Now Conan, though he was large-boned and strong, and very boastful in his speech, was a coward at heart, and more afraid of wounds and death than any man that ever lived.

So when he saw Dryantore coming towards him with his sword in his hand all dripping, he shouted aloud—

"Hold thy hand, Dryantore! Hold thy hand for a little while, and be not guilty of such treachery!"

But the giant, not heeding in the least Conan's words, raised his sword with his two hands and rose on tiptoe for a mighty blow. Then Conan, terrified beyond measure, put forth all his strength to free himself, and bounded from the floor clear outside the range of the sword; but left behind him, clinging to the floor, all the skin of his back, even from the points of his shoulders to the calves of his legs.

When he saw the giant still making towards him in a greater rage than ever for missing his blow, he again cried aloud—

"Hold your hand this time, Dryantore! Is it not

enough that you see me in this woful plight ? For
it is plain that I cannot escape death. Leave me,
then, to die of my wounds, and slay me not thus
suddenly !"

Dryantore held his hand ; but he told Conan that
he would for a certainty kill him next time he came,
if he did not find him already dead of his wounds.
Then he stalked out of the dungeon, and, shutting
close the door, left the Fena in gloom and sadness.

Though Lavaran had been only a little while in
the palace, he made good use of his time, and now
approaching Finn, he whispered in his ear—

"There is that in yonder palace which would
free us from those accursed spells if we only could
get at it."

And when Finn asked what it was, he replied,
"A magical golden drinking-horn of wondrous virtue.
I saw it in the palace among many other precious
jewels."

And when Finn again questioned him how he
knew of its secret power, he said—

"Glanlua, my wife, told me. For she said that,
being herself at the point of death, Ailna fetched this
drinking-horn and bade her drink. And when she
had drunk, she was immediately freed from spells and
sickness. She told me, moreover, that it would remove
the spell from the Fena, and bring back their strength
and heal their wounds, if they could get to drink
from it."

Conan, being near, overheard this conversation ;

and he inwardly resolved that he would try to secure
the drinking-horn, if perchance he might be able to
heal his wounds by means of it.

Not long after, the giant again came to the prison,
sword in hand, and addressed Conan in these words—

"Come forward now, O big, bald man, for 1 am
about to fulfil my promise to you! Come forward,
that I may strike off your large head; for 1 see that
your wounds have not killed you!"

But Conan, instead of coming forward, fell back
even to the farthest part of the dungeon, and replied—

"You must know, Dryantore, that I, of all men
alive, am the most unwilling to die any death unworthy of a brave hero. You see my evil plight, all
wounded and faint from loss of blood; and, being as I
am a valiant warrior, it would surely be a shameful
thing and a foul blot on my fame, to be slain while in
this state. I ask only one favour—that you cure me
of my wounds first. After this, you may put me to
death in any manner that is most agreeable to you."

To this Dryantore consented, seeing that Conan
was secure; and he called to Ailna and bade her fetch
him the magical golden drinking-horn. "For I wish,"
said he, "to heal the wounds of yonder big, bald man."

But Ailna replied, "Of what concern are his
wounds to us? Is it not better that he should die
at once, and all the other Fena with him?"

Conan spoke out from where he stood, "Lovely
Ailna, I seek not to escape death. I ask only to be
healed first and slain afterwards!"

Ailna went to the palace and soon returned, bringing, not the drinking-horn, but a large sheepskin, covered all over with a long growth of wool. Dryantore took it from her, and doing as she told him, he fitted it on Conan's back, where it cleaved firmly, so that his wounds were all healed up in an instant.

As long as Conan lived afterwards, this sheepskin remained on his back; and the wool grew upon it every year, even as wool grows on the back of a living sheep. And from that time forth, the other Fena were always mocking him and laughing at him and calling him nicknames.

As soon as Conan felt his wounds healed, he again spoke to the giant—

"It is my opinion, Dryantore, that it would be a very unwise thing for you to put me to death. I see plainly you want a servant. Now, although I am large of bone and strong of body, and very brave withal, still I am very harmless. And if you let me live, I shall be your servant for ever, and you will find me very useful to you."

The giant saw the force and wisdom of Conan's words; and he felt that he wanted a servant very much, though he never perceived it till that moment, when Conan reminded him of it.

So he said, "I believe, indeed, Conan, that your words are truth. Wherefore, I will not put you to death. You are now my servant, and so shall you be for the rest of your life."

He then led Conan forth from the dungeon towards

the palace; and he was in such good humour at having got a servant, that he forgot to kill any of the Fena on that occasion.

He called to him Ailna and Glanlua, to tell them of what he had done. And he said to them—

"I find that I need a servant very much. Wherefore, I have made Conan my servant. And I am now about to free him from the spell and give him back his strength by a drink from the golden drinking-horn, so that he may be able to wait on me and do my work."

For Conan, though his wounds were healed, was still so weak from the spell that he was scarce able to walk.

"I do not at all approve what you have done," said Ailna. "It would be, methinks, much better to put him straightway to death along with all the others. As long as he is with us as our servant, I shall never think myself free from danger; for the Fena are treacherous all alike."

"As for the other Fena," replied Dryantore, "you need not be in any trouble on their account, for their time is short. As soon as I have got Conan free from the spell, I will go straight to the dungeon and kill them, every man. And when they are fairly put out of the way, it seems to me that we need not fear danger from this big, bald man with the sheepskin on his back."

When Ailna heard that the death of the Fena was near at hand, she no longer gainsaid her brother. So

Dryantore led Conan to the palace; and placing the magical drinking-horn in his hand, bade him drink. And Conan drank; and immediately his strength and his spirits returned.

Now it so happened, while these things went on, that Finn asked Dara to play one of his sweet, sad tunes, that they might hear the music of his timpan before they died. And Dara took his timpan, and began to play; and historians say that no one either before or since ever played sweeter strains.

At the very moment that Conan had finished drinking, he and Dryantore heard the music sounding faintly in the distance; and the giant opened the door and stood on the threshold to listen. He was so charmed that he quite forgot all about Conan and the drinking-horn; and finding that he could not hear the music plainly enough where he stood, he walked hastily towards the dungeon, leaving Conan behind with the drinking-horn in his hand.

No sooner had he gone out than Conan hid the drinking-horn under his cloak, and went to the dungeon after him.

And when the giant saw him he said, "Why have you followed me; and what business have you here? Are you not my servant; and why have you come without being bidden by me?"

"I thought," replied Conan, "that you were about to put the Fena to death; and I came to look at them once more before they died."

Then suddenly Dryantore bethought him of the

drinking-horn, and he said, "Where is the golden
drinking-horn I gave you?"

"I left it," said Conan, "just where I found it in
the palace."

The giant ran hastily towards the palace to secure
the drinking-horn; and no sooner was he out of sight
than Conan, drawing forth the horn, put it to the lips
of each to drink, beginning with Finn. Only Finn
and Oscar had drunk, when they heard the heavy
steps of the giant running towards the dungeon; and
now they saw that he was indeed inflamed with fury.
Oscar seized his great, polished spear, and sprang to
the door; and the others raised a mighty shout of
joy; while Conan went on releasing the heroes one
by one.

When Dryantore saw Oscar, he uttered a roar of
rage and disappointment; and then called aloud to
Ailna to come to him. And she came forth; and
when she saw how matters stood, she was seized with
such grief and terror that she dropped down and died
immediately. Glanlua was standing near at hand,
rejoicing at the release of her husband and friends;
but when she saw Ailna fall to the ground dead, she
became sad, and, stooping down, wept over her.

All this Oscar saw from where he stood; and it
was with much ado he checked his tears. For though
my son was the bravest of the heroes, and the most
terrible in battle, he had a gentle heart, and never saw
a woman or a child in distress without being moved
to pity.

But Conan felt not the least pity. On the contrary, he was very glad to see Ailna dead; and he told Oscar that it was very well she was out of the way, for that she was a vicious woman, and had wrought the Fena much trouble and woe.

And now Oscar, casting his eyes again on Dryantore, hardened his heart for battle, and addressed the giant in these words—

"It has at last come to pass, O Dryantore, that you are in the power of the Fena; and there is no escape for you, though you are a large and strong giant, and a druid with powerful magical spells. But the Fena never yet treated an enemy ungenerously. You indeed dealt unfairly and treacherously with us; and meant to kill us all, after having taken away our strength and valour by your black, guileful magic. But even so, we give you your choice; and we challenge you now to single combat with any of our champions you may wish to choose."

To which Dryantore replied, "It is very true that the Fena have prevailed over me; and it is a just punishment for my folly in releasing Conan the Bald from my spells. I desire single combat. I will fight the Fena one after another, till I either fall myself or slay them all; and I will begin with you!"

Oscar then took his shield and made ready for battle. Meantime the giant, harbouring great wrath against Conan, approached him unawares; and when he had come near enough, he sprang suddenly on him, and aimed a blow with all his might at his head. But

Conan, springing aside, barely escaped the edge of the sword; and, running in great fear, called to Oscar with great outcry to save him from the giant.

Then Oscar ran between; and he and the giant fought a long and fierce fight, while we looked on with anxious hearts. The giant was furious and strong; but my son was active and watchful and fearless of heart; and Dryantore at length fell at the door of his own palace, pierced through and through by the long, smooth spear of Oscar.

When the Fena saw the giant fall, they raised three mighty shouts of joy. And Glanlua brought the magic drinking-horn to Oscar, from which he drank, so that his wounds were healed, and his strength straightway returned to him.

The Fena then went into the palace, where they found food in great plenty, with wine and mead in golden bowls and drinking-horns. And they ate and drank and made merry; after which they rested that night on soft beds and couches.

When they awoke in the morning, all was changed. The palace and the lake were gone; and the heroes found themselves lying on the heathy side of Slieve Fuad, at the selfsame spot where they had first started the deer; with the morning sun shining brightly over their heads.

OISIN IN TIRNANOGE;*

OR,

THE LAST OF THE FENA.

———✦———

[According to an ancient legend, Finn's son, Oisin, the hero-poet, survived to the time of St. Patrick, two hundred years (the legend makes it three hundred) after the other Fena. On a certain occasion, when the saint asked him how he had lived to such a great age, the old hero related the following story.]

A SHORT time after the fatal battle of Gavra,† where so many of our heroes fell, we were hunting on a dewy morning near the brink of Lough Lein,‡ where the trees and hedges around us were all fragrant with blossoms, and the little birds sang melodious music on the branches. We soon roused the deer from the thickets, and as they bounded over the plain, our hounds followed after them in full cry.

We were not long so engaged, when we saw a rider coming swiftly towards us from the west; and we soon perceived that it was a maiden on a white

---

* Tirnanoge, the Land of Youth.   (See note 19 at the end.)
† Gavra, now Garristown, in the north-west of the county Dublin. (For an account of this battle, see note 28 at the end.)
‡ Lough Lein, the Lakes of Killarney.

steed.　We all ceased from the chase on seeing the
lady, who reined in as she approached.　And Finn and
the Fena were greatly surprised, for they had never
before seen so lovely a maiden.　A slender golden
diadem encircled her head; and she wore a brown robe
of silk, spangled with stars of red gold, which was
fastened in front by a golden brooch, and fell from
her shoulders till it swept the ground.　Her yellow
hair flowed far down over her robe in bright, golden
ringlets.　Her blue eyes were as clear as the drops of
dew on the grass; and while her small, white hand
held the bridle and curbed her steed with a golden
bit, she sat more gracefully than the swan on Lough
Lein.　The white steed was covered with a smooth,
flowing mantle.　He was shod with four shoes of pure
yellow gold, and in all Erin a better or more beautiful
steed could not be found.

As she came slowly to the presence of Finn, he
addressed her courteously in these words—

"Who art thou, O lovely youthful princess?　Tell
us thy name and the name of thy country, and relate
to us the cause of thy coming."

She answered in a sweet and gentle voice, "Noble
king of the Fena, I have had a long journey this day,
for my country lies far off in the Western Sea.　I am
the daughter of the king of Tirnanoge, and my name
is Niam of the Golden Hair."

"And what is it that has caused thee to come so
far across the sea?　Has thy husband forsaken thee;
or what other evil has befallen thee?"

"My husband has not forsaken me, for I have never been married or betrothed to any man. But I love thy noble son, Oisin; and this is what has brought me to Erin. It is not without reason that I have given him my love, and that I have undertaken this long journey; for I have often heard of his bravery, his gentleness, and the nobleness of his person. Many princes and high chiefs have sought me in marriage; but I was quite indifferent to all men, and never consented to wed, till my heart was moved with love for thy gentle son, Oisin."

When I heard these words, and when I looked on the lovely maiden with her glossy, golden hair, I was all over in love with her. I came near, and, taking her small hand in mine, I told her she was a mild star of brightness and beauty, and that I preferred her to all the princesses in the world for my wife.

"Then," said she, "I place you under gesa,[12] which true heroes never break through, to come with me on my white steed to Tirnanoge, the land of never-ending youth. It is the most delightful and the most renowned country under the sun. There is abundance of gold and silver and jewels, of honey and wine; and the trees bear fruit and blossoms and green leaves together all the year round. You will get a hundred swords and a hundred robes of silk and satin, a hundred swift steeds, and a hundred slender, keen-scenting hounds. You will get herds of cows without number, and flocks of sheep with fleeces of gold; a coat of mail that cannot be pierced, and a sword that never missed a stroke and from which no one ever escaped alive. There are feasting and harmless pastimes each day. A hundred warriors fully armed shall always await you at call, and harpers shall delight you with their sweet music. You will wear the diadem of the king of Tirnanoge, which he never yet gave to any one under the sun, and which will guard you day and night, in tumult and battle and danger of every kind. Lapse of time shall bring neither decay nor death, and you shall be for ever young, and gifted with unfading beauty and strength. All these delights you shall enjoy, and many others that I do not mention; and I myself will be your wife if you come with me to Tirnanoge."

I replied that she was my choice above all the maidens in the world, and that I would willingly go with her to the Land of Youth.

When my father, Finn, and the Fena heard me say this, and knew that I was going from them, they raised three shouts of grief and lamentation. And Finn came up to me and took my hand in his, saying sadly—

"Woe is me, my son, that you are going away from me, for I do not expect that you will ever return to me!"

The manly beauty of his countenance became quite dimmed with sorrow; and though I promised to return after a little time, and fully believed that I should see him again, I could not check my tears, as I gently kissed my father's cheek.

I then bade farewell to my dear companions, and mounted the white steed, while the lady kept her seat before me. She gave the signal, and the steed galloped swiftly and smoothly towards the west, till he reached the strand; and when his gold-shod hoofs touched the waves, he shook himself and neighed three times. He made no delay, but plunged forward at once, moving over the face of the sea with the speed of a cloud-shadow on a March day. The wind overtook the waves and we overtook the wind, so that we straightway lost sight of land; and we saw nothing but billows tumbling before us and billows tumbling behind us.

Other shores came into view, and we saw many wonderful things on our journey—islands and cities, lime-white mansions, bright greenans * and lofty palaces. A hornless fawn once crossed our course, bounding nimbly along from the crest of one wave to the crest of another; and close after, in full chase, a white hound with red ears. We saw also a lovely young maiden on a brown steed, with a golden apple in her hand; and as she passed swiftly by, a young warrior on a white steed plunged after her, wearing a long, flowing mantle of yellow silk, and holding a gold-hilted sword in his hand.

I knew naught of these things, and, marvelling much, I asked the princess what they meant; but she answered—

" Heed not what you see here, Oisin; for all these

* Greenan, a summer-house; a house in a bright, sunny spot.

wonders are as nothing compared with what you
shall see in Tirnanoge."

At last we saw at a great distance, rising over the
waves on the very verge of the sea, a palace more
splendid than all the others; and, as we drew near, its
front glittered like the morning sun. I asked the
lady what royal house this was, and who was the
prince that ruled over it.

"This country is the Land of Virtues," she replied.
" Its king is the giant, Fomor of the Blows, and its
queen the daughter of the king of the Land of Life.[19]
This Fomor brought the lady away by force from her
own country, and keeps her in his palace; but she has
put him under gesa[12] that he cannot break through,
never to ask her to marry him till she can find a
champion to fight him in single combat. But she still
remains in bondage; for no hero has yet come hither
who has the courage to meet the giant."

"A blessing on you, golden-haired Niam," I replied; "I have never heard music sweeter than your
voice; and although I feel pity for this princess, yet
your story is pleasant to me to hear; for of a certainty
I will go to the palace, and try whether I cannot kill
this Fomor, and free the lady."

So we came to land; and as we drew nigh to the
palace, the lovely young queen met us and bade us
welcome. She led us in and placed us on chairs
of gold; after which choice food was placed before
us, and drinking-horns filled with mead, and golden
goblets of sweet wine.

When we had eaten and drunk, the mild young princess told us her story, while tears streamed from her soft, blue eyes; and she ended by saying—

"I shall never return to my own country and to my father's house, so long as this great and cruel giant is alive!"

When I heard her sad words, and saw her tears falling, I was moved with pity; and telling her to cease from her grief, I gave her my hand as a pledge that I would meet the giant, and either slay him or fall myself in her defence.

While we were yet speaking, we saw the giant coming towards the palace, large of body, and ugly and hateful in appearance, carrying a load of deerskins on his back, and holding a great iron club in his hand. He threw down his load when he saw us, turned a surly look on the princess, and, without greeting us or showing the least mark of courtesy, he forthwith challenged me to battle in a loud, rough voice.

It was not my wont to be dismayed by a call to battle, or to be terrified at the sight of an enemy; and I went forth at once without the least fear in my heart. But though I had fought many battles in Erin against wild boars and enchanters and foreign invaders, never before did I find it so hard to preserve my life. We fought for three days and three nights without food or drink or sleep; for the giant did not give me a moment for rest, and neither did I give him. At length, when I looked at the two princesses weeping in great fear, and when I called to mind my father's deeds in battle, the fury of my valour arose; and with a sudden onset I felled the giant to the earth; and instantly, before he could recover himself, I cut off his head.

When the maidens saw the monster lying on the ground dead, they uttered three cries of joy; and they came to me, and led me into the palace. For I was indeed bruised all over, and covered with gory wounds; and a sudden dizziness of brain and feebleness of body seized me. But the daughter of the king of the Land of Life applied precious balsam and healing herbs to my wounds; and in a short time I was healed, and my cheerfulness of mind returned.

Then I buried the giant in a deep and wide grave; and I raised a great carn over him, and placed on it a stone with his name graved in Ogam.

We rested that night, and at the dawn of next morning Niam said to me that it was time for us to resume our journey to Tirnanoge. So we took leave of the daughter of the king of the Land of Life; and though her heart was joyful after her release, she wept at our departure, and we were not less sorry at parting from her. When we had mounted the white steed, he galloped towards the strand; and as soon as his hoofs touched the wave, he shook himself and neighed three times. We plunged forward over the clear, green sea with the speed of a March wind on a hill-side; and soon we saw nothing but billows tumbling before us and billows tumbling behind us. We saw again the fawn chased by the white hound with red ears; and the maiden with the golden apple passed swiftly by, followed by the young warrior in yellow silk on his white steed. And again we passed many strange islands and cities and white palaces.

The sky now darkened, so that the sun was hidden from our view. A storm arose, and the sea was lighted up with constant flashes. But though the wind blew from every point of the heavens, and the waves rose up and roared around us, the white steed kept his course straight on, moving as calmly and swiftly as before, through the foam and blinding spray, without being delayed or disturbed in the least, and without turning either to the right or to the left.

At length the storm abated, and after a time the sun again shone brightly; and when I looked up, I saw a country near at hand, all green and full of flowers, with beautiful smooth plains, blue hills, and bright lakes and waterfalls. Not far from the shore stood a palace of surpassing beauty and splendour. It was covered all over with gold and with gems of every colour—blue, green, crimson, and yellow; and on each side were greenans shining with precious stones, built by artists the most skilful that could be found. I asked Niam the name of that delightful country, and she replied—

"This is my native country, Tirnanoge; and there is nothing I have promised you that you will not find in it."

As soon as we reached the shore, we dismounted; and now we saw advancing from the palace a troop of noble-looking warriors, all clad in bright garments, who came forward to meet and welcome us. Following these we saw a stately glittering host, with the king at their head wearing a robe of bright yellow satin covered with gems, and a crown that sparkled with gold and diamonds. The queen came after, attended by a hundred lovely young maidens; and as they advanced towards us, it seemed to me that this king and queen exceeded all the kings and queens of the world in beauty and gracefulness and majesty.

After they had kissed their daughter, the king took my hand, and said aloud in the hearing of the host—

"This is Oisin, the son of Finn, for whom my daughter, Niam, travelled over the sea to Erin. This is Oisin, who is to be the husband of Niam of the Golden Hair. We give you a hundred thousand welcomes, brave Oisin. You will be for ever young in this land. All kinds of delights and innocent pleasures are awaiting you, and my daughter, the gentle, golden-haired Niam, shall be your wife; for I am the king of Tirnanoge."

I gave thanks to the king, and I bowed low to the queen; after which we went into the palace, where we found a banquet prepared. The feasting and rejoicing lasted for ten days, and on the last day, I was wedded to the gentle Niam of the Golden Hair.

I lived in the Land of Youth more than three hundred years; but it appeared to me that only three years had passed since the day I parted from my friends. At the end of that time, I began to have a longing desire to see my father, Finn, and all my old companions, and I asked leave of Niam and of the king to visit Erin. The king gave permission, and Niam said —

"I will give consent, though I feel sorrow in my heart, for I fear much you will never return to me."

I replied that I would surely return, and that she need not feel any doubt or dread, for that the white steed knew the way, and would bring me back in safety. Then she addressed me in these words, which seemed very strange to me—

"I will not refuse this request, though your journey afflicts me with great grief and fear. Erin is not now as it was when you left it. The great king Finn and his Fena are all gone; and you will find, instead of them, a holy father and hosts of priests and saints. Now, think well on what I say to you, and keep my words in your mind. If once you alight from the white steed, you will never come back to me. Again I warn you, if you place your feet on the green sod in Erin, you will never return to this lovely land. A third time, O Oisin, my beloved husband, a third time I say to you, if you alight from the white steed, you will never see me again."

I promised that I would faithfully attend to her words, and that I would not alight from the white steed. Then, as I looked into her gentle face and marked her grief, my heart was weighed down with sadness, and my tears flowed plentifully; but even so, my mind was bent on coming back to Erin.

When I had mounted the white steed, he galloped straight towards the shore. We moved as swiftly as before over the clear sea. The wind overtook the waves and we overtook the wind, so that we straightway left the Land of Youth behind; and we passed by many islands and cities, till at length we landed on the green shores of Erin.

As I travelled on through the country, I looked closely around me; but I scarcely knew the old places, for everything seemed strangely altered. I saw no sign of Finn and his host, and I began to dread that Niam's saying was coming true. At length, I espied at a distance a company of little men and women,* all mounted on horses as small as themselves; and when I came near, they greeted me kindly and courteously. They looked at me with wonder and curiosity, and they marvelled much at my great size, and at the beauty and majesty of my person.

I asked them about Finn and the Fena; whether they were still living, or if any sudden disaster had swept them away. And one replied—

"We have heard of the hero Finn, who ruled the Fena of Erin in times of old, and who never had an equal for bravery and wisdom. The poets of the Gaels have written many books concerning his deeds

---

* The gigantic race of the Fena had all passed away, and Erin was now inhabited by people who looked very small in Oisin's eyes.

and the deeds of the Fena, which we cannot now relate; but they are all gone long since, for they lived many ages ago. We have heard also, and we have seen it written in very old books, that Finn had a son named Oisin. Now this Oisin went with a young fairy maiden to Tirnanoge, and his father and his friends sorrowed greatly after him, and sought him long; but he was never seen again."

When I heard all this, I was filled with amazement, and my heart grew heavy with great sorrow. I silently turned my steed away from the wondering people, and set forward straightway for Allen of the mighty deeds, on the broad, green plains of Leinster. It was a miserable journey to me; and though my mind, being full of sadness at all I saw and heard, forecasted further sorrows, I was grieved more than ever when I reached Allen. For there, indeed, I found the hill deserted and lonely, and my father's palace all in ruins and overgrown with grass and weeds.

I turned slowly away, and afterwards fared through the land in every direction in search of my friends. But I met only crowds of little people, all strangers, who gazed on me with wonder; and none knew me. I visited every place throughout the country where I knew the Fena had lived; but I found their houses all like Allen, solitary and in ruins.

At length I came to Glenasmole,* where many a

* Glenasmole, a fine valley about seven miles south of Dublin, through which the river Dodder flows.

time I had hunted in days of old with the Fena, and there I saw a crowd of people in the glen. As soon as they saw me, one of them came forward and said—

"Come to us, thou mighty hero, and help us out of our strait; for thou art a man of vast strength."

I went to them, and found a number of men trying in vain to raise a large, flat stone. It was half lifted from the ground; but those who were under it were not strong enough either to raise it further or to free themselves from its weight. And they were in great distress, and on the point of being crushed to death.

I thought it a shameful thing that so many men should be unable to lift this stone, which Oscar, if he were alive, would take in his right hand and fling over the heads of the feeble crowd. After I had looked a little while, I stooped forward and seized the flag with one hand; and, putting forth my strength, I flung it seven perches from its place, and relieved the little men. But with the great strain the golden saddle-girth broke, and, bounding forward to keep myself from falling, I suddenly came to the ground on my two feet.

The moment the white steed felt himself free, he shook himself and neighed. Then, starting off with the speed of a cloud-shadow on a March day, he left me standing helpless and sorrowful. Instantly a woeful change came over me: the sight of my eyes began to fade, the ruddy beauty of my face fled, I lost all my strength, and I fell to the earth, a poor, withered old man, blind and wrinkled and feeble.

The white steed was never seen again. I never recovered my sight, my youth, or my strength; and I have lived in this manner, sorrowing without ceasing for my gentle, golden-haired wife, Niam, and thinking ever of my father, Finn, and of the lost companions of my youth.

THE

VOYAGE OF THE SONS OF O'CORRA.*

———◦◇◦———

A PRINCELY upright hundred-herd brugaid† was born
one time in the lovely province of Connaught, namely,
Conall Derg O'Corra the fair-haired. And thus was
this brugaid (circumstanced) :—he was a fortunate,
rich, prosperous man ; and his house was never found
without three shouts in it—the shout of the brewers
brewing ale, and the shout of the servants over the

---

* I translated this tale fifteen years ago (as mentioned in Preface,
page xiii) from two Royal Irish Academy MSS., 23. N. 15 and 23.
M. 50; and I subsequently made some modifications after I had an
opportunity of consulting the more correct text of the Book of Fermoy.
This last text has since been published, with literal translation, by
Dr. Whitley Stokes, in the *Revue Celtique* (Jan. 1893). After com-
paring my somewhat free version with Dr. Stokes's close translation,
I have not thought it necessary to make any changes.

A few of the adventures in this tale are identical with those described
in the Voyage of Maildun : the description of these I have omitted
here. Lochan, Enna, and Silvester, the chief characters in this extra-
ordinary fiction, are historical : they were saints of the primitive Irish
church, and lived in the sixth century.

† *Brugaid,* a sort of local officer who maintained a large establishment
as keeper of a house of public hospitality. See my " Short History of
Ireland," p. 57.

caldrons distributing (meat) to the hosts, and the shout of the youths over the chessboards* winning games from one another.

The same house was never without three measures :— a measure of malt for making yeast, a measure of wheat for providing bread for the guests, and a measure of salt for savouring each kind of food.

His wife was Cairderga† the daughter of the Erenach‡ of Clogher.‖ They felt no want of any kind except being without children ; and it was not that they were without children (being born to them), but that the infants always died the moment after birth.

Then this brugaid said (one day) to his wife as she reclined near him on the couch :—" It is a sad thing for us," said he, " that we have no children who would take our place and fill it worthily when we are gone."

" What desire is in your mind in regard to that ? " says the wife.

" It is my desire," says the brugaid, " to make a bond with the demon to try if he would give us a son or a daughter who would take our place after us (since God has not done so)."

" Let us do that," said the woman.

---

* Chess-playing was a favourite amusement among the ancient Irish.

† Cairderga : original *Caer-derg*, red berry.

‡ *Erenach*, the holder or *impropriator* of a church and its lands : usually a layman.

‖ Clogher in Tyrone where there was a monastery.

They accordingly fasted (and prayed) to the demon; (and the demon hearkened unto them. And in due time) the pains and struggles of childbirth came upon the lady; and she bore three sons at that great birth, namely, a son at the beginning of the night, and a son at the middle of the night, and a son at the end of the night.

And they were baptised according to the baptism of the pagans (by which they were dedicated not to God but to the demon); and their names were Lochan, Enna, and Silvester   And after that, they were reared and carefully trained up till they were swift and active on sea and land; so that they were an overmatch for all the young people of their own age in every game and in every accomplishment. And they were in the mouths and on the tongues of all who saw or heard of them in their day.

One day when they were resting at the railings of the house of their father and mother, wearied after their hurling and their martial games, the housefolk said that they saw no fault or defect in these handsome much-renowned youths, except only their being baptised in the service of the devil. (And the youths hearing this said):—" If it be so," said they, " that the devil is our lord and master, it is very wrong of us not to bring ruin and wrath and woe on his enemies, that is to say, (we ought) to slaughter the clergy, and burn and spoil their churches."

Then did these three youths arise, (and collecting a band), and taking unto them their arms, they came to

Tuam-da-Gualann,* and spoiled and burned the town. And (after that) they plundered and made dreadful havoc on the churches and clergy throughout the province of Connaught, until their wicked and blood-thirsty ravages were noised over the four quarters of Erin. Thus did they run their evil course without ceasing for a whole year, during which time they destroyed more than half the churches of Connaught.

At the end of the year Lochan said to his brothers: "We have made one great mistake through forgetful-ness," says he, "and our lord the devil will not be thankful to us on account of it." "What is that?" said the other two youths. "Our grandfather," says he, "that is our mother's father—not to have killed him and burned his church."

So they set out straightway, journeying without sparing or respite (to Clogher), and this was how they found the erenach, namely, on the green of the church with a great company of his folk around him, (waiting for the O'Corras), in order to attend on them and to deal out to them the choice of every food and the best of every ale. And the intention that the elder had towards them, that indeed was not the intention they had towards him, but to murder him and to burn and spoil his church.

Then the O'Corras came to the spot where the elder was standing, and they made up their minds not to kill him or burn the houses till night, when the cows and

* Tuam-da-Gualann, where was formerly a celebrated ecclesiastical establishment: now Tuam in Galway.

the (other) cattle of the homestead would be housed, all in their own proper places.

The elder welcomed them and led them to the homestead ; and he now became aware of their intention. Nevertheless he put them in a goodly pleasant *Greenan*,* and they were served with food and ale till they became exhilarated and cheerful : after which couches were made ready for them on lofty bedsteads.

And now deep slumber and heavy sleep fell on them, and a wonderful vision was revealed in a dream to Lochan, the eldest of the sons of O'Corra, in which he was carried to see heaven and hell. And after this he awoke. The other two awoke at the same time, and they said :—"Let us now arise, for it is time to plunder and destroy the homestead."

"Seems to me," said Lochan, "that this is not the right thing for us to do : for evil is the lord we have served until now, and good is the Lord we have plundered and outraged.

"And last night I had," said he, "a fearful dream, in which I saw a vision of heaven and hell. And first I was taken to see hell, where were countless souls of men and vast crowds of demons suffering divers tortures, and plagues unexampled. And I saw the four rivers of hell, that is to say, a river of toads, a river of serpents, a river of fire, and a river of snow. I saw also a monstrous serpent with many heads and legs,

---

* Greenan : original *grianán*, literally a sunny place : a summer-house : the most lightsome, airy, and pleasant apartment of a house. See this word discussed in my " Irish Names of Places," vol. i. p. 291.

at sight whereof, even though it were only a single glance, all the men in the world would drop dead with loathing and horror.

"After this methought I was taken to see heaven; where I beheld the Lord Himself seated on His kingly throne, and angels in the shapes of white birds singing for Him. And among them was one great snow-white bird of dazzling brightness that excelled all the others in size and beauty and voice, chanting strains of surpassing sweetness. Women in travail and men sore wounded and sick people racked with pain would fall asleep if they heard the delightful harmony of his voice. And it was made known to me that this great bird who chanted such heavenly music to his mild Lord was Michael the Archangel.

"And now my brothers," said Lochan, "it is my counsel to you that you follow God henceforward."

"But," said the others, "will the Lord accept repentance from us for the dreadful evils we have already done?"

They go to the father of their mother, namely, the erenach, and they ask this thing of him. "He will accept your repentance without doubt," says the erenach.

"Well then," said Lochan, "let Mass be celebrated for us, and put us under instruction, and let us offer our confession to God. After that we will make staffs of the handles of our spears; and we will go to Finnen of Clonard,* the tutor of the saints and of the just

* For St. Finnen of Clonard in the County Meath, see my "Short History of Ireland," p. 175

men of all Erin.   He is a very holy man, and he will
advise us in regard to what we ought to do."

To this counsel they agreed; and on the morrow
they set out for the place where Finnen was; whom
they found on the green of Clonard with a number of
his clerics.

"Who are these coming towards us?" said the
clerics.   And one said, "They are the O'Corras the
robbers."   Hearing this they fled, like lightning, in
a body from their master, for they felt quite sure
that the O'Corras were coming to slay them; so that
Finnen was left quite alone before the three brothers.

"It is from us the clerics are fleeing:" says Lochan.
"Of a certainty it is," said his brothers.   "Let us,"
said Lochan, "cast from us our staffs, the only little
remnant of our arms left with us; and let us throw
ourselves on our knees before the cleric."

And this they did.   "What is your desire?" says
the cleric (Finnen).   "Our desire," said they, "is
faith and piety, and to serve God, and to abandon the
lord whom we have hitherto served, namely, the devil."

"That is a good resolution," says the cleric; "and
let us go now to the homestead yonder, the place where
live our brotherhood."

They go accordingly with him to the brotherhood;
and after the matter had been considered, it was arranged
to set apart a young cleric to teach them; and it was
decreed that they should not speak to any one except
their own master till the end of a year.

So they continued for a whole year till they had

read the Canons through, and by the time they had come to be able to read them, the whole brotherhood felt grateful (to God) for their piety and their gentleness.

At the end of the year they came to Finnen; and they knelt before him, and said to him :—" It is time now that we should be judged and sentence passed on us for the great crimes we have committed.

"What," said Finnen, "do ye not think it enough —the penance you have done already for a whole year among the brotherhood?" "It is not enough,' said they. "What then are the greatest crimes ye have committed?" says Finnen. "We have burned more than half the churches of Connaught; and neither priest nor bishop got quarter or protection from us."

"You cannot." replied Finnen, "give back life to the people you have killed; but do ye that which will be in your power, namely, to build up the churches ye have burned, and to repair every other damage ye have committed in them. And I will give to each man of you," says he, "the swiftness and strength of a hundred; and I will take from you all weariness of feet, of hands, and of body; and I will give you light and understanding which will have neither decay nor end."

So the O'Corras departed, and went first to Tuam-da-Gualann; and after that, they fared through the province, obedient to rule and working hard each day, until it came to pass that they had restored everything they had previously destroyed.

After that they came at the end of the year to speak with Finnen. "Have you been able," asks Finnen, "to repair everything ye destroyed belonging to the Church?" "We have," said they, "except one place alone, namely Kenn-Mara."[*] "Alas for that," says Finnen; "that is the very first place you should have repaired; for it is the homestead of the oldest of all the saints of Ireland, namely, the aged Camann of Kenn-Mara. And now go and carefully restore everything ye have destroyed in that homestead. And the sentence that holy man passes on you, fulfil it patiently."

So they went gladly to Kenn-Mara; and they repaired everything they had ruined there.

One day when they had come forth from the homestead, they sat on the margin of the little bay, watching the sun as it went westward. And as they gazed and reflected on the course of the sun, they began to marvel greatly, pondering whither it went after it had gone down beneath the verge of the sea. "What more wonderful thing is there in the whole world," said they, "than that the sea does not freeze into ice, while ice is formed in every other water!"

Thereupon they formed the resolution on the spot to bring unto them a certain artificer who was a fast friend of theirs, and to (get him) to make a three-hide curragh[†] for them. Accordingly the curragh was made, and a strong-sided one it was. And the reward the

---

[*] *Kenn-Mara*, now Kinvarra on Galway bay.

[†] *Curragh*, see note 17 at end. Some curraghs were made with two—some with three—hides, one outside another, for the better security.

artificer asked for building it was to be let go with them.

When the time had come, and they were about to embark, they saw a large crowd passing close by; and this crowd was a company of *crossans*.* When the *crossans* saw the curragh putting forth on the sea, they inquired:—" Who are yonder people that are launching this curragh on the sea?" said they.

The *furshore* (juggler) of the crossans said:—" I know them well; they are the sons of Conall derg O'Corra the fair-haired of Connaught, the destroyers and robbers, going on their pilgrimage on the sea and on the great ocean, to make search for their Lord." "And indeed," added the *furshore*, "my word for it, they do not stand more in need of seeking for heaven than we do."

" It is a long day I fancy till you go on your pilgrimage," said the leader of the band. " Say not so," answered the *furshore*: " for I will certainly go with these people on my pilgrimage now without delay."

" Upon our word," said the *crossans*, " you will not take away our clothes with you; for not a single article of the garments you wear belongs to you." " It is not so small a matter that would keep me with you," says he.

So they stripped off all his clothes, and sent him away mother naked to the curragh.

---

* *Crossans :* travelling gleemen : the clothes, musical instruments, &c., were the property of the company. This word is the origin of the Scotch and Irish family name Mac Crossan, now often changed to Crosbie. A company of crossans had always among them a *fuirseoir, i.e* a juggler or buffoon.

" Who and what in the world are you, good man?" asked the crew. "A poor wretch who wishes to go with you on pilgrimage," said he. "Indeed," said they, "you shall not by any means come with us, seeing that you are stark naked." "Say not so, young men," said he; "for the sake of God do not refuse me; for I will amuse you and keep your hearts cheerful (with my music and singing); and your piety will not be a whit the worse for it."

And (inasmuch as he had asked) for the sake of God they consented to let him go.

Now this is how it was with the crew:—each man of them had built a church and raised an altar to the Lord in his own district. Their number was nine; among whom was a bishop, and a priest, and a deacon; and they had one *gilla* (attendant) who was the ninth man.

" Let us go aboard our curragh now," says Lochan, " as we have finished our task of restoring the churches, and as we have, besides, each of us built a church to the Lord in our own district."

It was then they put up their prayers fervently to God in the hope that they might have fine weather; and that the Lord would quell the fury of the billows, and the might of the ocean, and the rage of the terrible sea monsters. So they embarked in their curragh, bringing their oars; and they began to question among themselves what direction they should take. "The direction in which this wind will bring us," says the bishop. And having commended themselves to God, one and all, they betook them to their oars. A great wind now arose, which drove them out on the waste of waters straight to the west; and they were forty days and forty nights on the ocean. And God revealed to them great and unheard of wonders.

They had not been long rowing when the *crossan* died; and sad and sorrowful were they for his loss, and wept much. While they were still mourning, they saw a little bird alight on the deck of the curragh. And the little bird spoke and said to them :—" Good people, tell me now in God's name what is the cause of your sorrow."

" A *crossan* that we had playing music for us; and he died a little while ago in this curragh; and that is the cause of our sorrow."

And the bird said :—" Lo, I am your little *crossan* : and now be not sorrowful any longer, for I am going straightway to heaven." So saying he bade them farewell and flew away.

I.

They row forward for a long time till there was shown to them a wonderful island, and in it a great grove of marvellous beauty, laden with apples, golden coloured and sweet scented. A sparkling rivulet of wine flowed through the midst of the grove; and when the wind blew through the trees, sweeter than any music was the rustling it made. The O'Corras ate some of the apples and drank from the rivulet of wine, and were immediately satisfied. And from that time forth they were never troubled by either wounds or sickness.

II.

Then they took to their oars; and after a time they came in view of another island, and four companies of people in it, such as had never been seen before. Now these people had divided the island into four parts: old greyheaded people were in the first division; princes in the second; warriors in the third; and servants in the fourth. They were all beautiful and glorious to behold; and they diverted themselves continually with games and pastimes. One of the crew went to them to ask news: (he was a comely, well-favoured youth, but) he seemed ugly and dark-visaged in presence of these glorious people. When he had got among them, he became in a moment beautiful like the others; and he joined in their games, and laughed, and made merry. Moreover he remembered nothing more of his companions; and he sojourned in the island after that for evermore. And the O'Corras were at length forced to depart, though much grieved for the loss of their companion.

III.

Then they set out and rowed for some time till they sighted another marvellous island. It stood up in the air high over the great sea; and it was propped up by a pillar like a single foot standing under it in the middle. And the crew heard great shouting and the loud conversation of people on the top of the island overhead; but though the O'Corras sailed round and round, they could not get a sight of them.

IV.

They row forward after that till they come to an island in which lived one lone cleric. Very lovely was that island, and glorious its history. Beautiful purple flowers covered all the plains, dropping honey in abundance; and on the trees were perched flocks of bright-coloured birds singing slow sweet fairy-music. The O'Corras went to ask the cleric about himself and about the island. And he spoke as follows:—

"I am a disciple of St. Andrew the Apostle, and Dega is my name. On a certain night I neglected to read my Matins; and it is for this that I was sent on a pilgrimage on the ocean; and here I am awaiting the Judgment day. And yonder birds that are singing those incomparable strains on the trees, these are the souls of holy men."

V.

They took leave of the old man and plied their oars, till they reached another island, with dead people on one side of it, and living people on the other side: and many of the living people had feet of iron. All round was a burning sea, which broke over the island continually in mighty waves. And the living people uttered fearful cries when the fiery waves flowed over them, for their torments thereby were great and terrible.

VI.

After leaving this they rowed on till they saw an island formed of great flat stones for ever burning red hot. And thereon they saw whole hosts of people burning in great torment; and many had red fiery spits thrust through their bodies. And they uttered great cries of pain without ceasing. The crew called out from a distance to ask who they were : whereupon one answered :—

"This is one of the flagstones of hell. We are souls who in life did not fulfil the penance imposed on us; and warn all men to avoid this place; for whosoever cometh hither shall never go hence till the Day of Judgment."

VII.

The next island they saw was very beautiful and glorious to look upon. It had a wall of copper all round it, with a network of copper hanging out from each corner ; and in the centre stood a palace. The crew left their curragh on the strand and went towards the palace. And when they had come nigh unto the wall, the wind, as it rustled and murmured through the copper network, made music so soft and sweet that they fell into a gentle slumber, and slept for three days and three nights. When they awoke they saw a beautiful maiden coming towards them from the palace. She had sandals of *findrina* (a sort of white metal) on her feet, and an inner garment of fine silk next her snow-white skin. She wore a beautiful gold-coloured vest, and over all a bright-tinted mantle, plaited five-fold on its upper border, and fastened at the neck with a brooch of burnished gold. In one hand she held a pitcher of copper, and in the other a silver goblet.

When she had come near she greeted them and bade them welcome. And she gave them food from the copper pitcher which seemed to them like cheese; and she brought them water in the silver goblet from a well on the strand. And there was no delicious flavour that was ever tasted by man that they did not find in this food and drink. Then the maiden said to them :— "Although we are all—you and I—of one race, yet shall ye go hence without delay, for your resurrection is not to be here."

So they bade her farewell and took to their oars once more.

VIII.

After rowing for some time they saw flocks of large birds of divers colours flying over the sea ; and their number was great beyond counting. One of them alighted on the deck of the curragh.

"It would be a delightful thing," said one of the clerics, "if this bird were a messenger from the Lord, sent to give us news."

"That would be quite possible with God," said the eldest ; and as he spoke he raised his eyes and looked at the bird. Whereupon the bird spoke and said :—

"It is indeed to converse with you that I have come ; for I am of the land of Erin."

Now this bird was crimson red all over, except three beautiful streaks on her breast, which shone as bright as the sun. And after a time she said to the same cleric :—

"I am the soul of a woman ; and I am your friend.

And come ye now," says she, " to hear yonder birds; for these are the souls that are permitted to come out of hell every Sunday."

" It is better that we leave this place at once," said the same old cleric.   And his companions said to him :—

" We will go with thee whithersoever thou goest." So they departed from that place; (and the crimson red bird went with them).

IX.

And as they went, they saw three wonderful streams, namely, a stream of otters, a stream of eels, and a stream of black swans.   Great flocks of birds arose from these three streams and flew past the voyagers ; and the black swans followed close after, tearing and tormenting the birds.   And the crimson red bird said :—

" Marvel not, neither be ye sad of heart ; for these bird-shapes that ye see are the souls of people suffering the punishment of their crimes.   And the black swans that follow them, these are devils who are for ever tormenting them ; and the birds scream fearfully, and are for ever trying to fly from the demons and to free themselves from their torment.

" And now as to me," continued the bird, " I am about to depart from you.   It is not permitted me to make known to you what is to befal you ; but in a little time another will tell you all that you need to know."

And the cleric said:—"Tell us, I beseech thee, what are those three beautiful streaks on thy breast."

"I will tell you that," answered the bird. "When I was in the world I was married; but I did not yield obedience to my husband, neither did I fulfil my lawful homely duties as a wife. And when a grievous sickness came upon him I left him to die. But thrice I went in pity to him :—once to see him and ask after his illness; once to bring him such food as befitted his state; and the third time when he was dead, to watch by the body and see it buried. These three good deeds are the three beautiful streaks that you see on my breast; and I should have been bright all over like these streaks if I had not violated my lawful marriage duties."

And having so spoken, the bird bade them farewell and flew away.

X.

They next discovered a very beautiful island. The grass was bright green, and it was all over intermingled with pretty purple-coloured flowers. Flocks of lovely little birds of many bright colours, and myriads of bees, flew among the trees and flowers, humming and singing harmonious music. The voyagers saw a venerable grey-headed old man with a harp in his hand. He played this harp on the island continually; and the music thereof was sweeter than any music they had ever heard. They saluted the old man, who saluted them in return, with a blessing. But immediately he bade them to depart.

XI.

So they rowed away till they came to another island, on which they saw a man digging in a field; and his spade was all fiery, and the handle thereof, which he held in his hand, was red hot. From the sea at one side arose at times a mighty wave all flaming red with fire, which flowed quite over the island and over the man. And ever when he saw the wave coming he cried out with fear; and when the burning torrent covered him, he strove to raise his head above the flames, and roared with his great torment. Now when one of the waves had retired they spoke to him and asked:—

"Who art thou, O wretched man?"

And he answered:—"Lo, this is my punishment for my misdeeds. For when I lived on earth I always worked on Sundays, digging in my garden; for which I am condemned to dig with this fiery spade, and to suffer the torments of these fiery waves. And now, for the sake of God, offer up your prayers for me, that my pains may be lightened."

And they prayed fervently; after which they departed from the island.

XII.

Soon after leaving this they saw a horseman of vast size riding on the sea; and the horse he rode was made of fire flaming red. And as he rode, great waves of fire came after him along the sea; and when a wave began to roll over him, he yelled aloud with fear and pain. Then they asked him why he was thus tormented; and he answered:—

"1 am he who stole my brother's horse; and after I had gotten him I rode him every Sunday. For this I am now undergoing my punishment, riding on this horse of fire, and tormented with these great waves of fire."

XIII.

After leaving this they came in sight of another island, full of people, all weeping and lamenting grievously. Great numbers of jet-black birds with beaks of fire and red-hot fiery talons followed and fluttered round about them, tearing and burning them with their talons, and rending away pieces of flesh, the full of their fiery beaks. Then the crew said aloud:—

"Who are ye, O miserable people?"

"We are dishonest smiths and artisans; and because we cheated while we lived, we are punished by these hateful fiery birds. Moreover, our tongues are burning, being all afire in our heads; for that we reviled people with bitter words and foul taunts."

XIV.

Coming now to another place, they saw a giant huge in size, and of a sooty black colour all over. His mouth was all on fire; and from his throat he belched forth great flakes of fire, each flake as it came from his mouth larger than the skin of a three-year-old wether. He held in his hand an iron club larger than the shaft of a mill wheel; and on his back he bore an immense faggot of firewood, a good load for a team of horses. Now this faggot often blazed up and burned him; and he tried to free himself from his torment by lying down so that the sea might flow over him. But ever as he did so, the sea around him turned to fire, and rose up in mighty burning billows, covering him all over, so that he made the place resound with his bellowings.

"Miserable wretch, who art thou?" asked the crew.

And he answered:—"I will tell you truly. When I lived I used to cut faggots and bring them home on my back every Sunday: and lo, here is my punishment."

xv.

They came after that to a sea of fire full of men's heads, all black, and continually fighting with each other. And many great serpents rose up among the heads and came with fury to attack the curragh, so that at one time they pierced through the outer hide. And one of the crew who looked on cried out in great horror, and said:—

"It is enough to strike one dead to behold the fearful things I see!"

And the whole crew when they saw the heads and the serpents fell flat with fear. But the elder (the bishop) comforted them, saying:—

"Be ye not afraid or troubled on account of these things; for God is able to protect us, even though we

were in a curragh of only one hide ; and if He wishes
to save us, these monsters cannot hurt us, however
furious they may be to slay us."

And they took courage after this, and rowed out
into the open sea.

XVI.

There was shown to them next another beautiful
island, having in one place an open wood. The trees
were laden with fruit, and the leaves dropped honey to
the ground. The sides of the hills were clothed with
purple blossomed heather, mixed with soft, green
grass to its very centre. In the midst of the island
was a pretty lake, whose waters tasted like sweet wine.
They rested for a week on the shore of this lake, and
cast off their weariness. And now, being about to
leave the island, as they turned to go to the curragh, a
monstrous reptile* rose up from the lake and looked
at them. And they trembled with fear at the sight of
this terrible beast; for each man thought that he himself would be the first to be attacked. But after a little
time the reptile dived again into the water, and they
saw no more of him.

XVII.

From this they rowed away ; and after a long
time they came at midnight to an island wherein

* According to very ancient legends, which are still vividly remembered and recounted all over the country, almost every lake in Ireland
has a tremendous hairy reptile in its waters. Some say they are demons,
sent by St. Patrick to reside at the bottom of the lakes to the Day of
Judgment.

was a community of Ailbe of Emly.* On the beach they found two spring wells; one foul, the other bright and clear. The gilla wished to drink of the clear well; but the elder (the bishop) told him it was better to ask leave, if there was anyone living on the island.

Then they saw a great light; and coming closer, they found the twelve men of the community at their prayers; and now they perceived that the bright light they saw came from the radiant faces of the twelve; so that these holy men needed no other light. One of them, an old man, comes towards the voyagers; and he bids them welcome and asks news of them. They tell him all their adventures, and ask his leave to drink from the well; whereupon he said to them:— " Ye may fill your pitchers from the clear well, if your elder (*i. e.* the bishop) gives you leave."

" Who are ye ?" asks the gilla.

" A community of Ailbe of Emly," says he: "and we are the crew of one of Ailbe's curraghs. God has permitted that we live here till the Day of Judgment, praying for everyone who is drowned at sea. And now leave this land before morning," he added, "for your resurrection is not to be here. And if ye have not left by the dawn, so much the worse for yourselves; for if once ye get a view of this island in the light of day, bitter will be your anguish of mind for leaving it

---

* St. Ailbe, the patron of Munster, was a contemporary of St. Patrick. He founded his great monastery and school at Emly in the County Limerick.

(on account of its surpassing loveliness).   So it is better for you to go away during the night."

And they did exactly all he told them to do.

" Shall we take away some of the pebbles of the strand ? " said they (talking among themselves).

" It is better to ask leave," answered the cleric.   So the gilla asked leave of the same old man.

" Yes, if you have the permission (of your bishop)," answered he.   " Nevertheless," he added, " those who take them will be sorry; and those who do not take them will be sorry also."

They pick up pebbles, some bringing away one, some two, some three.   (After which they row away in the dark night from the island.)   In the morning they drank some of the spring water of the island from their pitchers; which threw them into a deep sleep from that time till next day.   On wakening up, they examined their pebbles in the light; and some were found to be crystal, some silver, and some gold.   Then those who brought some away were in sorrow that they had not brought more ; and much greater was the sorrow of those who had brought away none.   So the words of the old man came true.

XVIII.

After leaving this they came to a lovely island on which was a church standing all alone : and when they drew nigh they heard the voice of a cleric singing the psalms with a sweet voice.   They came to the door and struck it with the hand-wood ; and straightway a beautiful bright-coloured bird came to speak with them.

When they had told him who they were and what they wanted, he flew back to the cleric, who bade him have the door opened for the pilgrims. And when they had come in, they found the cleric—a very old man with white hair—who sang his hymns continually. And they saluted each other; and the pilgrims stayed there that night. And an angel came and brought them supper, and ministered unto them On the morrow the old priest bade them depart, since that was not to be the place of their resurrection on the Judgment Day. But before they went he foretold all that should happen to them during the rest of their voyage.

XIX

From that they came to an island in which was a disciple of Christ. Glorious and beautiful was that island; and on it stood a church and a kingly shrine. As they came near they heard some one singing the Pater to God in the door of the church: whereupon one of the clerics said :—

"Welcome the prayer of our father and teacher, Jesus"

And the priest who stood praying at the door said ·—

"Why say you so? Who are ye; and where have ye seen Him?"

And when they had told him that they were servants of Jesus, he spoke again :—

"I too am one of His disciples. And when I first took Him for my Lord I was faithful and steady; but after a time I left Him and came to sea in my curragh, and rowed till I came to this island. For a long time I lived on fruit and herbs; till at length an angel came from heaven to visit me. And he said to me :—

"'Thou hast not done well: nevertheless thou shalt abide on this island, eating the same food without either decay or death till the Judgment Day.' And so I have lived here to this hour: and no daily meal is sent to me, but I eat of the herbs and fruit that grow on the island."

Then they all went together into one house; and being very hungry, they prayed fervently for food. And presently an angel came down from heaven; and while they looked on he placed a supper for them on a flagstone hard by the strand, namely, a cake with a slice of fish for each. And while they ate, whatsoever taste each man separately wished for, that taste he found on the food. In the morning, when they were about to bid the cleric farewell, he foretold all that should happen to them, saying :—

" Ye shall go from me now on sea till ye reach the western point of Spain. And as ye near the land, ye shall meet a boat with a crew of men fishing, who will bring you with them to land."

Then turning to the bishop, he said :—" Immediately after leaving the curragh, as soon as thou hast reached the land, prostrate thyself three times to God. And the place on which thou shalt first set thy foot, there a great crowd shall gather round thee from every quarter. And they will treat thee kindly, and will

give thee land on which they will build a church for
thee; and after this thy fame shall spread over the
whole world. And the successor of Peter (the Pope)
shall bring thee eastwards to Rome. Yonder priest
thou shalt leave as thy successor in the church, and the
deacon thou shalt leave to be his sacristan. That place
and that church shall be revered, and shall be preserved
for ever. And thou shalt leave the Gilla in Britain,
where he will live for the rest of his life."

After this they bade the old man farewell and
left the island. And all fell out just as he had foretold.
And the bishop went to Rome; and he afterwards re-
lated these adventures to Saerbrethach bishop of West
Munster, and to Mocolmoc, one of the holy men of
Aran, as we have set them down here.

Thus far the Voyage of the Sons of O'Corra.

NOTES.

———◆◇◆———

NOTE 1.—*The Dedannans.*

According to the old bardic legends, the first man who led a colony to Ireland after the Flood was Parthalon. Next came Nemed and his people; and after these the Firbolgs, who were conquered and succeeded by the Dedannans.

The legend relates that the Dedannans, in the course of their wanderings, spent some time in Greece, where they learned magic and other curious arts. From this they migrated to Lochlann, in the north of Europe (see note 6), from which they came through Scotland to their final resting-place, Ireland.

From the three queens of their three last kings, Ireland got the three names, Erin, Fōla, and Banba.

After the Dedannans had held sway in Ireland for about two hundred years, they were in their turn conquered by the last and greatest colony of all, the people of Milèd or Milesius, who are commonly known by the name of Milesians, and who are the ancestors of the leading Gaelic families of Ireland. The Milesians defeated the Dedannans in two great battles: one fought at *Tailltenn*, now Teltown, on the river Blackwater, between Navan and Kells, in Meath; and the other at *Druim-Lighean*, now Drumleene, about three miles from Lifford, in Donegal.

In the legendary and romantic literature of Ireland, the Dedannans are celebrated as magicians. By the Milesians and their descendants they were regarded as gods, and ultimately, in the imagination of the people, they became what are now in Ireland called "fairies."

After their defeat by the Milesians, they seem to have retired to remote and lonely places; and their reputation as magicians, as well as the obscure and mysterious manner in which they lived, gradually impressed the vulgar with the belief that they were supernatural beings.

The notion was that they lived in splendid palaces in the interior of pleasant green hills. These hills were called *sidh* (pronounced *shee*); and hence the Dedannans were called *Daoine-sidhe* (*Deena-shee*), or people of the fairy hills; *Marcra-sidhe* (*Markra-shee*), fairy cavalcade; and *Sluagh-sidhe* (*Sloo-shee*), fairy host.

Of this mysterious race, the following are the principal characters mentioned in these tales.

Mannanan Mac Lir, the Gaelic sea-god. In "Cormac's Glossary" (written A.D. 900), we are told that he was a famous merchant who resided in, and gave name to, *Inis-Manann*, or the Isle of Man; that he was the best merchant in Western Europe; and that he used to know, by examining the heavens, the length of time the fair and the foul weather would last.

The Dagda, whose name some interpret to mean "the great good fire," so called from his military ardour, who reigned as king of Ireland from A.M. 3370 to 3450.

Angus or Angus Oge, the son of the Dagda, who lived at *Brugh* or Bruga, on the north shore of the Boyne, a little below the village of Slane. Angus is spoken of as the wisest and the most skilled in magic of all the Dedannan race.

Nuada of the Silver Hand. (See note 4.)

Lir of Shee Finnaha, the father of the four "Children of Lir," and Bove Derg of Shee Bove, of whom we know little more than what is told of them in the "Fate of the Children of Lir." Shee Finnaha is supposed to have been situated near Newtown Hamilton, in Armagh; and Shee Bove was on the shore of Lough Derg, on the Shannon.

Luga of the Long Arms, who imposed the eric-fine on the three sons of Turenn for slaying his father Kian. (See note 7 for a further account of this Luga.)

Dianket, the great physician, of whose powers of cure extra-ordinary stories are told. He had a son Midac, and a daughter Armedda, more skilful than himself. The old legend relates that

Midac took off the silver arm which his father Dianket had put on Nuada (see note 4), and, having procured the bones of the real arm, he clothed them with flesh and skin, and fixed the arm in its place as well as ever " in three moments." Dianket was so enraged at being outdone by his son that he slew him. After Midac had been buried for some time, three hundred and sixty-five healing herbs grew up from his grave, one from every joint and sinew of his body —each herb to cure disease in that part of the human body from which it grew—all which were gathered by his sister Armedda, and placed carefully in her cloak in their proper order. But before she had time to study their several virtues fully, her father Dianket mixed them all up in utter confusion. (O'Curry, *Atlantis*, vii. and viii. 158.) Were it not for this churlish proceeding, Armedda would have found out, and we should now know, the exact herb to cure each particular disease of the human frame.

NOTE 2.—*The Feast of Age.*

This was also called the Feast of Gobnenn the Dedannan smith. It was instituted by Mannanan Mac Lir, and whoever was present at it, and partook of the food and drink, was free ever after from sickness, decay, and old age.

NOTE 3.—*The Druids.*

The ancient Irish druids do not appear to have been *priests* in any sense of the word. They were, in popular estimation, men of knowledge and power—" Men of science," as they were often designated; they knew the arts of healing and divination; and they were skilled above all in magic. In fact, the Irish druids were magicians, neither more nor less; and hence the Gaelic word for " druidical " is almost always applied where we should use the term "magical "—to spells, incantations, metamorphoses, etc. (See O'Curry, " Lectures on the Manners and Customs of the Ancient Irish," Lecture ix.)

NOTE 4.—*Nuada of the Silver Hand.*

Nuada of the Silver Hand was king of Ireland, according to the chronology of the Four Masters, from A.M. 3311 to 3330. He commanded the Dedannans in the first battle of Moytura (see note 11),

where his arm was cut off with a sword-blow by Sreng, the great
Firbolg champion. Afterwards Credne the artificer made him a
silver arm with a hand, which was fixed on by Dianket, the physician (see note 1). Nuada was slain in the second battle of Moytura,
by Balor of the Mighty Blows (see note 11).

Note 5.—*The Fomorians.*

"Fomor," the simple form of this word, means, according to
the old etymologists, a sea-robber, from *fo*, on or along, and *muir*,
the sea. The word is also used to denote a giant, or a gigantic
champion.

The Fomorians of Irish history were sea-robbers, who infested
the coasts, and indeed the interior, of Ireland, for a long series of
years, and at one time fortified themselves in Tory Island. They
are stated to have come to Ireland from Lochlann, in the north of
Europe (for which see next note); but they were originally from
Africa, being, according to the legend, the descendants of Ham the
son of Noah.

Note 6.—*Lochlann : The Lochlanns.*

Lochlann was the Gaelic designation of the country from which
came the people who are known in European history as Danes, *i.e.*
the country round the southern shores of the Baltic, including the
south part of Sweden. The Lochlanns, or Lochlannachs, or Danes,
it need hardly be said, make a very conspicuous figure in our early
history, and in our mediæval romantic literature.

In the Gaelic tales, the chief city of Lochlann is always Berva;
but whether this represents a real name, or is merely an invention
of the old story-tellers, I cannot tell.

Note 7.—*Luga of the Long Arms : The Ildana.*

Luga of the Long Arms was the son of Ethlenn, daughter of the
Fomorian king, Balor of the Mighty Blows (see note 9). His
father, Kian (who was slain by the three sons of Turenn), was a
Dedannan; so that Luga was half Fomorian and half Dedannan.
But he always took the side of the Dedannans against the
Fomorians.

Luga is often called The Ildana, the Man of many sciences, to signify his accomplishments as a warrior and a man of general knowledge.

It had been foretold that Balor would be slain by his own grandson. Accordingly, when Luga was born, Balor sent him off to be drowned. But Luga escaped, and lived to revenge the unnatural conduct of his grandfather, whom he slew in the second battle of Moytura (see note 11), after Balor had slain the Dedannan king, Nuada of the Silver Hand. Luga succeeded Nuada as king of Ireland, and reigned, according to the chronology of the Four Masters, from A.M. 3330 to 3370.

It was by Luga that the celebrated yearly assembly of Tailltenn was instituted, in honour of his foster mother *Taillte*, after whom the place was called. (See note page 93, *supra*.)

NOTE 8.—*The Land of Promise: Fairyland.*

In ancient Gaelic romantic tales, mention is often made of *Tir Tairrngire*, the Land of Promise, Fairyland, as being one of the chief dwelling-places of the Dedannans or fairy host. In many passages this Land of Promise is identified with *Inis-Manann*, or the Isle of Man, which was ruled over by Mannanan Mac Lir, the sea-god, and named from him.

NOTE 9.—*Balor of the Mighty Blows.*

Balor was king of the Fomorians from Lochlann in the north; his wife was Kethlenda; and his son, Bres. Balor is often called Balor of the Mighty Blows; and also Balor of the Evil Eye, for he had one eye which would strike people dead or turn them into stone, so that he kept it covered, except when he wished to use it against his enemies. Balor is remembered very vividly in tradition by the peasantry of Ireland, especially in Donegal and in Tory Island, where a very high, tower-like rock is called to this day Balor's Castle.

NOTE 10.—*Eric.*

The eric was a fine paid as compensation for murder or homicide The friends of the murdered person might accept an eric, or they might refuse it and seek instead the death of the murderer. An eric was often paid for other crimes or injuries against the individual, as well as for homicide.

Note 11.—*Battle of Moytura.*

There were two great battles, each called the battle of Moytura.

First Battle of Moytura. When the Dedannans came to invade Erin, they found the country occupied by the Firbolgs, who were by no means inclined to give up quiet possession to the new-comers. After some parleying and manœuvring, a great battle was fought between them, A.M. 3303, at Moytura, near Cong, in Mayo, lasting for four days, in which the Firbolgs were defeated with great slaughter, and their king slain; after which the Dedannans took possession of the country, leaving Connaught, however, to a powerful remnant of the Firbolgs who survived the battle. This is called the First Battle of Moytura, or the Battle of the Southern Moytura. On the plain where it was fought, there are still great numbers of mounds, cromlechs, and other sepulchral monuments. (See Sir William Wilde's "Lough Corrib," page 210.)

Second Battle of Moytura. King Nuada, who led the Dedannans in the first battle of Moytura, had his arm cut off by Sreng, one of the Firbolg champions. He was under cure for seven years; during which time Bres, the son of Elatha, who was a Fomorian by his father and a Dedannan by his mother, ruled Ireland as regent. But at the end of the seven years, Bres had to retire in favour of Nuada. Whereupon he repaired in anger to his father in Lochlann; and at his instigation an army of Fomorians was raised, after some years, for the invasion of Ireland, and placed under the command of Balor of the Mighty Blows.

Luga of the Long Arms seems to have foreseen this invasion. He knew that Bres would have to abdicate whenever Nuada's arm came to be healed, and he conjectured truly that he would not resign the sovereignty without a struggle. But the old tales would lead to the inference that Luga had some preternatural fore-knowledge of the battle. Anyhow, the legend says that for many years he made preparations for the coming struggle; and it was with this intention that he imposed the celebrated eric-fine on the sons of Turenn.

The Fomorians landed, and were met by the Dedannan army at the Northern Moytura, or, as it is often called, Moytura of the Fomorians, situated in the parish of Kilmactranny, barony of Tirerrill, county Sligo. The battle was fought on the eve of Samin, *i.e.* on the last day of October, A.M. 3330; and the Fomorians were defeated with the slaughter of their principal men and the best part of their army. In the course of the battle, Nuada of the Silver Hand, the Dedannan king, was slain by Balor; but soon after, Balor himself was killed by his grandson, Luga. Luga, we are told, flung a stone at him from a crann-tavall or sling (see note, page 240), and struck him in the evil eye with so much force that the stone went clean through his head and out at the back.

The site of this battle, like that of the Southern Moytura, abounds to this day in sepulchral monuments.

These two battles of Moytura form the subjects of two historic tales, which are still in existence, though they have never been published.

Note 12.—*Gesa.*

"Gesa" (pronounced *gessa*, the *g* hard, as in *get*) is plural: singular *geis*, plural *geasa* or *gesa*. Gesa means solemn vows, conjurations, injunctions, prohibitions. "I put you under gesa" means, I adjure you solemnly, so solemnly that you dare not disobey. It would appear that individuals were often under gesa or solemn vows to observe, or to refrain from, certain lines of conduct—the vows being either taken on themselves voluntarily, or imposed on them, with their consent, by others. Thus Dermat O'Dyna was under gesa never to pass through a wicket gate when entering or leaving a palace (page 282); Finn was under gesa not to sleep at Allen more than nine nights in succession (page 337); Dermat put Oisin under gesa not to loose any one whom he bound (page 312). It would appear, also, that if one person went through the form of putting another under gesa to grant any reasonable request, the abjured person could not refuse without loss of honour and reputation. Thus Midac places Finn under gesa to come to the banquet in the Fairy Palace of the Quicken Trees (page 189); and the witch-lady places gesa on Finn to search for the ring in the lake (page 354). And sometimes, on very solemn or urgent occasions, the gesa seem to have been imposed with spells, so as to draw down ill luck as well as loss of honour on the person who disregarded the injunction (page 281).

Geis or gesa also means a charm or spell.

NOTE 13.—*Tir-fa-tonn.*

The Gaelic tales abound in allusions to a beautiful country situated under the sea—an enchanted land sunk at some remote time, and still held under spell. In some romantic writings it is called *Tir-fa-tonn*, the land beneath the wave; and occasionally one or more of the heroes find their way to it, and meet with many strange adventures (page 253). Sometimes it is *O'Brasil*, that dim land which appears over the water once every seven years—" on the verge of the azure sea "—and which would be freed from the spell, and would remain permanently over water, if any one could succeed in throwing fire on it. (See Gerald Griffin's beautiful ballad, " O'Brasil, the Isle of the Blest.") The Island of Fincara (page 87), and the beautiful country seen beneath the waves by Maildun (page 147), are remnants of the same superstition.

This very old Celtic tradition is obviously the same as the legend of the continent of Atlantis, mentioned by Plato, which at some remote time was overwhelmed and sunk under the Atlantic Ocean. And it would seem that they have the same shadowy tradition in the East; for in "Lalla Rookh" Moore makes the Peri say, in her soliloquy:

> " I know where the Isles of Perfume are,
> Many a fathom down in the sea,
> To the south of sun-bright Araby."

NOTE 14.—*The Enchanted Well.*

Res autem sic revera evenit. Cum Angus magus equum giganteum Eochaidio et popularibus traderet, monebat homines nec stabulandi neque omnino requiescendi copiam equo faciendam; ne forte quiescendo urinam demitteret, quod si fieret exitio omnibus fore. Postea vero quam at Planitiem Silvulæ Cinereæ pervenissent, intenti adeo sarcinis ingentis equi dorso detrahendis incumbebant, ut monitorum Angi obliviscerentur; restitit autem equus, et subinde urinam demisit. Extemplo hinc fons ortus; qui cum scaturiisset, submersit omnes, sicuti in historiâ narratur.

Note 15.—*Conal Carna of the Red Branch.*

The Red Branch Knights of Ulster, a sort of militia in the service of the monarch, much like the Fena of later date (see note 23), flourished in the first century of the Christian era. Their home was the palace of Emania, near the city of Armagh; and they received their name from one of the houses of the palace in which they resided, which was called *Craebh-ruadh*, or Red Branch. They attained their greatest glory in the reign of Conor Mac Nessa, king of Ulster in the first century; and Conal Carna, mentioned in the story of "Liban the Mermaid," was one of their most illustrious champions.

Note 16.—*Ecca the Son of Marid: Comgall of Bangor.*

This Marid was king of Munster about the beginning of the second century of the Christian era. St. Comgall, one of the greatest saints of the early Irish Church, flourished in the sixth century, and was the founder of the celebrated monastery of Bangor in the county of Down.

Note 17.—*Curragh.*

It would appear that in Ireland, and indeed in England and Scotland as well, navigation was carried on in ancient times chiefly by means of curraghs. The curragh was a boat or canoe, consisting of a light framework of wood, covered over with the skins of animals. Curraghs are still used on many parts of the western coast of Ireland; but they are now covered with tarred canvas instead of skins.

Note 18.—*Conn the Hundred-fighter.*

Conn Ced-cathach or Conn the Fighter of a Hundred (not Conn of the Hundred Battles, as the name is generally translated), was king of Ireland from A.D. 123 to 158.

NOTE 19.—*Land of the Living : Land of Life, etc.*

The ancient Irish had a sort of dim, vague belief that there was a land where people were always youthful, and free from care and trouble, suffered no disease, and lived for ever. This country they called by various names:—*Tir-na-mbeo*, the land of the [ever-]living; *Tir-na-nóg*, the land of the [ever-]youthful; *Moy-Mell*, the plain of pleasure, etc. It had its own inhabitants—fairies; but mortals were sometimes brought there; and while they lived in it, were gifted with the everlasting youth and beauty of the fairy people themselves, and partook of their pleasures. As to the exact place where Tirnanoge was situated, the references are shadowy and variable; but they often place it far out in the Atlantic Ocean, as far as the eye can reach from the high cliffs of the western coast. And here it is identical with O'Brasil, of which mention has been made in note 13.

I have already remarked (see note 1) that the fairies were also supposed to live in palaces in the interior of pleasant green hills, and that they were hence called Aes-shee or Deena-shee, *i.e.* people of the *shee* or fairy hills; and hence also the word "banshee" *i.e.* a woman (*bean*) of the fairy hills. Tirnanoge was often regarded as identical with these bright, subterranean palaces. In my boyhood days, the peasantry believed that the great limestone cavern near Mitchelstown, in the county Cork, was one of the entrances to Tirnanoge.

NOTE 20.—*St. Brendan of Birra.*

I have already, in the preface (page xiii.), spoken of the celebrated voyage of St. Brendan of Birra (Birr, in King's County), undertaken in the sixth century. He set out from near Brandon Mountain, in Kerry, sailing westwards into the Atlantic Ocean, and, according to the belief of some, landed on the shore of America. He had many imitators, who ventured out on the great ocean in their curraghs as pilgrims; but none were so enterprising as himself, or met with such a variety of strange lands, if we except Maildun and the three sons of O'Corra, whose adventures are quite as surprising as those of Brendan.

Note 21.—*Brendan's Satchel.*

The ancient Irish saints, when on their missionary journeys through the country, kept their precious books, as well as the portable sacred utensils, in leather satchels, which they brought with them from place to place. These satchels were often highly ornamented, and, like other relics, were held in extraordinary veneration after the death of the owners. The Gaelic term for this kind of satchel is *polaire*. (See Petrie, "Round Towers," page 336.)

Note 22.—*Cormac Mac Art.*

Cormac Mac Art, the most illustrious of the Irish kings, who began his reign A.D. 254, was the son of Art the Lonely, who was son of Conn the Hundred-fighter. During his reign flourished the Fena or militia, spoken of in the next note; and the old chroniclers never tire of dwelling on the magnificence of his court at Tara, and the prosperity of the country during his reign. He was renowned for learning and wisdom, and he wrote a book called *Tegusc-righ*, or instruction for kings, copies of which are extant in the Books of Leinster and Ballymote. He also caused the records of the kingdom to be collected and written down in one great book called the Psalter of Tara, but no portion of this book is now known to exist; and he established three schools at Tara—one for military science, one for law, and one for history and chronology. He spent the last years of his life in retirement and study at Cletty on the Boyne, and died A.D. 277, forty years after he had ascended the throne.

Note 23.—*Finn and the Fena.*

The Fena or "Fena of Erin" were a sort of militia or standing army, permanently maintained by the monarch for the support of the throne, and regularly trained to military service. They attained their greatest glory in the reign of Cormac Mac Art (see previous note). Each province had its own militia under its own captain, but all were under the command of one general-in-chief. Their most renowned commander was Finn the son of Cumal, who of all the heroes of ancient Ireland is most vividly remembered in popular tradition. Finn had his palace on the top of the Hill of

Allen, a remarkable flat-topped hill, lying about four miles to the right of the railway as you pass Newbridge and approach Kildare, rendered more conspicuous of late years by a tall pillar erected on the top, on the very site of Finn's palace. Before the erection of the pillar, there were considerable remains of the old fort on the hill, but at present nearly every vestige is obliterated, cleared away partly to make room for the foundation of the pillar, and partly by cultivation; for the land has been tilled and cropped to the very summit. The whole neighbourhood, however, teems with living traditions of Finn and the Fena.

The Fena were divided into distinct tribes or clanns, belonging to the several provinces, each under its own commander. Of these, the Clann Baskin of Leinster, under the immediate command of Finn; and the Clann Morna of Connaught, commanded by Gaul Mac Morna, were rival tribes, and, for reasons stated in note 27, regarded each other with hatred and distrust.

The following are some of the principal characters celebrated in the romantic literature of the Fena.

Finn the son of Cumal, commander-in-chief of the Fena under king Cormac Mac Art (see note 22); brave, wise, and far-seeing, a man of supreme military ability. His foresight seemed so extraordinary, that the people believed it was a preternatural gift of divination, and the shanachies invented a legend to account for it (see note 25). Like many great commanders, he had a little of the tyrant in his character, and was unforgiving to those who injured him. But in the story of Dermat and Grania, he is drawn in too unfavourable a light. In his old age he was killed by a fisherman at a place called Athbrea on the Boyne, A.D. 284, as recorded in the Annals of Tighernach, of the Four Masters, and of Innisfallen.

Oisin or Ossian, Finn's son, the renowned hero-poet, to whom the bards attribute many poems still extant.

Oscar, the son of Oisin, youthful and handsome, kind-hearted, and one of the most valiant of the Fena.

Dermat O'Dyna, noble-minded, generous, of untarnished honour, and the bravest of the brave. He was as handsome as he was valiant, whence he is often styled Dermat of the Bright Face, Dermat of the White Teeth, etc. He was the idol of the ladies of Ireland, and hence he is often called Dermat-na-man, or Dermat of the Women (page 210). The Munster traditions represent him as a native of Kerry; but he was in reality a Leinsterman, though his descendants migrated to Munster at a very early period. Mr. O'Grady, in his edition of the story of Dermat and Grania (page 294), has given an ancient poetical genealogy of Dermat. This hero is equally celebrated in popular story in the Highlands of Scotland. According to Highland tradition, the great and illustrious Clann Campbell, represented by the Duke of Argyll, descend from him; and their crest is a boar's head, in memory of the manner of Dermat's death.* Dermat O'Dyna is, on the whole, the finest type of hero among the Fena—as fine indeed as can be found in any literature; and his noble character is very well maintained throughout the Ossianic tales.

Kylta Mac Ronan, Finn's nephew, renowned for his fleetness of foot.

Dering, the son of Dobar O'Baskin, who was not only a brave warrior, but also "a man of knowledge," gifted with some insight into futurity.

Ligan Lumina, also celebrated for swiftness of foot.

Fergus Finnvel, poet, warrior, and frequent adviser of the Fena.

Gaul Mac Morna, the leader of the Clann Morna or Connaught Fena, one of the mightiest of all the heroes. He served under Finn, but the two chiefs bore no love to each other, for Gaul had slain Finn's father, Cumal, in the battle of Knocka (see note 27).

Conan Mail or Conan the Bald, the best-marked and best-sustained character in the Ossianic romances; large-bodied, a great boaster, a great coward, and a great glutton. He had a venomous tongue, and hardly ever spoke a good word of any one. He belonged to the Clann Morna, and was always reviling the Clann Baskin. He was the butt for the gibes and mockery of the Fena, but they dreaded his foul tongue. The story-tellers never lose an opportunity of having a fling at Conan, and of turning him into ridicule for his cowardice, his big talk, and his gluttony.

---

* For a full account of the Highland traditions regarding Dermat, and of the Highland monuments that commemorate his name, see "Loch Etive and the Sons of Uisnach" (p. 255), a very valuable and interesting book, recently published, which came into my hands after I had written the above.

NOTE 24.—*Cooking-Places.*

The Fena, as related in the beginning of the story of the Gilla Dacker, were quartered on the principal householders during the winter half-year ; and maintained themselves chiefly by the chase during the summer months.   When they were on their hunting expeditions, we are told that they ate only one meal a day ; and for this meal they cooked the flesh of the animals brought down in the chase, in the following manner.   They first dug a deep pit in the earth near their camping-place, and, having lighted a great fire beside it, they heated a number of round stones.   They next covered the bottom of the pit with the hot stones, on which they placed the meat, bound up with sedge and grass ropes, and on this again they put another layer of heated stones ; and, having closely covered up the whole with branches, they let it stand till the meat was sufficiently cooked.   The remains of these old earth-ovens are still to be seen, and are called by the peasantry *fulachta-na-bhfiann*, the cooking-places of the Fena.

NOTE 25.—*Finn's Tooth of Knowledge.*

It had been prophesied of old that a man named Finn would be the first to eat of the salmon of knowledge, which swam in the pool of Linn-Fec, in the Boyne (near the present village of Slane) ; and that he would thereby obtain the gifts of knowledge and of divination.   A certain old poet named Finn, knowing this, hoped that he might be the lucky man ; so he took up his abode on the shore of Linn-Fec ; and he fished in the pool every day from morn till night, in the hope of catching the salmon of knowledge.   At this time, Finn the son of Cumal was a boy, fleeing from place to place from his hereditary enemies, the Clann Morna, disguised, and bearing the assumed name of Demna ; and, happening to come to Linn-Fec, the old poet took him as his servant.

After long watching and waiting, Finn the poet hooked the salmon at last, and gave it to Demna to broil, warning him very strictly not to eat or even taste of it.   Demna proceeded to broil the fish ; and soon the heat of the fire raised a great blister from its side, which the boy pressed with his thumb to keep it down, thereby scalding himself so severely that he unthinkingly thrust his thumb into his mouth.

When the salmon was cooked, the poet asked Demna had he eaten of it. "No," replied the boy; "but I scalded my thumb on the fish, and put it into my mouth." "Thy name is not Demna, but Finn," exclaimed the poet: "in thee has the prophecy been fulfilled; and thou art now a diviner and a man of knowledge!"

In this manner Finn obtained the gift of divination, so that ever after, when he wished to look into futurity, he put his thumb under his tooth of knowledge, as he did when cooking the salmon of Linn-Fec, and the whole future was revealed to him. There appears to have been some sort of ceremony used, however (see page 339, *supra*); and it would seem that the process was attended with pain (page 194), so that it was only on very solemn and trying occasions he put his thumb under his tooth of knowledge.*

Note 26.—*The Game of Chess.*

Chess-playing was one of the favourite amusements of the ancient Irish chiefs. The game is constantly mentioned in the very oldest Gaelic tales; as, for instance, in the "Cattle-Spoil of Cooley," in "The Book of the Dun Cow" (A.D. 1100). (See O'Donovan's "Introduction to the Book of Rights," page lxi.)

Note 27.—*Battle of Knocka.*

The battle of Knocka or *Cnucha* (now Castleknock, near Dublin) was fought in the reign of Conn the Hundred-fighter (see note 18).

---

* The above legend is taken from "The Boyish Exploits of Finn Mac Cumal," published, with translation, by John O'Donovan, LL.D., in the fourth volume of the Ossianic Society's Transactions, from a MS. *transcribed* in 1453, now lying in the Bodleian Library at Oxford. But the internal evidence of the language shows that the piece is far more ancient than the fifteenth century. The legend of Finn and the Salmon of Knowledge is still current among the peasantry; and a modern popular version of it may be seen in the *Dublin Penny Journal*, Vol. I. page 110.

As to the process of putting his thumb under his tooth of knowledge, even the English-speaking peasantry of the south still retain a tradition that it was painful; for they say that Finn "chewed his thumb from the skin to the flesh, from the flesh to the bone, from the bone to the marrow, and from the marrow to the *smoosagh*."

The contending parties were, on the one side, Conn with his royal forces, and the renowned hero, Gaul Mac Morna, with his Connaught Fena, the Clann Morna; and on the other side, Cumal, the father of Finn, with the Clann Baskin and the Leinster forces in general, aided by Owen More, heir to the throne of Munster, with a large army of Munstermen. The Leinster and Munster armies were defeated, chiefly through the valour of Gaul, who slew Cumal with his own hand. This was the cause of the irreconcilable enmity that existed ever after between the Clann Baskin and the Clann Morna.

When Finn the son of Cumal grew up to man's estate, he succeeded to the position held by his father as leader of the Fena. But though he made peace with Gaul Mac Morna, and though Gaul submitted to his command, there was always a feeling of ill-concealed hatred and distrust between them.

Note 28.—*Battle of Gavra.*

When Carbri of the Liffey, son of Cormac Mac Art, ascended the throne of Ireland, one of his first acts was to disband and outlaw the Clann Baskin; and he took into his service in their place their rivals and deadly enemies, the Clann Morna from Connaught. Whereupon the Clann Baskin marched southwards, and entered the service of Fercorb, king of Munster, Finn's grandson, in direct disobedience to king Carbri's commands. This led to the bloody battle of Gavra, celebrated in Ossianic literature, which was fought A.D. 284, at Garristown, in the north-west of the county Dublin, where the rival clanns slaughtered each other almost to annihilation. In the heat of the battle, Carbri and Oscar met in single combat; and, after a long and terrible fight, the heroic Oscar fell pierced by Carbri's spear, and died on the evening of the same day. But Carbri himself was dreadfully wounded; and, while retiring from the field, his own kinsman, Semeon, whom he had previously banished from Tara, fell on him, and despatched him with a single blow.

This battle is the subject of a poem which the bards ascribe to Oisin, and which has been published, with translation, in the first volume of the Ossianic Transactions. In this poem there is an affecting description of the death of Oscar, surrounded by his few surviving companions, and in presence of his father Oisin.

ALPHABETICAL LIST OF THE PRINCIPAL PROPER NAMES OCCURRING
IN THIS VOLUME, WITH THEIR ORIGINAL GAELIC FORMS, AND,
IN MANY CASES, THEIR MEANINGS.

Every writer who attempts to popularise the Gaelic literature of
Ireland and Scotland, finds the proper names a serious difficulty.
If they are given in their original Gaelic forms, they are not unfrequently unpronounceable and repulsive to the English reader;
if they are written phonetically, they are often strange and barbarous
looking. In this book, I have not followed any general principle
in reducing the names to forms suitable to readers of English. I
have dealt with each, as it were, on its own merits. Sometimes—
very often, indeed—I have given the original spelling; sometimes I have given the names phonetically; and frequently I have
mixed the two modes. But all through I have avoided any great
departure from the original forms, as will be seen by a glance
at the following list.

In all cases the names occurring through the book may be
pronounced just as the letters would indicate to the English reader.

Aed, *Aedh*, a flame of fire.
Ahaclee, *Ath-cliath*, hurdle-ford.
Ailna, *Ailne*, beauty, joy.
Aina, *Aine*.
Allil, *Ailioll, Ailell*, or *Oilioll*.
Allil Ocar Aga, *Ailell Ochair Aga*.
Alva, *Ailbhe*.
Balor, *Balar*.
Baskin, *Baoiscne*.
Begallta, *Beagalltach*, little fury.
Ben-Damis, *Beann-Damhuis*.
Beoc, *Beóc, Dabheóc*, and *Beoán*.
Berva, *Berbhe*.
Borba, *Borb*, proud.
Bran, *Bran*, a raven.
Bres, *Breas*.
Brian, *Brian*.
Brickna, *Briccne*.

Bruga of the Boyne, *Brugh-na-Boinne*.
Canta, *Cainte*.
Carn-Arenn, *Carnn-Airenn*.
Carricknarone, *Carraic-na-rón*, the rock of the seals.
Clann Navin, *Clann-Neamhuinn*.
Cloghan Kincat, *Clochan-chinn-chait*, the stepping-stones of the cat's head.
Coil Croda, *Cael-crodha*, the slender valiant [man].
Colga, *Colga*.
Colman, *Colman*, little dove.
Comgall, *Comhghall*.
Conal Carna, *Conall Cernach*.
Conan Mail, *Conan Mael*, Conan the Bald.

Conang, *Conaing*.

Conn the Hundred-fighter (not Conn of the Hundred Battles, as it is usually translated), *Conn-Cédcathach*.

Connla, *Connla*.

Coran, *Coran*.

Cormac Mac Art, *Cormac Mac Airt*.

Corr the Swift-footed, *Coir Cosluath*.

Cuan, *Cuan* or *Cuadhan*.

Culand, *Culand*.

Curnan the Simpleton, *Curnan Onmit*.

Curoi Mac Dara, *Curoi Mac Dáire*.

Dagda, *Dagda*.

Dara Donn, *Dáire Donn*.

Darvra, Lake, *Loch Dairbhreach*, the lake of oaks.

Dathkeen, *Dathchaoin*, bright-complexioned.

Decca, *Deoch*.

Dedannans, *Tuatha De Danann*.

Derdri of the Black Mountain, *Deirdre Duibhshleibhe*.

Dering, *Diorraing*.

Dermat O'Dyna, *Diarmait O'Duibhne*.

Dianket, *Diancecht*.

Diuran Lekerd, *Diuran Lecerd*.

Dobar O'Baskin, *Dobhar O'Baoiscne*.

Dooclone, *Dubhchluain*, dark-coloured meadow.

Dord-Fian, *Dord-Fiann*.

Dryantore, *Draoigheantóir*.

Ducoss, *Dubhchosach*, black-foot.

Eas-Dara, *Eas-Dara*.

Ebb, *Eab*.

Ebliu, *Ebliu*.

Ebric, *Aibhric*.

Ecca, *Eochaidh*, a horseman.

Enbarr, *Aenbharr*, splendid mane.

Encoss, *Aenchos*, one foot.

Ethnea, *Eithne*, sweet nut-kernel.

Etta, *Eitche*.

Eva, *Aeife*.

Eve, *Aebh*.

Failinis, *Failinis*.

Fatha Conan, *Fatha Chonain*.

Femin, *Feimeann*.

Fena, *Fianna*.

Ferdana, *Feardána*.

Fergor, *Fearghoir*, manly or strong voice.

Fergus, *Fearghus*, manly strength.

Fiaca Findamnas, *Fiacha Findamnais*.

Ficna, *Fiachna*, little raven.

Ficra, *Fiachra*.

Fincara, *Fianchaire*.

Fincoss, *Finnchosach*, white-foot.

Finn, *Finn* or *Fionn*, fair-haired.

Finnin, *Finghín*, fair offspring.

Finola, *Fionnghuala*, white shoulder.

Flidas, *Flidas*.

Foltlebar, *Folt-leabhar*, long hair.

Frevan, *Freamhainn*.

Ga-boi, *Ga-buidhe*, yellow javelin.

Ga-derg, *Ga-dearg*, red javelin.

Gael Glas, *Gaodhal-Glas*.

Garva, *Garbh*, rough.

Gaul Mac Morna, *Goll Mac Morna*.

Germane, *Germane*.

Gilla Dacker, *Giolla Deacair*, lazy fellow.

Glanlua, *Glanluadh*, pure-spoken.

Glas Mac Encarda, *Glas Mac Aeinchearda*.

Glore, *Glór*, a voice.

Ilbrec, *Ilbhreach*.

Ildana, *Ioldhanach*.

Inis Glora, *Inis Gluaire.*

Innia, *Innia.*

Innsa, *Inse.*

Inver-tre-Kenand, *Inbher-Tre-Cenand.*

Irann, *Irann.*

Iroda, *Ioruaidhe.*

Irros Domnann, *Iorrus Domnann.*

Island of the Torrent, *Inis Tuile.*

Kemoc, *Caemhoc* or *Mochoemhoc.*

Kenn-Avrat, *Ceann-Abhrat.*

Kenri, *Caenraighe.*

Kethen, *Cethen.*

Kethlenda, *Ceithleann* or *Ceithleand.*

Kian, *Cian.*

Kylta Mac Ronan, *Caeilte Mac Ronain.*

Largnen, *Lairgnen.*

Lavaran, *Lobharan.*

Liban, *Liban.*

Lidas, *Liadhas.*

Ligan Lumina, *Liagan Luaimneach,* Ligan the Bounding.

Lir, *Lir.*

Lobas, *Lobais.*

Lochlann, *Lochlann.*

Loskenn of the Bare Knees, *Loiscinn Lomghlúineach.*

Luath, *Luaith,* swift.

Luga of the Long Arms, *Lugh Lamh-fada.*

Mac-an-Lona, *Mac-an-Luin.*

Mac Luga, *Mac Luigheach.*

Mac-na-Corra, *Mac-na-Corra.*

Maildun, *Mail Duin,* chief of the fort.

Manissa, *Maighneis.*

Mannanan Mac Lir, *Manannan Mac Lir.*

Marid Mac Carido, *Mairid Mac Cairedo.*

Mergah, *Meargach.*

Micorta, *Miodhchuarta.*

Midac, *Miodhach* or *Mioch.*

Midir, *Midhir.*

Midkena, *Miodhchaoin.*

Milucra, *Miluchradh.*

Modan, *Muadhan.*

Morallta, *Moralltach,* great fury.

Moyle, *Mael,* a bare hill.

Moy-Mell, *Magh-Mell,* plain of pleasures.

Moytura, *Magh-tuireadh,* plain of towers.

Muman, *Mumha,* gen. *Mumhan.*

Muridach, *Muridach.*

Murthemna, *Muirthemhne.*

Niam, *Niamh,* beauty.

Nuada of the Silver Hand, *Nuadha Airgeatlaimh.*

Nuca, *Nuca.*

Oisin, *Oisin* (pronounced *Isheen'* in Munster, and *Osh'in* in Ulster and in Scotland).

Oscar, *Oscar.*

Owenaght, *Eoghanacht,* descendants of Owen.

Pezar, *Pisear.*

Racad, *Rachadh.*

Rib, *Rib.*

Sencab, *Seanchab,* old mouth.

Sharvan, *Searbhan,* a surly person.

Shee Finnaha, *Sidh-Fionnachaidh.*

Skeabrac, *Sciath-bhreac,* speckled shield.

Skolan, *Sceolaing.*

Slana, *Slánach,* healthy.

Sorca, *Sorcha.*

Sotal of the Large Heels, *Sotal Sálmhór.*

Taillkenn, *Tailcenn.*

Tinna the Mighty, *Tinne Mór.*

Tir-fa-tonn, *Tir-fa-thuinn,* country beneath the wave.

Tirnanoge, *Tir na n-óg,* land of youths.

Trencoss, *Treunchosach,* strong-foot.

Trenmore O'Baskin, *Treunmór O'Baoiscne.*

Triscadal, *Triscadal*

Tuis, *Tuis.*

Turenn, *Tuireann.*

Ur, *Uar.*

Urcar, *Urchar.*

THE END.